Geology of south Dorset and Devon and its World Heritage

In recognition of its outstanding geology, the coast between Orcombe Rocks in south-east Devon and Old Harry Rocks in south Dorset was granted World Heritage status in December 2001. The geology of this coast is described, together with the recently mapped 1:50 000 geological sheets 328 Dorchester, 341/342 West Fleet and Weymouth and 342/343 Swanage.

The diverse geology ranges from the Late Permian to Quaternary, representing more than 200 million years of geological time and many different ancient environments that included arid desert, subtropical seas and cold periglacial conditions. The stratigraphy is described in detail and incorporates revisions of the Triassic, Jurassic, Cretaceous and Palaeogene successions. The region is justly renowned for its rich variety of fossils, found especially in the Lower Jurassic rocks around Lyme Regis and Charmouth. Many scientifically important specimens have come from these crumbling mudstone cliffs, including marine reptiles first made famous by the work of the 19th century Lyme Regis fossil collector Mary Anning.

During the Quaternary, the district lay beyond the influence of the glaciers and outwash that covered much of northern Britain. Head and the residual clay-with-flints are the main deposits preserved from that period together with river alluvium and terrace deposits.

The structural geology is described in the context of basin evolution. This area was part of the Wessex–Channel Basin that developed throughout the Mesozoic. Numerous borehole records provide the basis for a detailed assessment of thickness variation and this is related to structural development. Mesozoic structures continued to influence later structural development. Periods of earth movement associated with the uplift of the Alps in southern Europe caused parts of the succession to be spectacularly folded, as seen for example at Durdle Door (*Cover photograph*).

Many past geomorphological studies have emphasised the close relationship between geology and the development of coastal landscape in the region, and there are a number of spectacular natural arches and sea stacks. Landslips, both active and dormant, are described and occur in a variety of forms unrivalled in the UK. Inland too, the influence of geology on the landscape is very strong, from the high rolling chalk downland north of Dorchester to the lower lying sandy heaths formed of Cenozoic (Palaeogene) sediments farther east around Wareham. In the Isle of Purbeck, picturesque Corfe Castle sits astride the sharply defined east–west ridge of the Purbeck Hills, formed by steeply dipping beds of chalk, part of a huge monoclinal fold that extends eastwards to the Isle of Wight.

Geology has also played a part in the development of the region, summarised in the *Economic geology* chapter. This region supplied the Portland Stone and Purbeck Marble that has been used in many great cathedrals and civic buildings. Palaeogene clays are an important source of raw material for ceramics, and the Wytch Farm Oilfield, near Bournemouth, is the largest onshore oilfield in the UK.

The text is fully referenced, and additional information includes a borehole and a fossil inventory.

The geological succession tabulated opposite summarises the age, stratigraphical classification, lithology and thickness of the rock types seen in south Dorset and on the World Heritage Coast.

Cover photograph
Durdle Door: a natural arch has been cut through steeply dipping Portland Stone Formation. Landward (left) of this are alternating hard and soft beds of the Purbeck Group and soft sandstones and siltstones of the Wealden Formation, which have been eroded back to form Durdle Cove in the foreground (J M Pulsford, P030749).

1. *Ichthyosaurus. Vulgaris.*
2. *Ichthyosaurus. Tenuirostris*
3. *Plesiosaurus. Dolichodeirus.*

DURIA ANTIQUIOR.

4. *Pterodactylus Macronyx.*
5. *Dapedium Politum*
6. *Pentacrinites Briareus.*

Frontispiece   An impression of prehistoric life in Dorset, sketched by Sir Henry de la Beche (1796–1855), the first Director of the Geological Survey.

BRITISH GEOLOGICAL SURVEY

C M BARTON
M A WOODS
C R BRISTOW
A J NEWELL
R K WESTHEAD
D J EVANS
G A KIRBY
G WARRINGTON

Contributors

Biostratigraphy
J B Riding

Stratigraphy
E C Freshney

Economic geology
D E Highley
G K Lott

Engineering geology
A Forster
A Gibson

Geology of south Dorset and south-east Devon and its World Heritage Coast

Special Memoir for 1:50 000 geological sheets 328 Dorchester, 341/342 West Fleet and Weymouth and 342/343 Swanage, and parts of sheets 326/340 Sidmouth, 327 Bridport, 329 Bournemouth and 339 Newton Abbot

Compiled by: M A Woods

Keyworth, Nottingham: British Geological Survey   2011

ISBN 978 0 85272 654 9

Bibliographical reference

BARTON, C M, WOODS, M A, BRISTOW, C R, NEWELL, A J, WESTHEAD, R K, EVANS, D J, KIRBY, G A, WARRINGTON, G, RIDING, J B, FRESHNEY, E C, HIGHLEY, D E, LOTT, G K, FORSTER, A, AND GIBSON, A. 2011. Geology of south Dorset and south-east Devon and its World Heritage Coast. *Special Memoir of the British Geological Survey.* Sheets 328, 341/342, 342/343, and parts of 326/340, 327, 329 and 339 (England and Wales).

Authors

M A Woods, BSc, FGS, CGeol, EurGeol
A J Newell, BSc, PhD
R K Westhead, BSc, PhD, CGeol
D J Evans, BSc, PhD, CGeol
G A Kirby, BSc, PhD
British Geological Survey, Keyworth

C M Barton, BSc, PhD
C R Bristow, BSc, PhD
G Warrington, DSc, CGeol
Formerly British Geological Survey

Contributors

J B Riding DSc, CGeol
E C Freshney BSc, PhD, CGeol
D E Highley BSc, CGeol, CEng
G K Lott BSc, PhD
A Forster BSc, CGeol
A Gibson BSc, MSc, FGS
British Geological Survey

Acknowledgements

A summary of the geology of the Dorset and south-east Devon coast was compiled by the members of the Technical Working Group of the World Heritage Steering Committee: Mr Tim Badman (Dorset County Council, Chairman), C M Barton (formerly BGS), Professor Denys Brunsden (Dorset Coast Forum/King's College London), Mr Richard Edmonds (Jurassic Coast Project), Dr Andy King (Natural England), Professor Vincent May (formerly Bournemouth University), Professor Michael House (formerly University of Southampton) and Mr Aiden Winder (Devon County Council). The nomination document, published in 2000 by Dorset County Council (Nomination, 2000), was based on the contributions of 67 earth scientists from the UK and overseas and has influenced the present text.

BGS has benefited from the co-operation and provision of data from numerous organisations and individuals in Dorset: Kaolin and Ball Clay Association, English Nature, English Heritage, the Countryside Agency, the Environment Agency, the National Trust, the Forestry Commission, the Farming and Rural Conservation Agency, MAFF and the Ministry of Defence. Mr David Harvey of Bridport kindly donated his photographic collection of the Dorset coast to the BGS and a number of his plates are reproduced here. A BGS assessment of the mineral resources of east Dorset, summarised here, was funded by the former DETR and is the subject of separate reports.

We gratefully acknowledge the assistance of local landowners who permitted access for the drilling of stratigraphical boreholes at Abbotsbury, Upton, Big Almer Wood and Studland.

This *Special Memoir* was compiled by M A Woods, and edited by M G Sumbler, K Ambrose, R W O'B Knox and A A Jackson. The comments of H C Ivimey-Cook, B M Cox and E Robinson are appreciated. Cartography by R J Demaine, L Noakes, H W Holbrook, and P Lappage: pagesetting by A Hill.

Notes

Throughout this memoir the word 'district' refers to the area indicated in Figure 1.

National Grid References are given in square brackets; those for boreholes are given in Appendix 1.

The authorship of fossil species is given in Appendix 2.

Numbers prefixed by the letter P refer to photographs in the British Geological Survey collection.

CONTENTS

FIGURES

TABLES

PLATES

FOREWORD

It is now more than half a century since the publication of Arkell's memoir *Geology of the country around Weymouth, Swanage, Corfe and Lulworth.* This classic work has been an inspiration to many students of geology, and continues to provide a foundation for modern geological interpretations of the region. Studies of the Dorset and south-east Devon successions have continued unabated, spurred on by new geological concepts such as sequence stratigraphy and cyclostratigraphy. In December 2001, the 95 miles of spectacular coast between Orcombe Rocks in south-east Devon and Old Harry Rocks in south Dorset became the first natural *World Heritage* site in England, in recognition of this unique landscape.

The purpose of this *Special Memoir* is to provide an overview of the formational stratigraphy of the south Dorset and south-east Devon district in the light of the work that has been undertaken since the publication of Arkell's memoir, and to provide an explanation of the newly published 1:50 000 geological map sheets 328 Dorchester, 341/342 West Fleet and Weymouth, and 342/343 Swanage.

In the last 50 years, exploration for hydrocarbons has added enormously to the geological understanding of south Dorset. Ball clays are important to the local and national economy. Detailed assessment of ball-clay reserves in the Wareham Basin has shown their stratigraphical distribution and led to new insight into the Palaeogene history of the area. Building stones of this district include Portland Stone and Purbeck Marble that has been used in many great cathedrals and civic buildings of Britain. Today, geology continues to influence the coastal environment. New research on the spectacular coastal landslides of the district shows how vital an understanding of geology is to the management of these processes.

With the award of *World Heritage* status to the south Dorset and south-east Devon coast come new opportunities and pressures for economic development. The attractive coastal scenery, which lures so many visitors each year, owes much of its character to its geology. Understanding and appreciation of this geological heritage will help to ensure that this unique area is available for the enjoyment of future generations.

Professor John Ludden, PhD
Executive Director

British Geological Survey
Kingsley Dunham Centre
Keyworth
Nottingham
NG12 5GG

ONE

Introduction

The coast from Orcombe Rocks [SY 021 794], at the mouth of the River Exe in Devon, to Old Harry Rocks [SZ 056 826], at the southern edge of Studland Bay in Dorset, was declared a World Heritage Site by UNESCO at a meeting in Helsinki on 13th December, 2001. This special status is in recognition of the outstanding geology (Figure 1); the coastline is the first natural World Heritage Site in England. The strata that are superbly exposed in the 95 miles of rocky headlands and bays designated as a World Heritage site represent nearly 200 million years of Earth history, and have been at the heart of scientific investigation since the birth of geology.

This *Special Memoir* describes the newly designated World Heritage Coast as well as the coastal area east to Hengistbury Head [SZ 178 904], in east Dorset. Inland, the area described includes the recently resurveyed Dorchester (328), West Fleet and Weymouth (341 and part 342) and Swanage (342 and part 343) sheets. The coastal area described is included in the Sidmouth (326 and 340), Bridport (327) and eastern part of the Newton Abbot (339) sheets in the west, and the western part of the Bournemouth (329) Sheet in the east (Figure 1). Most of the region described is protected through the UK statutory planning system either as Sites of Special Scientific Interest, Heritage Coasts or Areas of Outstanding Natural Beauty (Nomination, 2000).

GEOGRAPHICAL SETTING

The principal physical features of south Dorset and southeast Devon are directly related to the geology, and several subregions are recognisable (Figures 1; 2). Fertile rolling lowlands underlain by Permian and Triassic strata occur between the mouth of the River Exe in the west, and the River Otter. Farther east, broad outliers of Cretaceous Upper Greensand Formation and Chalk Group, capped by Quaternary clay-with-flints, form plateaux of higher ground between Sidmouth and Lyme Regis. There, the landscape is heavily dissected with extensive valley systems cut down into the softer underlying Triassic strata. Erosion between Sidmouth and Beer Head has cut a series of deep valleys at Salcombe Mouth, Weston Mouth and Branscombe Mouth and has formed impressive coastal cliffs.

The undulating and dissected ground of Marshwood Vale (Figure 2), north-east of Lyme Regis, is underlain by soft mudstone formations, with prominent outliers and resistant hill caps of Bridport Sand, Inferior Oolite and Upper Greensand that extend southward and eastward to the coast. Rolling chalk downlands occur around Dorchester and east of Bridport, and form some of the highest ground in the region, rising to over 265 m at Gore Hill [ST 637 038] in the north and 252 m on Eggardon Hill [SY 545 945] in the west. A prominent escarpment marks the edge of the Chalk outcrop, and the downlands are dissected by dry valleys and coombes.

Low-lying ground between Chesil Beach and Weymouth exposes mudstones and thin limestones in the core of the Weymouth Anticline, and contrasts with the low-lying sandy heathland formed by Palaeogene strata around Wareham and Bournemouth in the east of the district. Shallow waters and mud flats of Poole Harbour adjoin and pass into reed bed and marsh, wet heathland and ultimately dry heath and woodland. At the southern edge of the Wareham Basin, the Purbeck Hills form a ridge, 200 m high, of near-vertical Chalk. South of the Purbeck Hills, east–west ridges produced by the erosion of alternating limestone, sandstone and mudstone, dominate the Isle of Purbeck scenery.

The east Devon and west Dorset coast exhibits spectacular landslides, notably the Bindon Landslide between Axmouth and Lyme Regis, and Black Ven [SY 357 931] near Charmouth, the largest recorded coastal mudslide in Europe. Farther east, Chesil Beach is a gravel barrier beach that extends for 28 km between West Bay and Portland and encloses the Fleet, an important lagoon area that contains freshwater peats. The Isle of Purbeck coast is a classic location for demonstrating the evolution of caves and bays with many fine examples of rock arches and stacks, including the famous Durdle Door promontory (see *cover photograph*).

The River Frome has the largest catchment in the district, with its tributaries the Hooke River and Sydling Water in the west, and the River Cerne and South Winterborne farther east (Figure 1). The Frome drains the Chalk and Palaeogene strata of much of south central Dorset and the Wareham Basin. The River Piddle, subparallel and about 3 km north of the Frome for much of its length, also drains the Chalk of central Dorset and both rivers flow into the Wareham Channel in the western part of Poole Harbour. The north-east of the district forms part of the catchment of the River Stour which flows into Bournemouth Bay at Christchurch. Jurassic strata in west Dorset fall within the catchment of the River Brit, with its tributaries the Simene, the Mangerton River and the Asker. The River Bride may have formerly been a tributary of the Brit before marine truncation of the confluence (Wilson et al., 1958). Ground to the west lies within the Char catchment and includes a large number of small streams that drain Marshwood Vale. Farther west, the rivers Axe and Sid drain valleys cut into Permo-Triassic strata through ragged Cretaceous outliers. The western edge of the Cretaceous outcrop rises as an escarpment east of the River Otter, which meets the sea at Budleigh Salterton, and Orcombe Rocks at the mouth of the River Exe mark the western limit of the World Heritage Coast.

The economy of the area is largely based on agriculture, mineral extraction and tourism. The largest

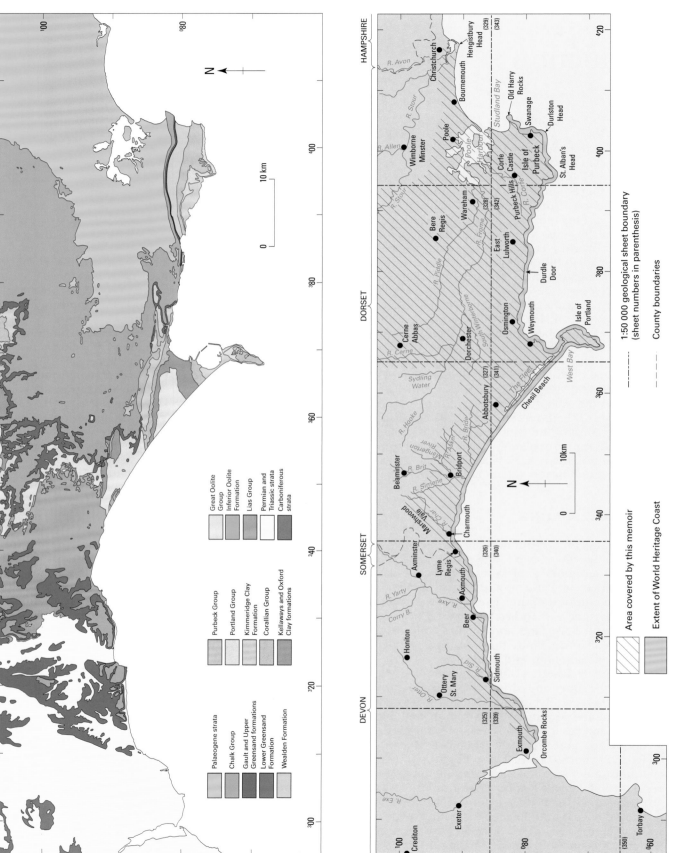

Figure 1 Geological and location maps of south Dorset and south-east Devon showing the area covered by this memoir and the World Heritage Coast region.

onshore oilfield in the UK is at Wytch Farm and there are important ball clay and aggregate deposits around Wareham.

GEOLOGICAL HISTORY

For much of the time between the Permian and the mid Cenozoic, Dorset and south-east Devon were covered by broad regions of fault-controlled subsidence. The Wessex — Channel Basin (Permian to Cretaceous) and Hampshire Basin (Paleocene to Oligocene) allowed thick accumulations of sedimentary rocks to be preserved, and these provide an almost unbroken record of Earth history for the last 200 million years.

The oldest rocks at outcrop on the World Heritage Coast are of Permian–Triassic age, the **Aylesbeare Mudstone Group**; this is overlain by Triassic **Sherwood Sandstone** and **Mercia Mudstone** groups *(inside front cover)*. These strata were deposited in a semi-arid desert environment; the mudstone formed mainly in ephemeral lakes created by seasonal flooding and periodically these became hypersaline as the water evaporated. In contrast, the sandstones represent wind-blown dunes and river deposits.

Mud and lime mud of the **Penarth Group** was deposited during a marine transgression that flooded the region in late Triassic times. This marked the beginning of a period of marine deposition, and a shallow epicontinental sea covered much of southern England during the latest Triassic and Early Jurassic. Limestone and calcareous mudstone of the **Blue Lias** and **Charmouth Mudstone** formations (lower Lias Group) accumulated at that time. Fossil remains of ammonites, belemnites and marine reptiles indicate an extremely rich and diverse marine environment. Arenaceous deposits in the upper part of the **Dyrham Formation** indicate a shallowing of the sea towards the end of the Pliensbachian. The overlying **Beacon Limestone Formation** formed in the latest Pliensbachian and early Toarcian when rising sea level reduced the supply of sediment and allowed a highly condensed limestone to form (Hesselbo and Jenkyns, 1998).

Shallow marine conditions prevailed from late Toarcian through to Mid Jurassic times. The **Bridport Sand Formation** (Toarcian to Aalenian) probably formed in a shallow storm-influenced shoal area that separated an area of shallow-water carbonate deposition to the north from a deeper basin farther south (Bryant et al., 1988). The **Inferior Oolite Formation** (Aalenian to early Bathonian) marks the spread of carbonate deposition into Dorset, and the sedimentation pattern was strongly influenced by contemporaneous movement along major faults. In the overlying Great Oolite Group, the **Fuller's Earth** and **Frome Clay** formations (Bathonian) are mainly mudstone that was deposited in deeper water, which, in turn, give way to the shallower water **Forest Marble** (Bathonian) and **Cornbrash** (Bathonian to early Callovian) formations at the top of the group. Towards the end of the Mid Jurassic Period, a marine transgression led to re-establishment of a shallow shelf sea over much of Britain. Sandy mudstone of the Kellaways Formation (Callovian) pass up into deeper

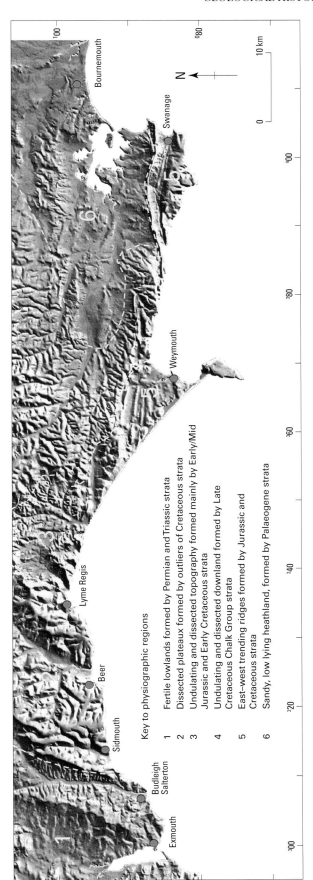

Key to physiographic regions

1   Fertile lowlands formed by Permian and Triassic strata

2   Dissected plateaux formed by outliers of Cretaceous strata

3   Undulating and dissected topography formed mainly by Early/Mid Jurassic and Early Cretaceous strata

4   Undulating and dissected downland formed by Late Cretaceous Chalk Group strata

5   East–west trending ridges formed by Jurassic and Cretaceous strata

6   Sandy, low lying heathland, formed by Palaeogene strata

Figure 2   Digital terrain model showing physiographic regions.

water mudstone of the Oxford Clay Formation (Callovian to Oxfordian). Ammonites and belemnites are abundant in the Oxford Clay, but the remains of reptiles are less common in Dorset than elsewhere in southern England.

A drop in sea level accompanied by a widespread influx of siliciclastic sediment interrupted mud deposition in the Late Jurassic, and the **Corallian Group** (Oxfordian to Kimmeridgian) is a mixed facies of sandstone, mudstone and carbonate. Sea level oscillated throughout the Oxfordian and early Kimmeridgian, producing disconformities and facies changes that can be correlated across much of Dorset. At this time, regional subsidence with syndepositional faulting became significant in the higher part of the Corallian Group (Newell, 2000). Widespread mudstone deposition was re-established, and the **Kimmeridge Clay Formation** was deposited during a period of high global sea level during the Kimmeridgian, although the maximum sea depth was probably not much in excess of 50 m. Synsedimentary faulting, related to rifting in the North Atlantic, continued to influence deposition and major changes in the thickness of the Kimmeridge Clay occur across the Purbeck Fault (e.g. Morgans-Bell et al., 2001).

Widespread marine regression at the start of the Portlandian led to withdrawal of the sea from much of the UK, and shallower marine conditions were established in the region. Siltstones and sandstones of the **Portland Sand Formation,** forming the lower part of the Portland Group, were followed by the development of a carbonate ramp and accumulation of limestone of the **Portland Stone Formation** (Coe, 1996). An arid climate at this time meant that there was little contamination of the limestone by land-derived material from rivers, and locally algal patch-reefs were formed, preserved in the upper part of the Portland Stone.

Retreat of the sea continued into earliest Cretaceous times, and the carbonate-dominated **Purbeck Group** (Portlandian to Berriasian) was deposited in lagoons, sabkhas and freshwater lakes. The lakes were liable to occasional, short-lived marine flooding, but the records of fossilised trees and dinosaur footprints show that land was nearby. Carbonate deposition ceased as rivers draining the land areas farther west and south spread sandy and silty sediment of the **Wealden Formation** (Valanginian to Early Aptian) across Dorset; finely laminated mud and sand accumulated in freshwater lagoons. Rapid basin subsidence and active faulting allowed thick successions to develop, especially on the downthrown side of the major faults. In contrast, the footwall blocks (e.g. South Dorset and Cranborne–Fordingbridge highs) were extensively eroded during the Early Cretaceous so that Upper Jurassic (and locally Middle Jurassic) strata were removed; this erosion surface is known as the Late Cimmerian Unconformity (Chadwick, 1986). Increasing marine influence in the upper Wealden Formation is a precursor to a major Aptian marine transgression that re-established a shallow sea across southern England and the dominantly arenaceous **Lower Greensand** was deposited. This markedly transgressive unit thins westwards across south Dorset, where the presence of lignite and brackish water molluscs suggest proximity to land.

Deeper water conditions were established in Mid Albian times with a major marine transgression that extended the mud deposition of the **Gault Formation** westwards across older formations. Later, a sandy facies, the **Upper Greensand**, derived from eroding land areas farther west, advanced eastwards over the Gault. In the latest Albian, a fall in sea level, perhaps accompanied by tectonic uplift (Gale, 2000a) induced erosion that cut into the top of the Upper Greensand, removing the youngest Albian sediments.

In Late Cretaceous times (Cenomanian to Campanian), with rising sea level, a long period of carbonate deposition was initiated across the UK; this is the **Chalk Group**. Basal sediments are clay-rich (**Grey Chalk Subgroup**), but pass upwards into increasingly pure limestone (**White Chalk Subgroup**) as global sea level rose. In parts of south Dorset rather different sediments formed. The Grey Chalk Subgroup is condensed and attenuated across a structural high (Mid Dorset Swell), and in south-east Devon the lower part of the Chalk Group is represented by highly condensed sandy bioclastic limestone (**Beer Head Limestone Formation**) that suggests formation in a shallow marine, near-shore environment (Durrance and Laming, 1985).

In the latest Cretaceous, structural inversion began along major tectonic lineaments. At the same time there was a major fall in sea level, which led to erosion of the top of the Chalk Group and initiation of terrigenous sedimentation in the Cenozoic Hampshire Basin (Chadwick, 1993). The earliest Palaeogene sediments of south Dorset formed in a broad, mangrove-fringed coastal zone; depositional conditions fluctuated between open-shelf, estuarine and fluvial environments in response to alternating marine transgression and regression resulting in a cyclical pattern of deposition. Miocene uplift terminated this cycle as the tectonic 'ripples' of the Alpine Orogeny spread to southern England. In Dorset, major east–west normal faults were reactivated as reverse faults and associated monoclines and anticlines were formed. Uplift allowed the onset of subaerial erosion, which continues to the present day.

During the Quaternary, Dorset lay beyond the southern limits of ice sheets that spread from highlands farther north. Weathering and deposition during the many phases of periglacial climate change led to the formation of clay-with-flints, gravel-rich river terrace deposits and solifluction debris (head). The raised beaches seen along the coast today were produced during periods of relatively higher sea level between these glacial phases. Today, the most significant geological processes affecting the region are soil erosion, particularly from arable areas, the deposition of this material as alluvium on river floodplains, coastal erosion and cliff recession particularly by the process of landslip.

HISTORY OF RESEARCH

Geological research on the Dorset and east Devon coast extends back for more than three hundred years, to the time when the abundance of fossils around Lyme Regis first became well known. Many of the important founders of earth science are known to have visited or lived in the area, including James Hutton (1726–1797), William Smith (1769–1839), William Buckland (1784–1856), Adam Sedgwick (1785-1873), William Conybeare (1787–1857), Roderick Murchison (1792–1871), Charles Lyell (1797–1875), Louis Agassiz (1807–1873) and Henry De la Beche (1796–1855), the founder of the Geological Survey.

The Dorset coast became famous during the early part of the 19th century as a result of important fossil vertebrate discoveries, particularly by Mary Anning (Tickell, 1996; Torrens, 1998). Although apparently poor and without formal education, Mary Anning became 'the greatest fossilist the World ever knew' (Torrens, 1998). With her family, she found the first ichthyosaur to receive scientific attention (1811–1812), the world's first complete plesiosaur (1823) and the first British pterodactyl (1828). Important mammal remains were also discovered on the Isle of Purbeck, particularly by Robert Damon (1814–1889) and Robert Ferris Damon (1845–1929).

Later scientific advances resulting from work on the Dorset and east Devon coast include pioneering work on ammonite zonation by the German palaeontologist Albert Oppel (1831–1865); the first biostratigraphical demonstration of diachronism by Sydney Savory Buckman (1860–1929) and a detailed systematic description of the Lower Jurassic succession by William Lang (published between 1912 and 1936). Aubrey Strahan (1895, 1898) first documented Cenozoic thrusts within the steep and overturned strata of south Dorset, providing the modern basis for understanding regional structural evolution, and Arkell used the Dorset coast as a standard reference for his world-wide study of the Jurassic system (Arkell, 1956). Undoubtedly it is the Jurassic geology of Dorset that has received most historical attention, but important works on Cretaceous stratigraphy include Rowe (1901, 1903) and Jukes-Browne and Hill (1900, 1903, 1904). Arkell's (1947) classic memoir, *The Geology of Weymouth, Swanage, Corfe and Lulworth*, has been an inspirational guide to countless geologists for over 50 years.

More recently, the geology of Dorset and south-east Devon has been the basis for numerous stratigraphical, palaeontological and structural studies. Theories about the influence of regular climatic oscillations on sedimentation have been developed from studies of the Blue Lias and Charmouth Mudstone successions (Weedon, 1986; Weedon and Jenkyns, 1990). Drummond (1970) and Kennedy (1970) showed how sedimentation in the Albian and Cenomanian had been influenced by a positive structural axis, named the Mid Dorset Swell, and Smith (1957, 1961a, 1961b, 1965) described the highly condensed Beer Head Limestone Formation (formerly 'Cenomanian Limestone') in south-east Devon. The Chalk of south-east Devon was discussed in a modern sedimentological context by Jarvis and Woodroof (1984) and Jarvis and Tocher (1987), and ammonites from the Chalk of Devon and Dorset form the basis of taxonomic descriptions by Wright and Kennedy (1981). Increasingly, geological successions in different regions are being interpreted as genetically related packages of sediment, controlled by changes in global sea level, and the superb outcrops of the Dorset coast have done much to underpin this approach (Coe, 1996; Hesselbo and Jenkyns, 1998; Newell, 2000). Finally, there are a number of publications that provide an overview of the Jurassic geology of Dorset (House, 1993; Callomon and Cope; 1995; Coe, 1995; Hesselbo and Jenkyns, 1995), and most recently there have been detailed accounts of Permo-Triassic, Jurassic, Cretaceous and Cenozoic outcrop successions published in the Geological Conservation Review series (Daley and Balson, 1999; Mortimore et al., 2001; Wright and Cox, 2001; Benton et al., 2002; Cox and Sumbler, 2002; Simms et al., 2004).

There is a long history of geological mapping in the area, stretching back to the mid 19th century; the early survey during the period 1850 to 1875 by H W Bristow at the scale of one inch to one mile (1:63 360) was published as [Old Series] sheets 15 to 18. Since then there have been more detailed surveys at 1:10 560 (six inches to one mile) and 1:10 000 scales, culminating in the publication of new 1:50 000 maps for Sheet 325 Exeter, Sheet 326 Sidmouth, Sheet 328 Dorchester, Sheet 341 and part of Sheet 342 West Fleet and Weymouth, Sheet 342 and part of Sheet 343 Swanage and Sheet 329 Bournemouth. Details of the history of surveying of these areas are given on the published maps.

There are recently published memoirs for the Newton Abbot (Selwood et al., 1984) and Bournemouth (Bristow et al., 1991) sheets, and a Sheet Explanation for Sidmouth (Edwards and Gallois, 2004). The remainder of the district has previously been described by Arkell (1947) and Wilson et al. (1958).

This memoir is in part based on detailed information contained in open-file reports (*see* Information sources), copies of which are available for consultation and purchase at the British Geological Survey, Keyworth, Nottingham, NG12 5GG.

TWO

Permian and Triassic

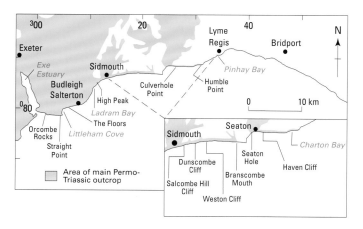

Map 1   Permo-Triassic outcrops.

Rocks of Permian and Triassic age are almost continuously exposed in cliff sections on the south-east Devon coast, between Torbay in the west and Pinhay Bay, near Lyme Regis, in the east (Figure 1). Most of the succession formed in arid and semi-arid desert environments, but a marine influence is evident near the top, indicating that a shallow sea had become established across the region just before the end of the Triassic Period.

The succession comprises, in ascending stratigraphical order, the **Exeter, Aylesbeare Mudstone, Sherwood Sandstone, Mercia Mudstone** and **Penarth** groups (Figure 3). The lowest (**Pre-planorbis**) beds of the **Lias Group** are also Triassic, but for convenience are dealt with in Chapter 3. The oldest strata occur in the west and successively younger units appear towards the east. These groups or, in the case of the Exeter Group, analogous units, also occur at depth farther east in the district where their character and extent has been determined from cuttings and geophysical logs of boreholes (Figure 4; Lott et al., 1982; Rhys et al., 1982; Whittaker et al., 1985; Penn et al., 1987; Holloway et al., 1989; Bristow et al., 1991; Hamblin et al., 1992; McClure et al., 1995; Butler, 1998; Hawkes et al., 1998; Smith and Hatton, 1998; Ruffell and Shelton, 1999), supplemented by information from sporadic cores (e.g. Lott and Strong, 1982; Knox, 1982) and from seismic sections.

As elsewhere in the UK, much of the Permian and Triassic succession seen on the World Heritage Coast is strikingly red-coloured, and many historical geological accounts have used the name 'New Red Sandstone' for the whole interval, although the sediments are actually more varied than this name implies. While conglomerates and sandstones are the dominant components of the Exeter and Sherwood Sandstone groups, the intervening

Aylesbeare Mudstone Group is clay-rich, as is the Mercia Mudstone Group, which also contains beds of gypsum and, at depth in Dorset, halite. The youngest Triassic deposits are grey mudstones, shales and limestones of the Penarth Group and the basal Lias Group.

Dating the succession is problematic as remains of marine macrofossils, which are usually the most useful for biostratigraphy, are absent from most of the succession. However, study of the sporadic remains of fossil spores and pollen (palynology), and isotopic and magnetostratigraphic data, indicate a Permian age for the Exeter Group and, less certainly, suggest that the Aylesbeare Mudstone spans the Permian–Triassic boundary. An Early Triassic age is also possible for the lower part of the Sherwood Sandstone, but the upper part is Mid Triassic. The Mercia Mudstone is Mid to Late Triassic, and the Penarth Group (with the basal Lias Group) is assigned to the latest Triassic (Figure 3).

Outcrops and boreholes show that the combined thickness of Permian? and Triassic strata around the Devon–Dorset border may approach 1600 m. Boreholes show that farther to the east substantial lateral thickness changes are controlled by major tectonic lineaments; for example, the Aylesbeare Mudstone is less than 200 m thick on the South Dorset High, but thickens to more than 1400 m in the Portland–South Wight Trough (Figure 4).

EXETER GROUP

The Exeter Group (Edwards et al., 1997; Edwards and Scrivener, 1999) crops out to the west of the Exe estuary (Figures 4a; 5), just beyond the limit of the World Heritage Coast, but is described herein for completeness. The group rests unconformably on folded Devonian and Carboniferous rocks and is succeeded, unconformably, by the Aylesbeare Mudstone Group. A further unconformity, representing a long intra-Permian phase of erosion and nondeposition (Warrington and Scrivener, 1988, 1990; Edwards et al., 1997; Edwards and Scrivener, 1999) can be used to subdivide the group into lower and upper parts. (Figure 3).

The succession mostly comprises coarse fluvial sandstones and conglomerates, becoming finer grained when traced eastwards and locally affected by syndepositional faulting (e.g. Crediton Trough; Figure 36) (Edwards et al., 1997; Edwards and Scrivener, 1999). These deposits are interpreted as having formed on large subaerial alluvial fans sourced mainly from uplands to the west. The group also includes the **Exeter Volcanic Rocks**, in the lower part, and the **Dawlish Sandstone Formation** in the upper part (Figure 3). The former are the eroded

Figure 3 Permo-Triassic stratigraphy of south-east Devon (outcrop) and south Dorset (subcrop).

remnants of basalt and lamprophyric lavas. The Dawlish Sandstone (Plate 1) includes substantial aeolian units, representing sand-dune and inter-dune deposits (Selwood et al., 1984; Jones, 1992; Clemmensen et al., 1994; Edwards and Scrivener, 1999; Newell, 2001). It is overlain around the Exe estuary by the **Exe Breccia** (Selwood et al., 1984).

Coarse clastic units occur beneath the Aylesbeare Mudstone in the Musbury Borehole, and between the Aylesbeare Mudstone and Variscan basement rocks in boreholes at Nettlecombe, Seaborough and Wytch Farm (*inside front cover;* Figure 4a). Though analogous to the Exeter Group in lithological character and stratigraphical position, these occurrences are not in proven continuity with, and cannot be related to, formations recognised at outcrop (Edwards et al., 1997; Edwards and Scrivener, 1999); their age is constrained only by their stratigraphical context.

Up to 607 m of Exeter Group strata occur in the south-east Devon coastal outcrop (Selwood et al., 1984), increasing to between 785 and 1115 m preserved in the Crediton Trough (British Geological Survey, 1995). In boreholes in Dorset, the analogous deposits range in thickness from about 48 m to more than 366 m.

Fossil burrows occur in the lower part of the group and vertebrate tracks near the top, but these are not useful for determining the age of the succession. However, radiometric age data from the Exeter Volcanic Rocks indicate an Early Permian (291–282 Ma: Asselian to Artinskian) age (Edwards et al., 1997; Edwards and Scrivener, 1999), and pollen from the upper part of the group, suggest an age no older than Mid Permian.

AYLESBEARE MUDSTONE GROUP

The Aylesbeare Mudstone Group crops out on the east side of the Exe estuary between Orcombe [SY 019 797] and Knowle [SY 056 814] (Figures 4a; 5).

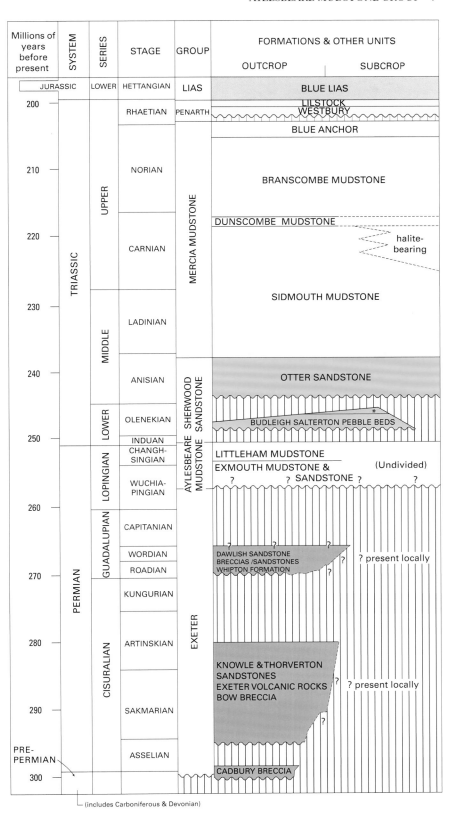

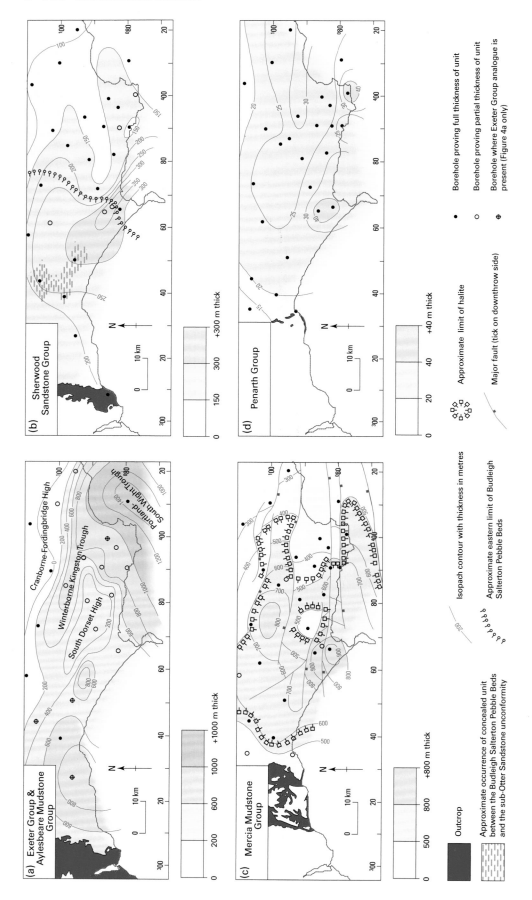

Figure 4 Isopachyte maps for stratigraphical intervals in the Permo-Triassic succession of Dorset and south-east Devon.

Plate 1 Dawlish Sandstone Formation, seen 1 km north-east of Dawlish [SX 972 775], looking north-east to Langstone Rock [SX 980 779], Devon. These distinctive cross-bedded sandstones are aeolian deposits, representing fossil sand dunes. Height of cliff is c. 20 m (P615352).

Unconformities separate it from the Exeter Group or, in most of the subcrop, Variscan basement rocks below, and from the Sherwood Sandstone above (Figure 3). As the name suggests, mudstone is the dominant lithology, but sandstones also occur in the lower part of the group, and evaporites (gypsum) are present locally (Henson, 1970; Selwood et al., 1984; Jones, 1992; Edwards and Scrivener, 1999). In the coastal outcrop the group comprises the **Exmouth Mudstone and Sandstone** and overlying **Littleham Mudstone** formations (Selwood et al., 1984; Edwards and Scrivener, 1999; Figure 3). The former includes sandstones that appear to persist eastwards at depth, at least as far as the Musbury Borehole, but which pass northwards into mudstone in the Exeter district (Edwards and Scrivener, 1999). The group is interpreted as representing deposition under alternating lacustrine and desiccated mudflat conditions in an arid–semi-arid sabkha-playa environment. Thick fluvial and aeolian sandstones in the Exmouth Mudstone and Sandstone may represent relatively proximal situations over which the finer, more distal, deposits of the Littleham Mudstone subsequently transgressed. The siltstone and thin coarser intercalations were probably deposited from sheet-floods (Jones, 1992; Edwards and Scrivener, 1999). Possible climatic controls on the deposition of the Exmouth Mudstone and Sandstone were investigated by Clemmensen et al. (1994).

On the Devon coast the Aylesbeare Mudstone is 530 m thick (Selwood et al., 1984). A similar, though incomplete thickness occurs in the Winterborne Kingston Borehole (Rhys et al., 1982), and about 867 m were proved in Wytch Farm X14 Borehole in south Dorset, from where the group thickens eastwards and southwards into the Portland–South Wight Trough (Figure 4a), with 1463 m proved in offshore borehole 98/11-2. The group is present at depth throughout most of south Dorset, to the south of faults that define the northern margin of the Winterborne Kingston Trough (Whittaker, 1985; Holloway et al., 1989; Hamblin et al., 1992; Butler, 1998; Figure 36), but is absent farther north, in the Cranborne and Spetisbury boreholes on the Cranborne–Fordingbridge High (Figure 4a). In the Wytch Farm X14 Borehole, a breccia about 48 m thick (**Wytch Farm Breccias**) was considered by Butler (1998) to be a locally derived basal unit of the Aylesbeare Mudstone rather than a representative of the older Exeter Group.

Although the Aylesbeare Mudstone lacks stratigraphically useful fossils, burrows (Henson, 1970; Selwood et al., 1984; Mader, 1985a, b), sporadic plant fragments and reworked Devonian and Carboniferous miospores (Warrington, 1971; Owens, 1972) have been recorded. Indirect biostratigraphical evidence and magnetostratigraphy indicates that the group is Late Permian (Lopingian) to Early Triassic (Induan or Olenekian) in age (Figure 3).

Exmouth Mudstone and Sandstone Formation

The Exmouth Mudstone and Sandstone Formation is 255 m thick on the Devon coast, where all but the lowest beds are exposed in the cliffs between Orcombe Rocks [SY 019 797] and Littleham Cove [SY 040 802] (Figure 5). The formation comprises reddish brown mudstones with up to 60 per cent of interbedded brown, red and green sandstones. Five fining-upwards cycles occur (Selwood et al., 1984), each with a sharp, probably erosional, base overlain by planar-bedded and large-scale cross-bedded sandstones, some with a basal mudstone intra-clast conglomerate. The sandstones grade upwards into mudstones with beds of poorly sorted sandy siltstone. The undersurfaces of sandstones show load casts, and polygonal mudcracks are common in mudstone interbeds. Some of the sandstones have sedimentary features that are consistent with deposition in a braided fluvial channel, whereas others, at Straight Point [SY 037 795] (Selwood et al., 1984, figure 17, bed j) and Orcombe Point (Plate 2) include large-scale cross-bedded sets that represent aeolian dunes formed by a southerly wind (Jones, 1992).

Littleham Mudstone Formation

The Littleham Mudstone Formation is exposed between Straight Point and the east end of 'The Floors' cliff [SY 056 814] near Budleigh Salterton (Figure 5), and is about 275 m thick. The contact with the under-lying Exmouth Mudstone and Sandstone is seen on the east side of Straight Point and at Littleham Cove [SY 039 803]. The top of the formation, overlain discon-formably by the Sherwood Sandstone, dips eastwards between the top of 'The Floors' cliff [SY 045 810] and the base of the cliff about 1.2 km farther east.

Nearly structureless, reddish brown mudstones with scattered pale green spots form the bulk of the Littleham Mudstone; they comprise hematite-stained silt (30 to 50 per cent) and clay (40 to 70 per cent), dominantly illite but with kaolinite and chlorite, with 2 to 7 per cent fine sand-grade quartz and feldspar grains. There are also persistent beds of silty sandstones and sandy siltstones up to 0.6 m thick. The sandstones fine upwards, have sharp, planar, or slightly undulating bases, small-scale cross-bedding and corrugated lamination (Selwood et al., 1984). The lowest beds of the formation contain numerous ellipsoidal and stellate concretions, up to 0.2 m in diameter, comprising dark radioactive and vanadiferous cores surrounded by pale green haloes (Harrison, 1975; Selwood et al., 1984).

SHERWOOD SANDSTONE GROUP

The Sherwood Sandstone Group is exposed on the Devon coast between Budleigh Salterton [SY 045 810] and Sidmouth [SY 132 873], where it is about 235 m thick (Figure 5). It overlies the Aylesbeare Mudstone unconformably and is succeeded conformably by the Mercia Mudstone. At outcrop the Sherwood Sandstone comprises a conglomeratic lower part, the **Budleigh Salt-erton Pebble Beds Formation**, disconformably overlain by the thicker and predominantly finer grained **Otter Sandstone Formation** (Figure 3).

Boreholes show that whilst the Sherwood Sandstone has a more extensive subcrop than the underlying Ayles-beare Mudstone, the Budleigh Salterton Pebble Beds are restricted to south-east Devon and west Dorset (Figure 4b). The Sherwood Sandstone proved in the Nettlecombe Borehole is 303 m thick, and includes about 65 m of strata not seen at outcrop, between the

Budleigh Salterton Pebble Beds and an angular uncon-formity at the base of the Otter Sandstone (Butler, 1998). More than 356 m of Sherwood Sandstone are present in the Hewish Borehole in south Dorset, and about 130 m of Otter Sandstone occur in the Spetisbury Borehole in central Dorset.

The Sherwood Sandstone is Early to Mid Triassic in age, based on the stratigraphical context of the Budleigh Salterton Pebble Beds, and vertebrate fossils and magne-tostratigraphic data from the Otter Sandstone (Figure 3).

Budleigh Salterton Pebble Beds Formation

On the coast, the Budleigh Salterton Pebble Beds Forma-tion is about 26 m thick, and can be seen dipping east-wards from the top of 'The Floors' cliff [SY 045 810] to the base of the cliff about 1.2 km farther east [SY 056 814], near Budleigh Salterton (Figure 5). It consists largely of medium brown conglomerates, with subrounded to rounded boulders, cobbles and pebbles in a matrix of gravel and silty sand; beds of paler brown sandstone also occur (Plate 3). Clasts, up to 0.45 m in diameter, are predominantly metaquartzite, but include schorl, vein quartz, porphyry, rhyolite and sandstone. Locally, large-scale cross-bedded and fining-upward cobble-pebble-sand units infill scour hollows. Erosion surfaces, commonly marked by pebble pavements, occur where conglomerates overlie sandstones. Some sandstone units, which are laminated and lack large clasts and mica, may be aeolian. There are sporadic, thin mudstones, some with mudcracks, that are locally reworked as intraclasts in the conglomerates.

There is a contrast between the lower and upper parts of the formation. The lower part contains sheets and lenses of planar cross-bedded conglomerates that pass laterally into horizontally bedded conglomerates, cross-bedded sandstones and muddy sandstones. In the upper part, horizontally bedded conglomerate is overlain by sandstone with large-scale trough cross-bedding (Smith, 1990). The top of the formation is marked by a red, clay- and silt-rich sand, overlain by a layer of ventifacts. This unit is interpreted as a palaeosol, indicative of a substantial break in sedimentation and a long period of weathering and pedogenesis (Wright et al., 1991). The ventifacts mark an aeolian deflation surface (Leonard et al., 1982). In the subcrop, this depositional hiatus is more clearly marked by an angular unconformity (Butler, 1998). Sedimentological data suggest that the Budleigh Salterton Pebble Beds were deposited on a braided river plain or 'wet' alluvial fan, by northward-flowing streams (Selwood et al., 1984; Smith, 1990; Smith and Edwards, 1991; Warrington and Ivimey-Cook, 1992).

In boreholes, the Budleigh Salterton Pebble Beds range from 19.5 m thick at Musbury to more than 46 m at Hewish; their absence from easterly parts of Dorset (Figure 4b) has been attributed to non-deposition (Smith and Edwards, 1991) or erosion prior to deposi-tion of the overlying Otter Sandstone (Holloway et al., 1989; Butler, 1998).

The Budleigh Salterton Pebble Beds contain reworked Ordovician and Devonian fossils that are possibly derived

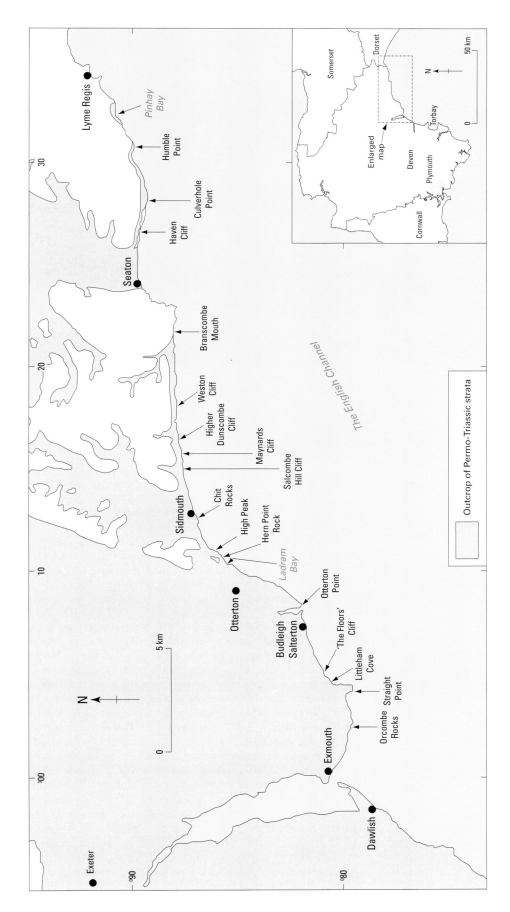

Figure 5   Key coastal localities for examination of the Permo–Triassic succession.

Plate 2 Exmouth Mudstone and Sandstone Formation, seen at Orcombe Point [SY 0204 7951], south-east of Exmouth. Prominent planar tabular cross bedding can be seen in the middle of the aeolian sandstone, representing the migration of a dune. Wind-rippled sandstones occur in the adjacent units/beds (P615356).

Mudstones with thin aeolian sandsheet sandstones

Aeolian sandstones

from sources in Brittany and Normandy (Cocks, 1989, 1993). In the absence of indigenous fossils or other direct evidence, the age of the formation is indicated only tentatively as Olenekian (Early Triassic; Figure 3), from its position between the Aylesbeare Mudstone and the Otter Sandstone.

Otter Sandstone Formation

The coastal outcrops of the Otter Sandstone Formation extend from west of Budleigh Salterton [SY 056 814] to east of Sidmouth [SY 132 873] (Figure 5) (Jones, 1993; Hounslow and McIntosh, 2003; Gallois, 2004). The lowest beds rest disconformably upon the Budleigh Salterton Pebble Beds west of Budleigh Salterton and are exposed discontinuously eastwards [to SY 073 820]. To the east of the River Otter, the higher beds are exposed in a 4.5 km-long section that extends north-north-east-wards from Otterton Point [SY 078 818] to cliffs below High Peak [SY 105 862]. Faulting repeats the outcrop of the higher beds farther east, at Chit Rocks [SY 121 868] and immediately east of the River Sid [SY 130 873].

The Otter Sandstone is about 210 m thick at outcrop, based upon the Monks Wall S10 Borehole, Otterton. Three units are recognisable on the coast: a lower unit of sandstone; a middle unit comprising vertically stacked sandstone sheets with conglomerates, the latter typi-cally overlying channel-form erosion surfaces; an upper unit of sandstones interbedded with mudstones tran-sitional to the succeeding Mercia Mudstone Group. The middle unit forms the bulk of the succession, and includes bedding-parallel sheets and vertical pipe-like concentrations of calcrete in cliffs at Budleigh Salterton

[SY 068 818] and between Otterton Point and Ladram Bay [SY 096 850] (Plate 4). An early diagenetic origin for these concretions is indicated by their presence as intra-clasts in the conglomerates, especially in the higher part of the formation. The pipe-like concretions, commonly more than a metre long (Mader, 1990), are interpreted as rhizocretions, formed by calcification around the tap roots of plants (Purvis and Wright, 1991).

Boreholes at Nettlecombe and Seaborough proved the occurrence of up to 65 m of anhydritic mudstones and siltstones with thin sandstones that are not repre-sented in the exposed coastal succession. These beds were originally regarded as part of the Otter Sandstone (Holloway et al., 1989), but are now considered to be a separate older, unit (Butler, 1998). Seismic sections show that an unconformity, perhaps similar to that recog-nised in the Triassic successions of the Southern North Sea (Geiger and Hopping, 1968) and Cheshire Basin (Evans et al., 1993), and identified with the 'Hardegsen Diskordanz' in the German Buntsandstein, appears to separate these strata from the succeeding Otter Sand-stone (Butler, 1998). Elsewhere in Dorset, the Otter Sandstone is generally thinner than at outcrop in south-east Devon, with between 160 and 170 m in the Coombe Keynes, Waddock Cross and Winterborne Kingston bore-holes; it is markedly thicker in the Chickerell Borehole, near Weymouth, where it exceeds 300 m. The Otter Sandstone is an important reservoir unit in the Wytch Farm Oilfield (Colter and Havard, 1981; Dranfield et al., 1987; Bristow et al., 1991; Bowman et al., 1993; McClure et al., 1995; McKie et al., 1998; Hogg et al., 1999; Katten-horn and Pollard, 2001). There the formation is around 160 m thick and has been divided by McKie et al. (1998)

Plate 3 Budleigh Salterton Pebble Beds Formation, seen in sea cliffs at Budleigh Salterton (yellow note book is 16 cm long). These gravel-rich beds represent braided river or alluvial fan deposits (P615351).

into a lower, largely fluvial sandstone interval, and an upper part with more common lacustrine and floodplain rocks, particularly mudstones.

The sedimentology of the Otter Sandstone (Lott and Strong, 1982; Jones, 1993) shows that the bulk of the succession was deposited in a braided river system, from gravel bars, sinuous dunes and migrating bars formed in frequently shifting channels. The numerous levels of rhizocretions indicate repeated colonisation of inactive parts of the river system by plants, which in turn attracted a fauna including herbivorous reptiles, such as *Rhynchosaurus spenceri*, and their dependant predators. Wind-blown sands occur locally in the basal part of the formation, and in the upper part, fluvial deposition, in channels, interacted with and was gradually superseded by deposition in a playa environment or an open body of water. The anhydrite-bearing unit, present locally below the Otter Sandstone in the subcrop (Figures 3; 4b), probably formed in an evaporitic playa or sabkha environment.

Following its deposition, the Otter Sandstone has undergone a complex diagenetic history. Initially this involved the creation of secondary porosity through grain and cement dissolution, but some porosity was then lost through the later precipitation of calcite and dolomite cements (Burley, 1984; Strong and Milodowski, 1987).

Despite the abundant evidence for an in-situ flora provided by the rhizocretions in the Otter Sandstone (Plate 4), no spores or pollen have been found. Invertebrate macrofossils are sparse and comprise crustaceans, an insect wing and arthropod cuticle (Benton et al., 1994, 2002; Benton, 1997). Remains of vertebrates, including fish, amphibians and reptiles (Huxley, 1869; Whitaker, 1869; Johnston-Lavis, 1876; Seeley, 1876; Metcalfe, 1884; Carter, 1888; Paton, 1974; Spencer and Isaac, 1983; Milner et al., 1990; Benton, 1990, 1997; Benton et al, 1993, 1994, 2002; Benton and Spencer 1995; Benton and Gower, 1997; Dineley and Metcalf, 1999; Spencer and Storrs, 2002) are more numerous and indicate an Anisian (early Mid Triassic) age, compatible with magnetostratigraphical evidence (Hounslow and McIntosh, 2003).

MERCIA MUDSTONE GROUP

The Mercia Mudstone Group is exposed discontinuously over a distance of about 20 km on the south Devon coast between the Ladram Bay area, south-west of Sidmouth, and Humble Point [SY 305 899], midway between Seaton and Lyme Regis (Figure 5). It rests conformably upon the Sherwood Sandstone and is succeeded, above a minor unconformity, by the Penarth Group (Figure 3). Inland the outcrop is extensively masked by Cretaceous rocks.

At outcrop, the group consists predominantly of red-brown, silty, dolomitic, gypsiferous mudstone. Thin grey to green, silty, dolomitic mudstone and siltstone units occur, mainly in the middle of the group, where they are associated with fine-grained sandstones, and also in the highest part. Sulphate evaporites (gypsum and anhydrite) are concentrated in red mudstones in the upper part of the group, and halite is present lower in the succession at depth in Dorset. Biostratigraphic and magnetostratigraphic evidence indicates that the group ranges in age from latest Anisian (late Mid Triassic) to Rhaetian (late Late Triassic) (Figure 3).

Plate 4 Rhizocretions in the Otter Sandstone Formation seen at Otterton Ledge [SY 0785 8190], c. 1 km east of Budleigh Salterton (subdivisions on pole are 50 cm). The rhizocretions formed by calcification around the roots of plants, which periodically colonised inactive parts of the braided river system in which the Otter Sandstone was deposited (P615357).

The lithostratigraphical nomenclature of the Mercia Mudstone Group on the east Devon coast is based largely on the scheme introduced by Gallois (2001). The group comprises, in ascending order: the **Sidmouth Mudstone, Dunscombe Mudstone** and **Branscombe Mudstone** formations (Gallois, 2001), and the **Blue Anchor Formation** (Warrington et al., 1980) (Figure 3). This nomenclature is retained in the following account for consistency with published BGS maps and sheet explanations for the Sidmouth and Lyme Regis (Sheet 326/340) district (Edwards and Gallois, 2004), which includes the east Devon coast section. However, in a revised national lithostratigraphical scheme for the Mercia Mudstone Group, Howard et al. (2008) refer the lower part of the Dunscombe Mudstone to the Arden Sandstone Formation and place the upper part in the Branscombe Mudstone Formation.

Boreholes show that the Mercia Mudstone is present at depth below southern Dorset. This concealed succession includes a halite-bearing unit, the 'Dorset Halite' (Whittaker, 1985; Smith and Hatton, 1998) or 'Dorset Halite Formation' (Harvey and Stewart, 1998). This unit is here included within the Sidmouth Mudstone, but the halite may be partly coeval with the overlying Dunscombe Mudstone (Gallois, 2001, 2003; Howard et al., 2008; Figures 3; 4c).

The group is about 475 m thick at outcrop on the east Devon coast. Greater thicknesses occur where the halite is present in south-central and west Dorset (Figure 4c); there the group is mostly between 600 and 700 m thick (Butler 1998), ranging from about 623 m at Marshwood to 695 m at Winterborne Kingston, but reaching about 975 m at Chickerell. Generally, thinner successions occur where halite is absent, with about 365 m at Wytch Farm and about 399 m at Lytchett. Determination of the original depositional thickness of the group is problematic where halite is present; the halite forms a *décollement* zone within which later listric faults sole-out, and the subsequent load-induced movement of this salt (halokinesis) has resulted in considerable variation in the thickness of the Mercia Mudstone in the hanging walls of these faults (Butler, 1998).

Sidmouth Mudstone Formation

The Sidmouth Mudstone Formation (equivalent to 'Mudstone I' of Jeans, 1978) is about 220 m thick in the vicinity of the coast section (Howard et al., 2008, fig. 3). The lower part occurs west of Sidmouth, at Hern Rock Point [SY 099 853], and in cliffs between High Peak [SY 101 856] (Plate 5) and Chit Rocks where it is well exposed (Figure 5). The outcrop is repeated by faulting east of Sidmouth and extends for more than 4 km east of the River Sid to Weston Cliff [SY 169 879]. Cretaceous rocks rest unconformably on the formation in Higher Dunscombe Cliff and overstep westwards onto progressively lower beds in Maynards and Salcombe Hill cliffs.

The formation comprises red-brown, mostly structureless, dolomitic mudstone with sporadic, thin beds of siltstone and fine-grained sandstone, contrasting with the thick, cross-bedded sandstones of the underlying Sherwood Sandstone. The lower beds, seen west of Salcombe Mouth [SY 146 877], contain scattered sandstone lenses, patches and laminations, sand-filled desiccation cracks, carbonate nodules and rhizocretions. Green reduction spots and mineral-filled solution hollows also occur (Jones, 1993). Higher beds, seen in Maynard's Cliff, generally lack these features, although green reduction spots persist and secondary gypsum veins appear about 110 m above the base of the formation. The sandstone beds have sharp bases with load structures or scour marks, and current and wave rippled tops. In the lower 45 m, beds are moderately thick (up to 1.2 m), but higher in the succession they are usually very thin and more commonly green coloured.

Boreholes show that there are thick developments of halite beneath some 1200 km² of western, central and southern Dorset. The northern extent of the halite corresponds with the northern margin of the Winterborne Kingston Trough (Figure 4c). In these areas, the Sidmouth Mudstone is generally much thicker than at outcrop or in boreholes where halite is absent; the thickest developments are in south Dorset, possibly as much as 540 m is present at Chickerell and Martinstown for example. The thickness is very variable, and ranges from 55 m at Creech to 360 m at Chickerell; individual units of relatively pure halite are typically between 20 and 40 m thick, but locally exceed 60 m (Highley et al., 2001). They occur interbedded with mudstone (e.g. Harvey and Stewart, 1998, figure 2).

The Sidmouth Mudstone was deposited partly under subaerial conditions and partly in shallow water in pools, lakes and lagoons that were periodically connected to the sea. The thin beds of coarser sediment in the succession probably result from flash-floods, but the halite formed in shallow hypersaline lakes and the sulphate evaporites (Plate 6) in the sediment of the sabkhas that bordered them (Warrington and Ivimey-Cook, 1992). Periodic replenishment of the brines from the Tethys Ocean, combined with syndepositional faulting, was responsible for the accumulation of the thick halite deposits (Warrington, 1974).

Biostratigraphical evidence for the age of the Sidmouth Mudstone consists of Carnian (early Late Triassic) miospores from the topmost 65 m of the formation (Warrington, 1971, 1997; Fisher, 1985). Lower beds have not yielded age-diagnostic material, but a latest Anisian and Ladinian (Mid Triassic) age is indicated by magnetostratigraphic evidence (Hounslow and McIntosh, 2003) and from the position of the formation above the Anisian Otter Sandstone (Figure 3).

Dunscombe Mudstone Formation

The Dunscombe Mudstone Formation is about 35 m thick on the east Devon coast. The type section is in cliff faces below Higher Dunscombe Cliff [SY 152 877 to 156 878] but the formation is more easily examined in cliffs and slipped masses below Weston Cliff [SY 168 880 to 171 880] (Gallois, 2001) (Figure 5).

The formation consists predominantly of green and purple mudstone but includes beds of red-brown and dark grey mudstone, pale grey dolomitic siltstone and very fine- to fine-grained cross-bedded and ripple-bedded sandstone, and mudstone breccias; much of the sequence is laminated. The dolomitic units range up to about 4 m in thickness, and have a sand content of up to 50 per cent. Breccias in the lower part of the formation consist of angular clasts in a mudstone matrix and may be autobreccias formed by repeated penecontemporaneous growth and dissolution of sulphate evaporites. In the upper part, coarser breccias with pervasive pinkish brown staining may be collapse breccias produced by dissolution of sulphates, and possibly halite, long after deposition. (Gallois, 2001; Edwards and Gallois, 2004). Bioturbation, particularly by sub-horizontal burrows, is common, and large specimens of the branchiopod crustacean *Euestheria* occur. The formation is dated as Carnian (early Late Triassic) on palynological evidence

(Warrington, 1971; Fisher, 1985). The depositional environment of the formation in the coastal section is interpreted as lacustrine, with brackish incursions (Edwards and Gallois, 2004). However, on a regional scale, the equivalent Arden Sandstone Formation (see below) comprises sand-filled distributary channels and interdistributary mudflat deposits that formed in deltaic or estuarine environments (Warrington and Ivimey-Cook, 1992).

The lower beds (c. 24 m) in the coastal sections are equivalent to the Arden Sandstone Formation of the national lithostratigraphical scheme for the Mercia Mudstone Group (Howard et al., 2008), and include the Weston Mouth Sandstone of Warrington et al. (1980) and Warrington and Scrivener (1980). Howard et al. (2008) incorporate the upper beds (c. 11 m) in the Branscombe Mudstone Formation.

Branscombe Mudstone Formation

The Branscombe Mudstone Formation (equivalent to 'Mudstone III' of Jeans, 1978) is about 220 m thick in the coastal section. The lower part crops out from Weston Cliff to east of Branscombe Mouth [SY 218 881], but exposures in this area are affected by landslip. Faulting repeats the outcrop at Seaton Hole [SY 235 895], and the highest 45 m of strata crop out in Haven Cliff [SY 257 897]. In the national lithostratigraphic scheme for the Mercia Mudstone Group (Howard et al., 2008) the upper 11 m of the Dunscombe Mudstone Formation of Gallois (2001) are incorporated in this formation.

The Branscombe Mudstone comprises predominantly red-brown, apparently largely structureless mudstone with sporadic, very thin beds of green, very fine-grained sandstone. Sand lenses and patches and carbonate nodules occur sporadically, and some green reduction spots and mottling are present. Gypsum occurs as nodules and veins; a prominent concentration of gypsum (Red Rock Gypsum of Gallois, 2001) occurs about 75 m above the base of the formation and crops out [SY 191 880] about 1 km west of Branscombe Mouth. An 'anhydrite marker', corresponding to this concentration of sulphate evaporites, is recognised by low gamma-ray and very high sonic velocity profiles on geophysical logs. The upper 19 m of the Branscombe Mudstone includes thin beds of green or grey mudstone, siltstone and sandy siltstone that grade upwards to the base of the Blue Anchor Formation.

The Branscombe Mudstone shows evidence of deposition in a range of arid continental environments that is similar to the underlying Sidmouth Mudstone. High evaporation across extensive sabkhas produced mineral-enriched pore waters and hypersaline lakes from which sulphate minerals were deposited. Occasional marine incursions helped maintain the formation of evaporitic brines (Warrington and Ivimey-Cook, 1992).

With the exception of one sparse miospore assemblage, reported by Fisher (1985) and others, from the upper 36 m of the formation (Warrington, 2000a), the Branscombe Mudstone has proved unfossiliferous. It is

Plate 5 Sherwood Sandstone overlain by Mercia Mudstone below High Peak [SY 1055 8600], west-south-west of Sidmouth. The Sherwood Sandstone is the prominently bedded lower unit forming the steep cliffs up to the level of the arrow in the photograph. The height of the cliff is c. 150 m (P615358).

considered to be Carnian to Norian (early to mid Late Triassic) in age, on the basis of magnetostratigraphic evidence and its position between the Carnian Arden Sandstone and the Norian(?) to Rhaetian Blue Anchor Formation (Figure 3).

Blue Anchor Formation

The Blue Anchor Formation crops out discontinuously between Haven Cliff and Humble Point. It is fully exposed between Haven Cliff and Culverhole Point [SY 273 893] (Figure 5), where the thickness has been recorded as 23 m (Richardson, 1906) or 29 m (Gallois, 2001). These compare with 25 m seen in a borehole at Lyme Regis (Warrington and Scrivener, 1980), and 73 m in the Chickerell Borehole.

The predominant lithology is grey-green to greenish grey silty mudstone. Beds of cream-coloured, dolomitic siltstone and dark grey mudstone and silty mudstone are also present, the former mainly in the lower part of the formation and the latter in the upper part. The lower part also has a few thin beds of red-brown mudstone. This succession records the commencement of a transgression that established marine conditions throughout much of Britain in latest Triassic times. Mainly supratidal sabkha deposits at the base alternate with and are succeeded by those formed in intertidal sabkhas and shallow marine environments (Warrington and Ivimey-Cook, 1992).

Palynomorph assemblages from the formation at outcrop (Warrington, 1971, 1999, 2000b; Stevenson and Warrington, 1971; Orbell, 1973; Fisher, 1985) and core from the Lyme Regis Borehole (Warrington, 1997) are indicative of a late Norian(?) to Rhaetian age.

PENARTH GROUP

The Penarth Group, which overlies the Blue Anchor Formation unconformably, is exposed discontinuously over some 5 km, from near Culverhole Point to Pinhay Bay [SY 319 908], west of Lyme Regis (Figure 5). The main section, between [SY 270 894], near Culverhole Point, and the east side of Charton Bay [SY 303 900] is faulted and affected by landslip and is relatively poorly exposed. The outcrop is repeated farther east by a north–south normal fault at Pinhay Bay where exposure is better. Inland, Cretaceous rocks overstep westwards from the Lias Group onto the Penarth and Mercia Mudstone groups, and partially mask the outcrop. The Penarth Group is 18.5 m thick near Lyme Regis, based upon the cored Lyme Regis Borehole (Warrington and Scrivener, 1980); its maximum recorded thickness is 42 m in the Chickerell Borehole in south Dorset, but successions proved in many other boreholes in the district are also thicker than at outcrop (Figure 4d).

Unlike most of the Permian and Triassic succession, the group is almost entirely of marine origin, and has yielded rich palynofloras and both microfossil and macrofossil assemblages of Rhaetian (late Late Triassic) age. The group comprises the **Westbury Formation**, overlain by the **Lilstock Formation** (Figure 3; Knox, 1982; Ivimey-Cook, 1982).

Westbury Formation

The Westbury Formation is characterised by dark grey to black fossiliferous shaly mudstones. The outcrop is commonly affected by landslip and exposures are

Plate 6 Sidmouth Mudstone Formation with gypsum (thin pale-coloured horizons) seen at Higher Dunscombe Cliff [SY 156 878], looking west towards Sidmouth. In the middle distance is Salcombe Hill Cliff, with the lower part of Sidmouth Mudstone Formation resting on Otter Sandstone Formation, which is also repeated in cliffs in the background (P615353).

discontinuous and variable. The formation is about 9.9 m thick on the coast, based on the record of the Lyme Regis Borehole (Warrington and Scrivener, 1980). The base may be seen at Culverhole Point and in Charton Bay, depending upon the condition of the exposures; only higher beds can be seen farther east,

in Pinhay Bay. At depth, the formation locally exceeds 12 m in thickness.

The base is marked by a 'bone-bed', containing fish scales, teeth and coprolites, that rests unconformably on the eroded top of the Blue Anchor Formation and infills borings and fissures in that formation. The remainder

Plate 7 Langport Member (Lilstock Formation) overlain by basal Lias Group exposed in Pinhay Bay [SY 3200 9085], south-west of Lyme Regis. The arrow marks the junction of the two units. Thin undulating surfaces seen in the thick unit a little below the arrow are slump bedding. Length of hammer is 0.3 m (P615354).

of the Westbury Formation consists of black fissile mudstones with a few thin, grey limestones and sporadic sandstone laminae. Deposition largely occurred in low-energy, stagnant or weakly oxygenated sea water, with periodic interruption by higher energy phases.

At outcrop (Orbell, 1973) and in boreholes (Warrington, 1982, 1997, 2005) the formation has yielded assemblages of spores, pollen and marine organic-walled microplankton; the fauna includes bivalves (notably *Protocardia rhaetica*, *Rhaetavicula contorta* and *Chlamys valoniensis*, and fish remains (Richardson, 1906; Ivimey-Cook, 1982; Callomon and Cope, 1995).

Lilstock Formation

The outcrop of the Lilstock Formation is commonly affected by landslip, and exposures are discontinuous, although the constituent Cotham and Langport members can be seen at Culverhole Point and in Pinhay Bay (Figure 5). The formation is about 8.6 m thick at outcrop, based on the record of the nearby Lyme Regis Borehole (Warrington and Scrivener, 1980), but thicknesses at subcrop commonly exceed 12 m.

In the coastal sections and the Lyme Regis Borehole, the **Cotham Member** comprises about 1.9 m of poorly exposed, green, grey, yellow or brown calcareous shales and thin cream-coloured limestones. Thickness variations at depth are uncertain as the member is difficult to distinguish from the Westbury Formation on most borehole geophysical logs. It has yielded few macrofossils compared with the underlying Westbury Formation, but bivalves, ostracods, fish scales, reptilian bones and coprolites are recorded (Richardson, 1906). Near the top of the member at outcrop (Mayall, 1983, fig. 2), a thin bed of algal limestone with a mamillated upper surface comprises a development of the 'Cotham Marble'

(Hamilton, 1961). Fresh or brackish water conditions, with periodic emergence, have commonly been inferred for the depositional environment of this member, but palynomorph assemblages including rich organic-walled microplankton associations similar to those known from the Westbury Formation (Warrington, 1982, 1997, 2005), indicate a marine influence. A bed of disturbed sediment towards the middle of the member has been interpreted as a seismite (Mayall, 1983; Simms, 2003).

On the coast (Plate 7) and in the Lyme Regis Borehole, the **Langport Member**, formerly the 'White Lias' (Warrington et al., 1980), comprises about 6 m of pale cream-coloured limestones with thin shale interbeds that initially accumulated in warm, very shallow marine water. Hallam (1960), Hesselbo and Jenkyns (1995), Wignall (2001) and Hesselbo et al. (2004) have documented evidence of penecontemporaneous movement in these deposits, including slumps and debris flows containing limestone intraclasts. Hesselbo et al. (2004) interpreted the Langport Member in the coastal section as comprising gravity-flow deposits shed from a storm-dominated carbonate ramp.

Fossils from the member include assemblages of spores, pollen and marine organic-walled microplankton (Orbell, 1973; Warrington, 1982, 1997, 2005), conodonts (Swift, 1995) and macrofossils, including bivalves, solitary corals and echinoderm remains (Richardson, 1906; Callomon and Cope, 1995; Swift and Martill, 1999).

The upper surface of the 'Sun Bed', at the top of the Langport Member, is an erosion surface penetrated by *Diplocraterion* burrows, syneresis cracks and borings. It is succeeded abruptly by a very finely laminated fissile mudstone at the base of the **Blue Lias Formation** of the Lias Group (Plates 7; 8; 9). The basal few metres are latest Triassic, but as most of the Lias Group is Jurassic these beds are described in Chapter 3.

THREE

Jurassic

The Jurassic succession of Dorset comprises large-scale, repeated rhythms of mudstone, sandstone and limestone related to global increases of the contemporary sea level and subsequent build-up of sediment. Shallow marine limestones in the Penarth Group, near the top of the Triassic, mark the beginning of a major marine transgression, and brackish and fresh water limestones in the Purbeck Group, mark the beginning of a widespread marine regression at the end of the Jurassic. Small-scale rhythms, interpreted in terms of orbitally forced climatic changes, also occur throughout much of the succession.

In Dorset, Lower Jurassic strata are represented by the **Lias Group**, comprising a succession of mudstones and thin limestones in the lower part, overlain by sandstones and limestones with subordinate mudstone-rich intervals. There are two principal shallowing-up cycles represented by the progression from mudstone, through sandstone, to limestone. The top of the second of these cycles is represented by the **Inferior Oolite Formation** at the base of the Middle Jurassic. This condensed, fossil-rich limestone is overlain by the **Great Oolite Group**. The lower formations of the Great Oolite, the **Fuller's Earth** and **Frome Clay**, are a predominantly deeper water mudstone facies, which, in turn, pass upwards into the shallower water sandstone and sandy mudstone and limestone facies of the **Forest Marble Formation** and thin limestones of the **Cornbrash Formation**.

The upper part of the Middle Jurassic succession consists of sandy mudstone of the **Kellaways Formation** and mudstone of the lower part of the **Oxford Clay Formation**. In the Upper Jurassic, the upper part of the Oxford Clay (Weymouth Member) is overlain by shallow-water sandstones and limestones of the **Corallian Group**. Another phase of relatively deep water sedimentation is represented by the mudstones of the overlying **Kimmeridge Clay Formation,** with dark, organic-rich intervals that reflect a poorly oxygenated marine environment. Upwards, the mudstone gives way to the dolomitic sandstone and limestone of the **Portland Group**, which record progressive shallowing of the Late Jurassic marine environment in Dorset, culminating, in the **Purbeck Group**, with marginal marine hypersaline lagoons and increasing evidence of terrestrially influenced depositional conditions.

The coastal succession is famous for its ammonite and marine vertebrate faunas, and has furnished some of the earliest scientifically described fossils. Ammonites are the basis of the standard biostratigraphical subdivision of the Jurassic succession into zones and subzones. For the Jurassic as a whole, averaged time resolution using ammonites may approach a million years for a zone, and half this for a subzone (Torrens, 1980a). Recognition of finer subdivisions, called 'horizons' or 'zonules', based on brief acmes of one or more species, has added to the biostratigraphical refinement of parts of the Lias Group (Phelps, 1985; Page, 1992, 2002; Bloos and Page, 2002) and in the much-condensed Inferior Oolite Formation (Callomon and Cope, 1995). The Jurassic ammonite zones are regarded by many workers as the basis of chronozones (units of chronostratigraphy; Torrens, 1980a), referred to by species name, written in Roman script.

In parts of the Jurassic succession in which ammonites are less common, other fossil groups become important for correlation. Brachiopods and bivalves locally dominate the faunas, and give their names to particular marker beds in the Great Oolite Group and Kellaways Formation. In the Cornbrash Formation, a brachiopod-based biozonation is often used, which allows finer subdivision than the ammonite faunas.

Fossils and particularly fossil reptiles have earned the Dorset coast world-wide fame. Reptile remains are most abundant in the Lias Group, but also occur sporadically at higher levels. The most famous fossils are of ichthyosaurs and plesiosaurs, first brought to scientific attention by Mary Anning, a 19th century fossil collector and dealer who lived in Lyme Regis. There are also rare finds of land-dwelling dinosaurs such as *Scelidosaurus harrisoni* near Charmouth and flying pterosaurs (e.g. *Dimorphodon macronyx*) from Lyme Regis.

LIAS GROUP

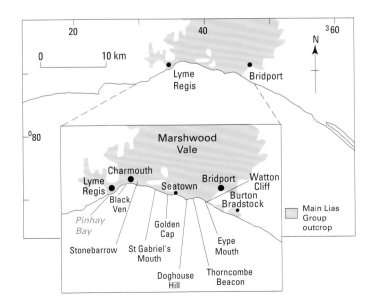

Map 2 Lias Group outcrops.

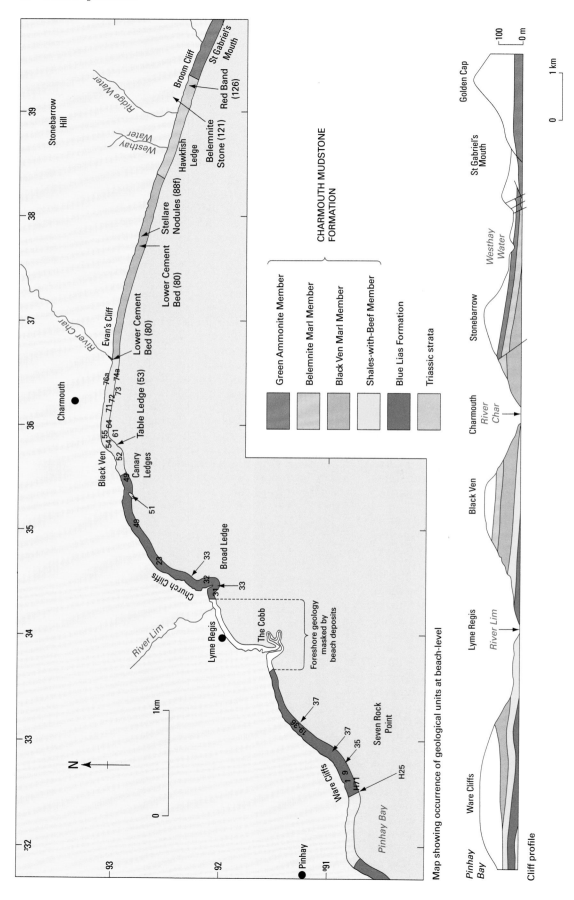

Map showing occurrence of geological units at beach-level

Figure 6 Lias Group strata and key marker beds in cliff and foreshore exposures between Pinhay Bay and St Gabriel's Mouth. Bed numbers correspond with those used in Figures 8, 10, 11, 12, 13 (based on figures by House, 1989 and Hesselbo and Jenkyns, 1995).

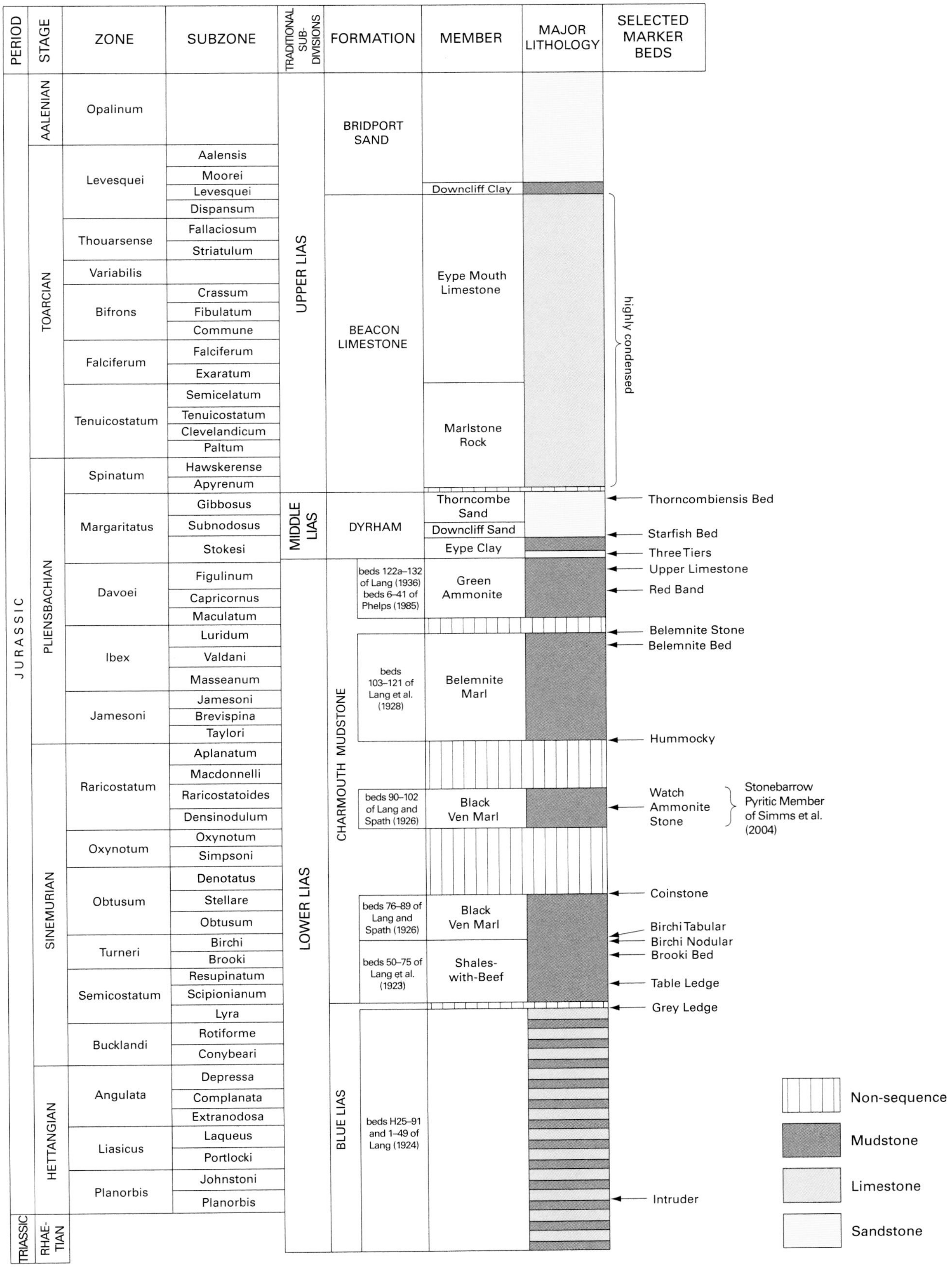

Figure 7 The stratigraphy of the Lias Group of the Dorset coast (based on Hesselbo and Jenkyns, 1995, and Bloos and Page, 2002). Not to scale.

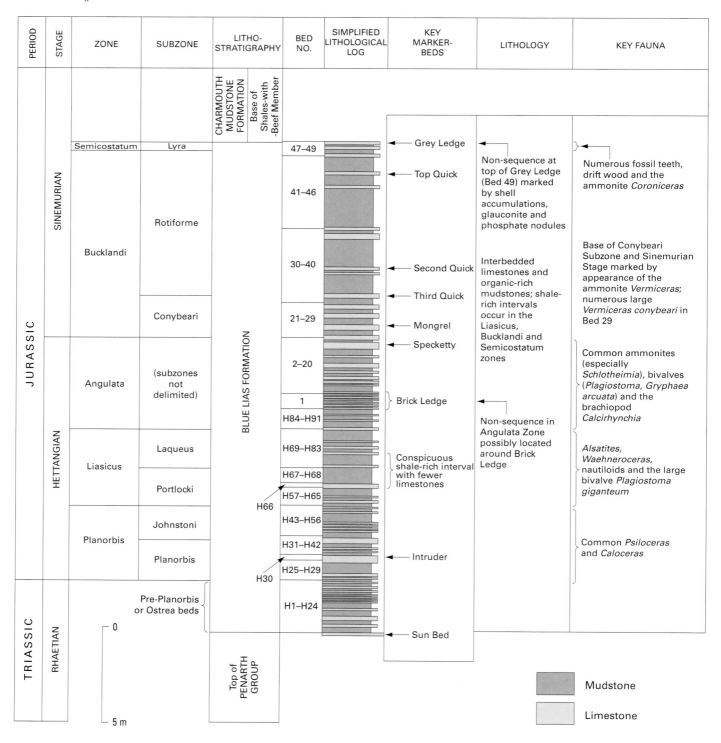

Figure 8 The stratigraphy of the Blue Lias Formation, based on sections in Pinhay Bay [SY 318 908] and at Seven Rock Point [SY 328 910] (from figures by Hesselbo and Jenkyns, 1995).

Strata of the Lias Group occur in west Dorset, between Lyme Regis and Burton Bradstock, and represent about 30 million years of marine sedimentation (Figure 6). The base of the Lias Group rests unconformably upon limestones of the Penarth Group, while the top is usually an eroded surface beneath the lowest limestone of the Inferior Oolite Formation. The base of the Jurassic System is defined by the base of the Planorbis Zone, taken at the lowest occurrence of the ammonite *Psiloceras planorbis*. It lies about 2.5 m above the base of the Lias

Group near Lyme Regis; underlying Lias strata are therefore Triassic.

The mudstone facies that predominates in the lower part of the Lias Group reflects deposition across a relatively deep, open marine shelf, below normal wave base (Hallam, 1992). The change to sandy and silty facies in the Late Pliensbachian reflects a shallowing of the depositional environment, caused by the basinward progradation of coarser grained sediments during a sea-level highstand and, possibly fall. Later with a return to deeper water conditions, sedimentation rates were dramatically reduced and limestone formed in a highly condensed sequence during the Toarcian (Hesselbo and Jenkyns, 1998). Sandstone, forming the top of the Lias Group, eventually prograded into the district, perhaps accompanied by a fall in sea level in the late Toarcian (Hesselbo and Jenkyns, 1995).

The Lias Group thickens progressively southward across the district, from 300 to 400 m in north Dorset to more than 1100 m in south Dorset (e.g. 1146 m in the Kimmeridge 5 Borehole). However, the pattern is not uniform and important thickness changes occur across faults; in the northern block of the Purbeck Monocline only 351 m and 436 m are present in boreholes at Bushey Farm (A1 Borehole) and Creech respectively.

In Dorset, the Lias Group comprises five formations that replace the imprecise divisions of Lower, Middle and Upper Lias of traditional usage (Cox et al., 1999, Figure 7). The limestone-rich **Blue Lias Formation**, at the base of the Lias Group, is overlain by the predominantly argillaceous **Charmouth Mudstone Formation**, the thickest subdivision. The succeeding sandy and silty beds comprise the **Dyrham Formation**. The **Beacon Limestone Formation** (formerly the 'Junction Bed') is a much-reduced equivalent of the succession developed farther north in England. The uppermost strata of the Lias Group comprise the arenaceous **Bridport Sand Formation**.

The lower part of the group is known from the very detailed measurements of the coastal succession by Lang and co-workers (Lang, 1914, 1924, 1936; Lang et al., 1923, 1928; Lang and Spath, 1926), who numbered beds from the base of the Blue Lias up to the top of the Green Ammonite Member (Figure 7).

Blue Lias Formation

Although the type area for the Blue Lias Formation is around Bath and Bristol (Torrens and Getty, 1980; Donovan and Kellaway, 1984), the cliffs between Pinhay Bay and Lyme Regis provide the primary reference section [SY 320 908 to 333 914] (Lang, 1924; Hallam, 1960b; Callomon and Cope, 1995; Hesselbo and Jenkyns, 1995; Cox et al., 1999; Simms, 2004; Figure 8). The formation comprises rhythmic alternations of argillaceous limestone ('cementstone') and mudstone (Plate 8), and ranges from 20 m in a borehole at Wytch Farm to more than 200 m in the Winterborne Kingston and Kimmeridge 5 boreholes (Figure 9). About 30 m is present around Lyme Regis, with 35 m in the Nettlecombe Borehole, increasing eastwards to 116 m and 129 m in boreholes at Martinstown and Chickerell respectively.

Most of the limestones are either tabular or highly nodular with common fossils and bioturbation. However, two groups of tabular limestones in the lower part of the formation (Johnstoni Subzone; Figure 8) are distinctly laminated and virtually lack evidence of benthonic body or trace fossils (Simms, 2004). Limestones occur interbedded with calcareous mudstone, siltstone or less commonly, laminated, bituminous fissile mudstone ('paper-shale'). Individual limestone beds are typically 0.1 to 0.3 m thick, and intervening mudstones, which may contain limestone nodules, are generally less than 1 m thick. A more substantial unit of mudstone with relatively few limestone beds (Saltford Shale Member) occurs in the type area and elsewhere, but is not well developed in Dorset. Several features of the limestone beds, including undeformed vertical burrows, suggest that the limestone–mudstone alternation is a primary sedimentological feature (Hallam, 1960b), perhaps related to sea level and/or orbitally forced climate changes (House, 1985, 1989; Weedon, 1986). However, Moghadam and Paul (2000) proposed an entirely diagenetic origin for the limestones linked to primary differences in the sediment (Simms, 2004).

The base of the Blue Lias is a marked non-sequence, with limestone, mudstone or 'paper-shale' overlying the eroded, commonly bored surface of the 'Sun Bed' at the top of the Langport Member, seen in the foreshore in Pinhay Bay (Plate 9). There, the lowest 2.5 m of the formation are Triassic, and have been referred to as 'Ostrea Beds' (after the abundance of the oyster *Liostrea*) or Pre-Planorbis Beds (Cope et al., 1980). The base of the Jurassic is at the base of a 0.15 m-thick mudstone (Bed H25; Figure 8) containing the lowest occurrence of the ammonite genus *Psiloceras*, an approximately synchronous event in the UK (Torrens and Getty, 1980; Warrington et al., 1980). About a metre higher in the succession at Pinhay, a conspicuous, fine-grained tabular limestone, containing centimetre-wide fissures part infilled with bioclastic limestone (Simms, 2004), is named the 'Intruder' (Bed H30), and forms a prominent ledge on the eastern foreshore of Pinhay Bay. The formation top is taken at the marked upward decrease in abundance of limestone beds; in the coastal sections, it corresponds with the top of a limestone band named Grey Ledge (Bed 49 of Lang, 1924) (Figure 8), characterised by accumulations of glauconite, pyritised fossils, limestone intraclasts and phosphatic nodules, seen in the foreshore east of Lyme Regis, between Broad Ledge [SY 3535 9290] and Canary Ledge [SY 354 930].

The Blue Lias Formation ranges from the latest Rhaetian to the lower part of the Semicostatum Zone (Lyra Subzone) in the Lower Sinemurian. Ammonites are a major component of the macrofauna (Plate 10), and include common *Psiloceras* and *Caloceras* in the lower part, succeeded higher in the succession by *Alsatites*, *Waehneroceras* and *Schlotheimia*. *Vermiceras* appears in the Conybeari Subzone, around the middle of the succession, which marks the base of the Sinemurian stage

Plate 8 Blue Lias Formation overlying the Penarth Group at Pinhay Warren [SY 319 909], with Charmouth Mudstone Formation above. The lower interval of closely spaced limestone beds in the Blue Lias Formation includes the Pre-Planorbis Beds (latest Triassic) and Intruder Limestone Marker (Early Jurassic). The slightly higher group of limestone beds includes the Brick Ledge and Third Quick limestone markers. Height of cliff c. 25 m (P226902).

(Callomon and Cope, 1995). Traditionally the succession at Lyme Regis was regarded as a standard reference section for the base of the Sinemurian, but a more complete basal Sinemurian ammonite fauna has recently been discovered at East Quantoxhead, Somerset (Page, 1995; Bloos and Page, 2002). The Blue Lias Formation also contains brachiopods (*Calcirhynchia*), bivalves (*Gryphaea arcuata* and especially large specimens of *Plagiostoma giganteum*; Plate 10) and the nautiloid *Cenoceras* (Callomon and Cope, 1995). Fossil burrows made by soft-bodied organisms (particularly *Chondrites*, *Diplocraterion* and *Thalassinoides*) are abundant and conspicuous in the limestones, but are lacking in the finely laminated black shales (Callomon and Cope, 1995; Hesselbo and Jenkyns, 1995).

Charmouth Mudstone Formation

The type area of the Charmouth Mudstone Formation is between Charmouth and Seatown, where the formation is well exposed in a series of cliff sections and on the foreshore (Figure 6). Inland, the formation occupies about 30 km² of low-lying ground in the Char valley and Marshwood Vale (Figure 1). The principal lithologies are dark grey, laminated fissile mudstone and dark to pale grey and bluish grey mudstones. In addition, the formation contains sporadic concretionary and tabular beds of argillaceous limestone, phosphatic and sideritic nodules, organic-rich fissile mudstone ('paper shales'), and, in the upper part, silty and sandy beds. The formation is about 147 m thick on the coast, but ranges up to a maximum of 364 m in the Kimmeridge 5 Borehole (Figure 9). In south Dorset, boreholes proved 248 m at Chickerell, 218 m at Martinstown and 194 m at Nettlecombe. Thin successions occur north of the Purbeck Monocline and on the Cranborne–Fordingbridge High, with about 70 m in the Bushey Farm A1 Borehole and 125 m in the Creech Borehole. Farther north, the Winterborne Kingston Borehole proved 127 m (Rhys et al., 1982).

The lower boundary, at the top of Grey Ledge (Bed 49 of the Blue Lias) on the coast, coincides with marked upward decrease in abundance of limestone beds, associated with a decrease in their individual thickness and lateral persistence. The upper boundary corresponds to an upward change to coarser siliciclastic deposits of the Dyrham Formation (= basal Eype Clay Member) (Hesselbo and Jenkyns, 1995).

Well-established formational subdivisions in Dorset, are now formalised as members, and comprise in ascending order: the **Shales-with-Beef Member**, the

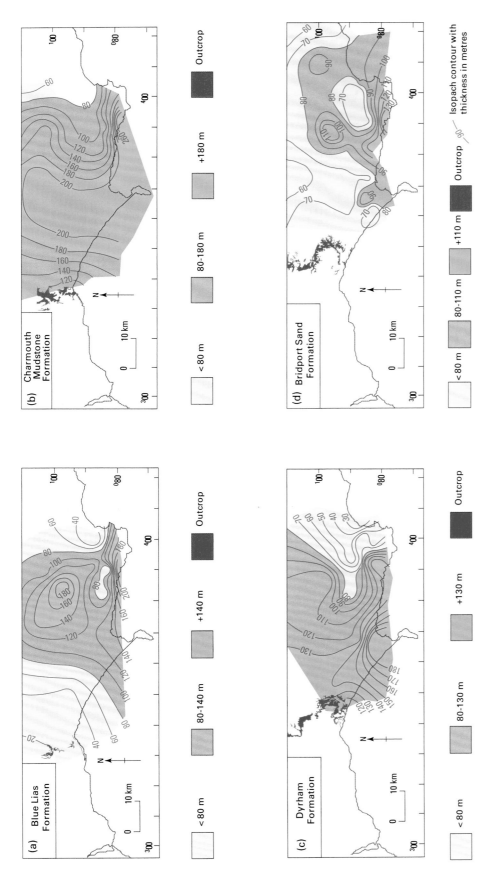

Figure 9 Generalised isopach maps for Lower Jurassic formations in Dorset and south-east Devon.

Labels on image (right side): Blue Lias Formation; Top of Sun Bed; Top of Penarth Group

Plate 9 Blue Lias Formation overlying Penarth Group at the east end of Pinhay Bay [SY 3245 9080] (P226907).

Black Ven Marl Member, the **Belemnite Marl Member** and the **Green Ammonite Member**. Their northward extent is uncertain, pending further mapping and interpretation of geophysical borehole logs in Somerset.

The Charmouth Mudstone Formation spans the greater part of the Sinemurian and Pliensbachian stages, ranging from the lower part of the Semicostatum Zone (Scipionianum Subzone) at the base, to the Margaritatus Zone (Stokesi Subzone) at the top. Ammonites are the most important elements of the fauna (Plate 10) and, in conjunction with lithological data, have helped to identify three major periods of erosion or intervals when the sequence became condensed. These are identified:

- within the upper Obtusum Zone and Oxynotum Zone (in the Black Ven Marl Member)
- in the upper Raricostatum Zone (at the junction of the Black Ven Marl Member and Belemnite Marl Member)
- at the top of the Ibex Zone and lower Davoei Zone (within the Green Ammonite Member) (Callomon and Cope, 1995; Hesselbo and Jenkyns, 1995; Figure 7).

Shales-with-Beef Member

The Shales-with-Beef (Lang, 1914, p. 313) occurs on the foreshore below Black Ven and as far east as the mouth of the River Char; the lower part reappears in a gentle syncline and can be seen in the cliffs as far west as Lyme Regis (Figure 6). The formation is dominated by dark, organic-rich, finely laminated mudstones with locally common thin seams of 'beef' (vertically oriented fibrous

Plate 10 Some characteristic fossils from the Lower Jurassic (Lias Group) of Dorset and south-east Devon. Scale bars represent 10 mm (P669422).

1	*Psiloceras planorbis* (Blue Lias)
2a–b	*Schlotheimia* (Blue Lias)
3a–b	*Arnioceras* cf. *semicostatum* (Blue Lias)
4	*Calcirhynchia* (Blue Lias)
5	*Caloceras* aff. *johnstoni* (Blue Lias)
6	*Plagiostoma giganteum* (Blue Lias)
7a–b	*Liparoceras* aff. *obtusinodum* (Belemnite Marl)
8	*Oxytoma inequivalve* (Black Ven Marl)
9	Ichthyosaur skull (Lias Group)
10a–b	*Amaltheus* aff. *margaritatus* (Dyrham)
11a–b	*Caenisites turneri* (Shales-with-Beef)
12	*Palaeocoma milleri* (Dyrham)
13a–b	*Dactylioceras* aff. *athleticum* (Beacon Limestone)
14	*Pentacrinites fossilis* (Black Ven Marl)
15a–b	*Prionorhynchia serrata* (Beacon Limestone)
16a–b	*Gibbirhynchia muirwoodae* (Dyrham)
17a–b	*Gibbirhynchia thorncombiensis* (Dyrham)
18	*Passaloteuthis elongatus* (Belemnite Marl)

calcite of diagenetic origin), and ranges from about 37 m thick in coastal exposures at Charmouth to a maximum of 130 m in the Kimmeridge 5 Borehole. Elsewhere, boreholes proved about 57 m at Chickerell and Martinstown, 34 m at Wytch Farm, 72 m at Creech and 62 m at Winterborne Kingston. Farther north, about 40 m was proved in a borehole at Mappowder.

Two principal lithologies comprise the Shales-with-Beef Member (Wilson et al., 1958; Callomon and Cope, 1995). The lowest 24.7 m of strata, up to the base of Little Ledge (Bed 74a), are bluish grey mudstones and calcareous mudstones with thin argillaceous limestones and a few seams of 'beef'. The base of the member is marked by a concentration of glauconite, pyritised fossils, fossil teeth and limestone intraclasts associated with erosion surfaces that truncate large ammonites such as *Coroniceras* (Callomon and Cope, 1995). This horizon is interpreted as an erosional winnowing and condensed surface formed at a time of elevated sea level that resulted in sediment starvation of basinal areas like Dorset (Hesselbo and Jenkyns, 1998). The upper 12.3 m of strata (Beds 74a to 75b) comprise brownish grey paper shales with numerous seams of 'beef' (Figure 10). A prominent line of nodules, the Birchi Nodule Bed (named for the ammonite *Microderoceras birchi*), occurs near the top (Plate 11); the nodules are up to 1 m in diameter and enclosed in 'beef'. A thin limestone known as the Birchi Tabular Bed occurs about 0.3 m higher; its base marks the top of the member.

Most fossils are poorly preserved, but the most important records are the ammonites *Arnioceras* and *Euagassiceras* in the Resupinatum Subzone, *Cymbites* and *Caenisites* in the Brooki Subzone and *Microderoceras* and *Promicroceras* in the Birchi Subzone (Callomon and Cope, 1995; Figure 10). Near the base of the succession (Bed 70c of Lang et al., 1923), in the Resupinatum Subzone, a friable, richly fossiliferous mudstone contains the ammonites *Arnioceras* and *Pararnioceras*, the bivalves *Liostrea*, *Gryphaea* and *Chlamys* and the brachiopod *Spiriferina* (Wilson et al., 1958). Slightly higher in the Resupinatum Subzone (Bed 72a of Lang et al., 1923), an indurated calcareous mudstone is packed full of the bivalves *Plagiostoma gigantea* and *Oxytoma* (Wilson et al., 1958). Fossil insects occur in the Birchi Nodular Bed near the top of the succession (Ziegler, 1962; Whalley, 1985).

Black Ven Marl Member

The type section of the Black Ven Marl Member extends along the foreshore from Black Ven, just west of the mouth of the River Char [SY 367 920], eastwards to Stonebarrow [SY 380 927], but much of the succession is landslipped (Plate 12). An extensive area of Black Ven Marls also crops out inland, in the core of the Marshwood Pericline (Figure 1). The principal lithology is a dark grey, pyritous mudstone and shale with sparse, thin beds and nodules of limestone. The base of the member is taken at the base of the Birchi Tabular Bed (Bed 76a, Lang and Spath, 1926) and the top is a non-sequence beneath the Hummocky limestone (Figure 11; Bed 103). The thickness of the Black Ven Marl Member ranges from 48 m

in the coastal sections at Charmouth, and 50.8 m in the Martinstown Borehole, to 137.6 m in the Kimmeridge 5 Borehole. In common with other parts of the Lias Group, the unit is attenuated north of the Purbeck Monocline, with 23 m in the Creech Borehole, and 18.9 to 26.8 m in boreholes at Wytch Farm. Farther north, 36 m occur in the Winterborne Kingston Borehole.

The main concretionary horizons are the Lower Cement Bed (Figure 11; Bed 80) and the Pavior or Upper Cement Bed (Bed 82) at about 12 and 18 m above the base, respectively, the Stonebarrow Flatstone (Bed 83) at 20 m above the base, the Stellare Nodules (Bed 88f) at 31 m above the base with the Coinstone just above it (Bed 89). The Obtusum Shales are dark mudstones that occur locally near the middle of the succession, for example at Stonebarrow and Black Ven, and include the Pentacrinite Bed (Bed 84b), which is composed almost entirely of the crinoid *Pentacrinites fossilis* (Simms, 1989). The crinoids, together with locally abundant trace fossils (especially *Chondrites*) and bivalves seen higher in the succession, indicate a normal marine palaeoenvironment, but the presence of abundant pyrite suggests that anoxic conditions occurred at some depth within the sediment (Callomon and Cope, 1995). Highly pyritic strata above the Coinstone, forming the upper part of the Black Ven Marl Member, contain relatively few limestone concretions and horizons of 'beef', and have been renamed the Stonebarrow Pyritic Member by Simms et al. (2004). In this unit, uncrushed pyritised ammonites are distinctive, particularly *Crucilobiceras*, *Eoderoceras*, *Echioceras* and *Oxynoticeras*.

The top surface of the Coinstone has a rich encrusting fauna that includes serpulids, bryozoans and oysters, which led Hallam (1969) to recognise it as a hardground. The sea-bed scouring responsible for the formation of this hardground may have been aided by the burrowing activities of marine organisms; their 'roughening' of the sea-bed sediment surface perhaps facilitating erosion by even relatively weak bottom-currents (Hesselbo and Jenkyns, 1995). A non-sequence (Figure 7) is developed above the Coinstone (Lang and Spath, 1926), although this appears to be less significant inland, where stream sections between Marshwood Manor [SY 396 992] and near Lodge House Farm suggest younger horizons of the Stellare Subzone than are present on the coast (Lang, 1932; Wilson et al., 1958; Cope et al., 1980). On the coast, there are further non-sequences in the lower part of the member, above the Pavior and at the base of the Obtusum Shales (Cope et al., 1980; Hesselbo and Jenkyns, 1995); at Stonebarrow these may be related to synsedimentary movement of the Char Fault (Hesselbo and Jenkyns, 1995).

Belemnite Marl Member

The Belemnite Marl Member is exposed in cliffs below Stonebarrow [SY 376 928 to 389 924] (Figure 12), between Westhay Water [SY 386 925] and Ridge Water [SY 391 924] (Plate 13) and below Golden Cap as far to the east as Seatown (upper strata only). Inland, the member forms an inlier in Marshwood Vale and in the

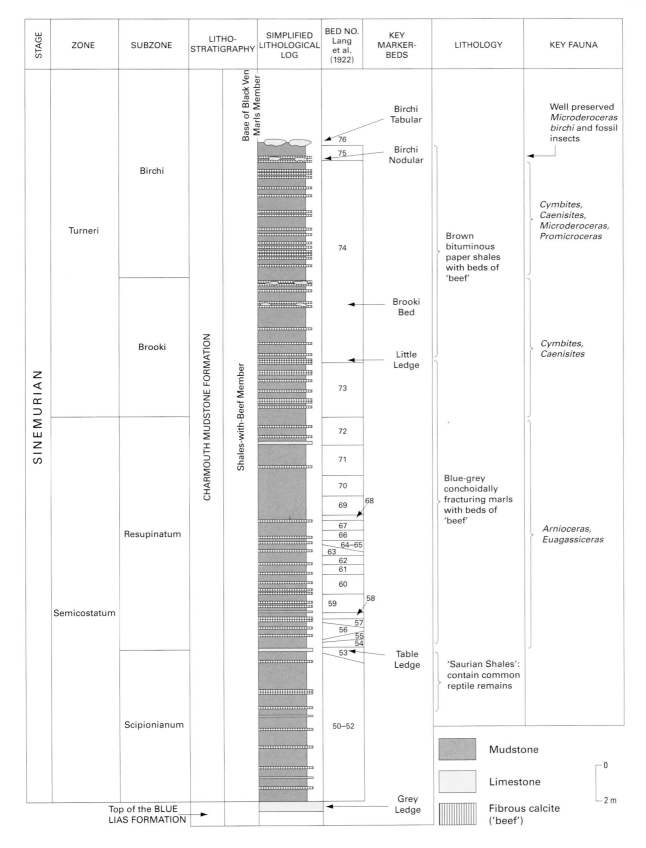

Figure 10   The stratigraphy of the Shales-with-Beef Member, based on sections at Seven Rock Point and below Black Ven [SY 356 930 to 364 930] (from a figure by Hesselbo and Jenkyns, 1995).

Black Ven
Marl
Member

Birchi
Tabular

Shales-
with-
Beef
Member

Plate 11 Shales-with-Beef Member, with Birchi Tabular in the upper cliff, overlain by Black Ven Marl Member (Charmouth Mudstone Formation), Charmouth Ledges [SY 361 930]. Height of cliff is c. 50 m (P672220).

Char valley. The characteristic lithology is a calcareous mudstone with distinctive alternations of pale and dark grey layers and, particularly in the upper part, there are abundant belemnites. The base and top are marked by thin limestones (0.1–0.15 m thick), the Hummocky (Bed 103) and the Belemnite Stone (Bed 121) respectively. The Hummocky is a nodular limestone with irregular surfaces overlain by a non-sequence where the Macdonnelli and Aplanatum subzones are absent. The Belemnite Stone is a light grey-brown concretionary horizon with a condensed faunal succession. The thickness of the Belemnite Marl Member increases toward the south from about 25 m in the cliffs at Stonebarrow, and 22.3 m in the Nettlecombe Borehole, to 35 m in the Martinstown Borehole, 48 m in the Hewish Borehole, 53 m in the Chickerell Borehole and 63.7 m in the Kimmeridge 5 Borehole. North of the Purbeck Monocline, it is 21.5 m thick in the Winterborne Kingston Borehole.

The distinctive cyclicity of pale (carbonate-rich, carbon-poor) and dark (carbonate poor, carbon-rich) mudstones is paralleled by changes in macrofossil and trace fossil assemblages, possibly reflecting climatic variations that affected detrital input of clays and/or plankton productivity (Donovan et al., 1979). The trace fossils *Rhizocorallium*, *Thalassinoides* and *Chondrites* are particularly conspicuous in the pale units (Sellwood, 1970). The light and dark-coloured mudstones form decimetre-scale bed couplets (Weedon and Jenkyns, 1990), which progressively increase in thickness in the lower and middle parts of the member, and then progressively decrease in thickness in the upper part of the member. These thickness changes indicate increasing and then decreasing net sedimentation rates (Hesselbo and Jenkyns, 1995). Belemnite abundances at first decrease and then increase concomitantly, and the member top is greatly condensed.

In general, the member is poorly fossiliferous. However, two condensed fossiliferous horizons occur in the top 0.5 m of the member, the Belemnite Bed and Belemnite Stone (Bed 120c and 121 respectively of Lang et al., 1928); these can be seen in the core of an anticline between St Gabriel's Mouth and Golden Cap and inland north of Shave Cross Inn [SY 4150 9855] (Wilson et al., 1958). The Belemnite Bed is a dark grey, pyritous and friable organic-rich mudstone containing abundant belemnites together with bivalves and the ammonite *Acanthopleuroceras*, and belongs to the Valdani Subzone. The Belemnite Stone, at the top of the Belemnite Marl Member, is similarly rich in bivalves, belemnites and ammonites (*Beaniceras*, *Lytoceras*, *Liparoceras*, *Tragophylloceras*, *Dayiceras*) and belongs to the younger Luridum Subzone (Wilson et al., 1958; Callomon and Cope, 1995; Hesselbo and Jenkyns, 1995).

Green Ammonite Member

The Green Ammonite Member (Day, 1863, p.291), named for the pale green calcite infill of ammonite fossils at some levels, is best seen in the coastal section below Golden Cap, from St Gabriel's Mouth [SY 396 923] in the west to Seatown [SY 419 918] in the

? Green Ammonite Member

Belemnite Marl Member

Top of foreground cliff →

Black Ven Marl Member

Plate 12 Black Ven Marl Member exposed in foreground cliff face, overlain by Belemnite Marl Member in background cliff face (Charmouth Mudstone Formation) at Stonebarrow [SY 375 928]. Height of cliff is c. 70 m (P672656).

east (Figure 6; Plate 14). The member crops out inland, in Marshwood Vale, but is typically concealed beneath sandy material derived from overlying strata (Wilson et al., 1958). The thickness of the member increases eastward along the coast from 15 to 37 m between Stonebarrow Cliff and Golden Cap (Lang, 1936, p. 429), perhaps as a result of synsedimentary movement of the Seatown Fault (Hesselbo and Jenkyns, 1995). Farther east, the Green Ammonite Member reaches 40.9 m in the Nettlecombe Borehole, but the thickest successions occur in boreholes in south central Dorset, with 74.6 m at Martinstown, 79.3 m at Chickerell and 98.6 m at Hewish. The member is relatively thin in boreholes at Kimmeridge (32.9 m), Creech (18.2 m) and Wytch Farm (20.4 m), while farther north only 7.5 m are present in the Winterborne Kingston Borehole. Inland, Lang (1932) claimed that the member showed a north-westerly thinning-out, resulting from a non-sequence at the base of the overlying Dyrham Formation, but this is now known to be an artefact of large-scale landslipping (Wilson et al., 1958; Cope et al., 1980).

The principal lithology is a medium or dark grey mudstone, silty to sandy in the upper part (Figure 13). Beds were numbered 6 to 41 by Phelps (1985) and this system supersedes Lang's (1936) numbering {given in parenthesis in the following text}. The base of the member is taken at the top of the Belemnite Stone and the top of the member is the base of a micaceous sandstone, known as the Three Tiers. Decimetre scale storm-generated scours, infilled with crinoid debris, belemnites, brachiopods and fossil wood indicate an unconformable junction with the underlying Belemnite Marl Member

(Hesselbo and Jenkyns, 1995), also marked by the absence of the upper part of the Luridum Subzone and lower part of the Maculatum Subzone. Marker-beds occur at three levels, the Lower Limestone (Bed 14) {123a} about 9 m above the base, the Red Band (Beds 21 to 23) {126} in the middle of the succession, about 19 m above the base, and the Upper Limestone (Beds 32 to 34) {129}, about 28 m above the base. In the lower part of the succession, the belemnites *Hastites* and *Passaloteuthis* are very abundant, together with small gastropods (*Coelodiscus*), the bivalves *Nucula* and *Parainoceramus,* and the ammonites *Aegoceras, Androgynoceras* and *Liparoceras* (Wilson et al., 1958). The Red Band, about 1 m thick, comprises a locally reddish brown weathering succession of limestones and mudstones, and also contains an association of small gastropods and *Nucula,* as well as the crinoid *Balanocrinus* (Wilson et al., 1958). In the top 3 m of the member the ammonites *Amaltheus stokesi* and *Protogrammoceras occidentale* are characteristic, and indicate the Stokesi Subzone of the Margaritatus Zone (Callomon and Cope, 1995). The uppermost 2 m of mudstones, beneath the Three Tiers, are extremely pyrite rich.

Dyrham Formation

The type area of the Dyrham Formation (formerly the Dyrham Silts of Donovan and Kellaway, 1984 and the Pennard Sands of Kellaway and Wilson, 1941) is at Dyrham in Gloucestershire. However, the finest and primary reference section is in the cliff and foreshore exposures between Seatown and Eype Mouth [SY 447 910], on the Dorset coast (Cox et al., 1999).

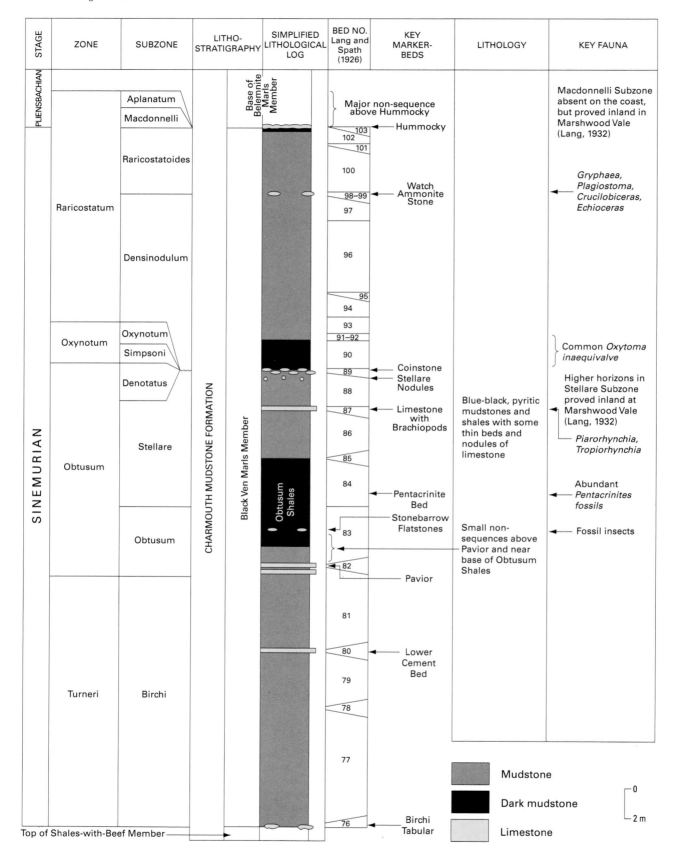

Figure 11 The stratigraphy of Black Ven Marl Member, based on the cliff section below Stonebarrow [SY 368 930 to SY 380 927] (from a figure by Hesselbo and Jenkyns, 1995).

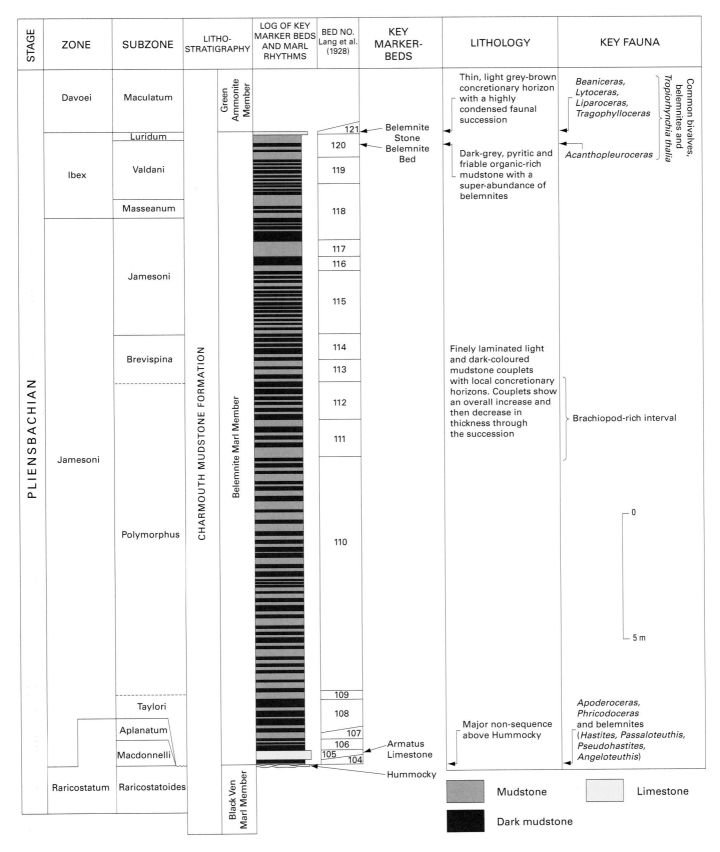

Figure 12 The stratigraphy of Belemnite Marl Member, based on the cliff sections from below
Stonebarrow [SY 380 927] to Seatown [SY 416 917] (from a figure by Hesselbo and Jenkyns, 1995).

Plate 13 Belemnite Marl Member overlain by Green Ammonite Member (Charmouth Mudstone Formation) at Westhay Water [SY 385 925]. Height of cliff is c. 25 m (P226928).

Inland, the formation forms an outcrop 2 to 4 km wide around the Marshwood Vale Pericline. The main lithologies (Figure 14) comprise pale to dark grey and greenish grey, micaceous mudstone and sandy mudstone, with interbeds of siltstone or very fine sandstone (in some cases muddy or silty), that weather to brown or yellow colours (Plate 15). Impersistent beds or concretions/doggers, of ferruginous limestone (some ooidal) and fine-grained sandstone, which may be laminated and show sedimentary structures or bioturbation, occur at the tops of sedimentary rhythms. In the upper part, the succession comprises poorly cemented fine-grained sandstone that includes occasional large argillaceous, silty or sandy limestone nodules. On the coast around Eype (Figure 9), the formation is about 115 m thick, but in boreholes ranges from a patchy development of 35 to 44 m in the Wareham Basin (Wareham 2 and Bushey Farm A1 boreholes), to a maximum of 212 m at Hewish in south Dorset. Thick successions are present in boreholes at Creech (144.6 m), Kimmeridge 5 (124.2 m), Martinstown (129.5 m) and Nettlecombe (141.5 m). Farther north, in the Winterborne Kingston Borehole, the formation is 125.4 m thick.

The lower boundary is marked by the gradational downward change from silty or finely sandy sediments to the smoother textured, predominantly mudstone lithology of the Charmouth Mudstone Formation. This coincides generally with a negative change of slope and spring line corresponding to a sandy bed that on the coast has three cemented bands, and is known as the Three Tiers (Bed 6 of Howarth, 1957; Hesselbo and Jenkyns, 1995) (Plate 14). The upper boundary is the base of the conglomeratic limestones of the Beacon Limestone Formation. The subdivisions of the formation recognised on the Dorset coast are, in ascending stratigraphical order: the **Eype Clay Member**, the **Down Cliff Sand Member** and the **Thorncombe Sand Member**.

The formation belongs wholly to the Margaritatus Zone of the Upper Pliensbachian, representing the greater part of the Stokesi Subzone, the Subnodosus Subzone and the Gibbosus Subzone (Cope et al., 1980). It is less uniformly fossiliferous than the underlying Charmouth Mudstone Formation, much of the fauna being concentrated at particular horizons.

Eype Clay Member

The Eype Clay Member is well exposed in the cliffs from Golden Cap [SY 4055 9185] to Eype [SY 4470 9103] with accessible sections east of Seatown (Plate 15). The member has a narrow inland crop around the Marshwood Vale Pericline, and occurs as an elongate inlier in the valley of the River Britt, north of Bridport, though is rarely exposed. The thickness of the Eype Clay is about 65 m in coastal exposures, and a similar thickness is present in boreholes at Hewish, Creech and Kimmeridge. Thinner successions occur in boreholes at Coombe Keynes (42.5 m) and Nettlecombe (50.9 m).

The Eype Clay Member comprises bluish grey, micaceous mudstone with impersistent beds of calcareous sandstone and abundant siderite nodules. It includes at its base an interval, up to 9 m thick, of sandstone, siltstone and sandy mudstone known as the Three Tiers (Day, 1863, p. 278; Plate 14). The 'Tiers' comprise three hard, weakly laminated, calcareous sandstone beds with *Thalassinoides* burrows and planar and ripple bedding, each about 0.5 to 1 m thick, and separated by intervals of sandy calcareous mudstone. They are well seen in deep gullies below the summit of Golden Cap [SY 407 919; SY 406 919; SY 4020 9201] and contain the ammonites *Amaltheus stokesi*, *Tragophylloceras loscombi*, *Lytoceras fimbriatum* and *Protogrammoceras occidentale* associated with common *Thalassinoides* bioturbation (Callomon and Cope, 1995; Hesselbo and Jenkyns, 1995).

There are two concretionary horizons, one about 47 m above the base and the other at the top of the succession, named respectively the Eype Nodule Bed and Day's Shell Bed (Wilson et al., 1958; Figure 14). The Eype Nodule Bed, at beach level at Seatown and Eype Mouth, comprises one or two beds of hard, calcareous nodules, rarely more than 70 mm in diameter, that are locally reworked and incorporated into the base of the overlying bed of calcareous shelly sandstone. Reworking of the nodules was related to synsedimentary movement of the Eype-

Plate 14   Green Ammonite Member (Charmouth Mudstone Formation) overlain by the Three Tiers sandstone at the base of the Eype Clay Member (Dyrham Formation), Golden Cap east [SY 407 919]. Height of cliff is c. 60 m (P672593).

mouth Fault, lateral changes in the extent of reworking varying with proximity to this structure (Simms, 2004). The nodule bed contains the ammonites *Amaltheus stokesi*, *A. wertheri*, *A. bifurcus*, *Amauroceras ferrugineum*, *Tragophylloceras loscombi*, *Protogrammoceras occidentale* and *Lytoceras fimbriatum*; the bivalve *Oxytoma inequivalve* and the crinoid *Isocrinus* also occur (Wilson et al., 1958; Callomon and Cope, 1995). Just above the nodule bed, in the overlying calcareous sandstone, a brachiopod fauna (*Lingula, Spiriferina* and *Furcirhynchia*) occurs with *Amaltheus* (Callomon and Cope, 1995). About 18 m higher, just below the top of the member, Day's Shell Bed is a thin (less than 0.3 m), laterally impersistent indurated shelly and crinoidal mudstone containing small carbonate concretions (Simms, 2004). The bed is well exposed 200 m east of Seatown [SY 4230 9161] and contains an exceptionally rich fauna (up to 60 species) of mostly juvenile gastropods and bivalves (particularly *Pseudolimea, Gryphaea, Lucina* and *Astarte*), but brachiopods, belemnites, echinoids and crustaceans also occur (Palmer, 1966; Callomon and Cope, 1995; Hesselbo and Jenkyns, 1995).

Down Cliff Sand Member

The Down Cliff Sand Member is best exposed in Ridge Cliff, and between Thorncombe Beacon [SY 4330 9135] and Eype Mouth [SY 4495 9090]. Inland, it cannot be separated from the overlying Thorncombe Sand Member. The member is typically about 27 m thick in coastal exposures; it thins eastward and ranges from 30.5 m below Thorncombe Beacon to 21.3 m at Eype Mouth (Wilson et al., 1958). The upper 12 m of the member is cut out by the overstep of Cretaceous strata on Golden Cap.

The member comprises an upward-coarsening succession of poorly cemented, grey to brown muddy siltstone and fine-grained sandstone that contains thin lenticles of more strongly cemented calcareous sandstone. Thick-shelled fossils, suggestive of a high-energy marine environment, are common and include the bivalves *Gryphaea cymbium* and *Pseudopecten aequivalvis* and the brachiopod *Gibbirhynchia muirwoodae* (Callomon and Cope, 1995; Plate 10). The well-known Starfish Bed, a nodular, greenish grey micaceous and calcareous sandstone, 1.4 m thick (Woodward, 1893, p. 197), forms the basal bed, about 1 m above Day's Shell Bed (Figure 14). It is so named because of the abundance of the brittle-star *Palaeocoma milleri* on the lower surface, preserved as a result of rapid deposition of sand (Ensom, 1983); it is visible near beach level beneath Thorncombe Beacon. The bed contains several alternations of laminated, bioturbated and locally hummocky cross-stratified sandstone (Goldring and Stevenson, 1972; Simms, 2004), and inland, provides an important mappable feature where it is associated with strong

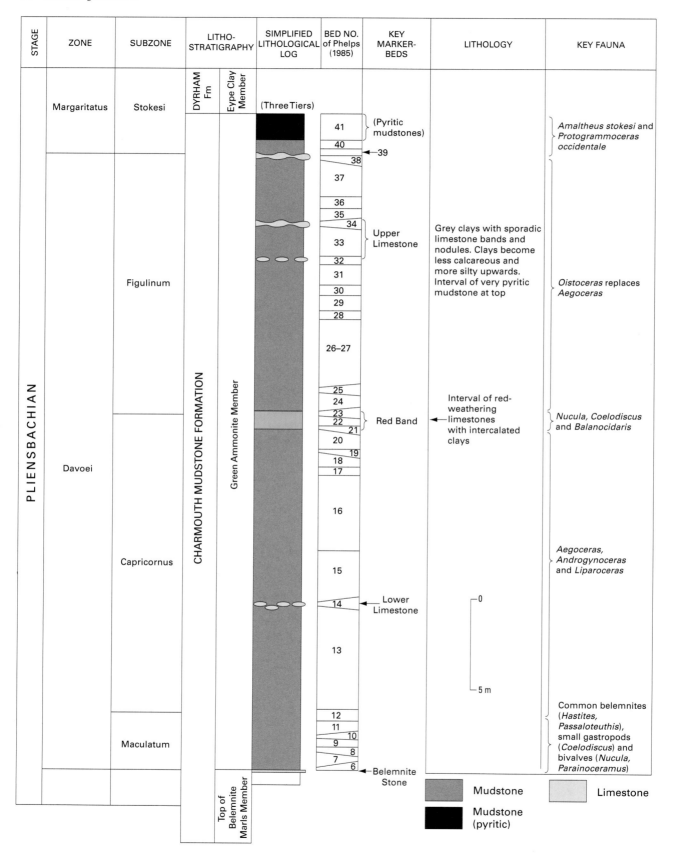

Figure 13 The stratigraphy of the Green Ammonite Member, based on the cliff sections around Golden Cap [SY 413 918 and SY 402 920] (from a figure by Hesselbo and Jenkyns, 1995).

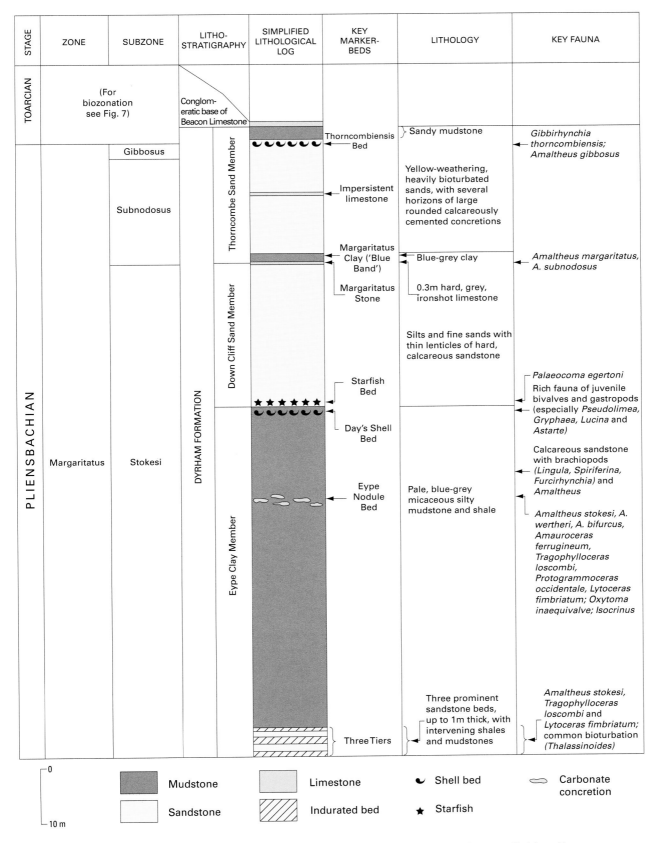

Figure 14 The stratigraphy of the Dyrham Formation, based on the cliff sections at Golden Cap [SY 406 919] and Thorncombe Beacon [SY 430 914 to 435 914] (from a figure by Hesselbo and Jenkyns, 1995).

Eype Clay
Member

Approximate
horizon of Eype
Nodule Bed

Plate 15 Eype Clay Member (Dyrham Formation) exposed at beach level at Ridge Cliff [SY 424 915]. The higher (vegetated) part of the cliff includes the Downcliff Sand and Thorncombe Sand members (Dyrham Formation), Beacon Limestone Formation (equivalent to 'Junction Bed'), and Down Cliff Clay Member (Bridport Sand Formation). Height of cliff c. 80 m (P672297).

ferruginous springs (Wilson et al., 1958). A few metres above the Starfish Bed, a 0.2 m-thick marl is characterised by abundant ossicles of the crinoid *Isocrinus* [? = *Balanocrinus* of Simms (1989)] (Wilson et al., 1958). The Margaritatus Stone, a 0.3 m thick, blue-centred, yellow-weathering, slightly conglomeratic ironshot limestone, marks the top of the Down Cliff Sand. Its ammonite fauna includes *Amaltheus margaritatus* and *Amaltheus subnodosus*, indicative of the Subnodosus Subzone (Callomon and Cope, 1995).

Thorncombe Sand Member

The Thorncombe Sand Member is best exposed in often inaccessible cliff sections between Doghouse Hill [SY 4275 9128] and Eype Mouth. The thickness of the Thorncombe Sand Member is about 27 m in coastal exposures, comparable with the underlying Down Cliff Sand Member. The combined thickness of the two units is comparable in boreholes at Martinstown (65.1 m), Chickerell (54.9 m), Coombe Keynes (65.2 m) and Kimmeridge 5 (59.4 m). Thicker successions were recorded in boreholes at Creech (82.8 m), Nettlecombe (90.6 m), and Hewish (146.9 m).

Most of the member comprises a succession of predominantly yellow-brown, weakly cemented, fine-grained or very fine-grained sandstone with large, stronger calcareous sandstone concretions or 'doggers'.

It is typically more yellow-weathering than the underlying Down Cliff Sand, and is extensively bioturbated with *Thalassinoides* burrows (Callomon and Cope, 1995) and contains hummocky cross-stratification (Sellwood et al., 1970). The basal bed, or Blue Band, comprises 2 m of blue-grey, shelly mudstone that succeed the Margaritatus Stone and forms a conspicuous marker in cliff sections, particularly between Ridge Cliff and Eype Mouth. The fauna of the lower and greater part of the member comprises bivalves (*Gryphaea cymbium* and *Pseudopecten aequivalvis*), belemnites and the ammonites *Amaltheus margaritatus, A. subnodosus, A. striatus* and *Amauroceras ferrugineum*, indicative of the Subnodosus Subzone (Callomon and Cope, 1995). Rhynchonellids commonly occur in clusters in the sands, or on the weathered surfaces of more indurated horizons (Wilson et al., 1958). There is an impersistent limestone about 0.3 m thick around the middle of the member, and at the top is a 0.35 m thick unit of brown calcareous mudstone and limestone named the Thorncombiensis Bed (Wilson et al., 1958), overlain by 2.3 to 4.6 m of grey sandy mudstone (Figure 14). The Thorncombiensis Bed contains abundant specimens of the brachiopod *Gibbirhynchia thorncombiensis* (Plate 10) and an ammonite fauna that includes *Amaltheus gibbosus*, indicative of the Gibbosus Subzone (Callomon and Cope, 1995). Strata above the Thorncombiensis Bed thin progressively between Thorncombe Beacon and Eype Mouth, east of which they have been completely removed by erosion, probably as a result of synsedimentary fault movement. The top of the member is defined by the base of the overlying Beacon Limestone Formation.

Beacon Limestone Formation

The Beacon Limestone Formation (formerly Junction Bed *sensu lato*) of Dorset is a highly condensed succession of limestones with erosion surfaces and non-sequences. The type section is the cliff exposure beneath Thorncombe Beacon [SY 4354 9148], from which the formation takes its name (Cox et al., 1999). Inland, the formation forms a prominent feature, giving rise to small plateaux north of Bridport (Wilson et al., 1958). At Thorncombe Beacon, the formation is typically 0.6 to 1.5 m thick, and reaches its maximum coastal thickness at Watton Cliff [SY 451 909], where 3.65 m is present; elsewhere the formation is locally absent. The Winterborne Kingston Borehole, proved 3.29 m (Ivimey-Cook, 1982; Rhys et al., 1982).

The predominant lithology is limestone, ferruginous and ooidal in the lower part, fine-grained, nodular and rich in ammonites in the upper part, and sporadically conglomeratic throughout. Variable grey, pink, reddish brown and brown colours are typical. Many ammonites are preserved in vertical orientation, consistent with preservation by episodic and rapid sedimentation (Hallam, 1967); many others are planed through at erosional surfaces suggesting that they were lithified at the time of erosion (Callomon and Cope, 1995). The sharp lower boundary is non-sequential and taken at the upward change from argillaceous, silty or sandy beds of the Dyrham Formation. The upper boundary is also non-sequential and taken at the base of mudstones of the Bridport Sand Formation. The formation is divided into two members, the **Marlstone Rock Member**, overlain by the **Eype Mouth Limestone Member** (Cox et al., 1999).

The formation ranges from the upper Pliensbachian Spinatum Zone to the upper Toarcian Levesquei Zone. Within a maximum of less than 4 m of strata there are at least six ammonite zones and up to 15 ammonite subzones (Figure 7). However, the pervasive development of non-sequences in the succession and degree of reworking mean that much of the time represented by these biozones (about 6 million years; Cope et al., 1980; Sellwood and Wilson, 1990) is not preserved as sediment. In contrast, coeval deposits in Yorkshire are at least 120 m thick.

Marlstone Rock Member

The Marlstone Rock Member is a thin brown, grey and locally pink limonitic limestone with ooids, sandstone pebbles and a conglomeratic base. Typically the member is 0.1 to 0.2 m thick on the coast, but slightly thicker (0.3 to 0.45 m) at Thorncombe Beacon and inland (0.66 to 0.89 m) at Symondsbury [SY 4450 9365] (Wilson et al., 1958). Up to four thin subdivisions were distinguished by Howarth (1992), using a combination of lithology and fauna. However, the succession at any given locality is seldom complete because of localised non-sequences

associated with the development of erosion surfaces, one of which is responsible for the complete absence of the member at Watton Cliff, where erosion has occurred down to the Thorncombiensis Bed (Figure 14) at the top of the Thorncombe Sand (Howarth, 1957).

The Marlstone Rock Member equates with the greater part of the Spinatum Zone at the top of the Pliensbachian, and the Tenuicostatum Zone at the base of the Toarcian (Hesselbo and Jenkyns, 1995). A persistent non-sequence at the junction with the underlying Thorncombe Sand Member is attributed to the lower part of the Apyrenum Subzone (Howarth, 1957; Figure 7). The lower, conglomeratic part of the member (Apyrenum Subzone) is characterised by common brachiopods and the ammonite *Pleuroceras solare* (Howarth, 1957). The higher, ferruginous ooidal limestone part, belongs to the Hawskerense Subzone, and contains the ammonites *Pleuroceras* spp., *Protogrammoceras paltum* and *Dactylioceras directum*, together with a distinctive brachiopod fauna that includes *Prionorhynchia serrata* (Plate 10) and *Rudirhynchia egretta* (Howarth, 1957).

Eype Mouth Limestone Member

The Eype Mouth Limestone Member comprises a highly condensed unit of pink, pinkish grey, red and yellow, locally conglomeratic, hard, micritic limestone. The member is typically 0.4 to 0.6 m thick at Ridge Down Cliff [SY 4262 9141], Doghouse Cliff [SY 4290 9132] and Thorncombe Beacon. The maximum thickness recorded in coastal exposures is 3.65 m at Watton Cliff and relatively thick successions (over 0.86 m) occur inland at Symondsbury. The base of the member is taken at the first massive pink and red limestone, up to 0.23 m thick, that overlies brown, limonitic limestone of the Marlstone Rock Member. Up to five lithological and faunal divisions were recognised by Howarth (1992), of which the upper two comprise pale or white conglomeratic limestone a few centimetres thick.

The Eype Mouth Limestone was episodically deposited through the greater part of the Toarcian, and contains a rich ammonite fauna representing (in ascending stratigraphical order) the Tenuicostatum Zone, Falciferum Zone, Bifrons Zone, Variabilis Zone (locally absent), Thouarsense Zone and basal Levesquei Zone (Cope et al., 1980; Callomon and Cope, 1995; Figure 7). The succession of ammonite zones is locally affected by the variable development of non-sequences associated with erosion surfaces, and some lateral changes in thickness of the member and anomalies in the ammonite faunal succession may be attributable to synsedimentary fault movements (Jenkyns and Senior, 1991). These authors show that some fine-grained limestones occur in horizontal tectonic fissures that were infilled by a random sequence of ammonites during faulting.

Bridport Sand Formation

The Bridport Sand Formation of Dorset is superbly exposed in coastal cliffs between West Bay [SY 465 905] and Burton Bradstock [SY 488 889] that provide the type

Plate 16   Bridport
Sand Formation,
East Cliff, West Bay
[SY 470 899–903].
A thin brownish
grey horizon at the
base of the cliff is
the Downcliff Clay
Member, overlain by
an interval containing
thin, undulating
sandstone beds.
Height of cliff c. 40 m
(P672325).

section (Plate 16). Additional cliff sections occur below Thorncombe Beacon and the adjoining Doghouse Hill. Inland, the formation has an arcuate, 2 km-wide crop in the area between Broadwindsor [ST 437 026] and Burton Bradstock. The formation averages 135 m in south Dorset (Figure 9), but thicker successions occur in boreholes at Bushey Farm A1 Borehole, Coombe Keynes and Kimmeridge 5, where it is over 200 m thick. It is thinner near the coastal exposures in west Dorset, with 87.5 m in the Martinstown Borehole and 101.5 m in the Nettlecombe Borehole. The Winterborne Kingston Borehole is a primary reference section, and proved 186.7 m (Ivimey-Cook, 1982; Knox et al., 1982; Rhys et al., 1982).

The principal lithologies are rhythmic alternations of friable micaceous siltstone or fine-grained sandstone, and cemented beds or doggers of calcareous sandstone. The succession is greenish grey when fresh, weathering to a distinctive yellow or brown colour. Sandy bioclastic limestones are present locally. A unit of variably sandy mudstone, the **Down Cliff Clay Member** (Buckman, 1922), occurs at the base. The lower formation boundary is taken at the base of the mudstone resting non-sequentially on limestone of the Beacon Limestone Formation, and the upper boundary is the base of the lowest limestone of the Inferior Oolite (= base of Scissum or Bottom Bed; Bed 6a of Callomon and Cope, 1995) in the type section (Richardson, 1928). A late Toarcian sea level highstand and subsequent fall may account for the change to sandy facies of the Bridport Sand in Dorset (Hesselbo and Jenkyns, 1998).

The friable sandstones, which form the bulk of the succession, are up to 2 m thick. They are extensively bioturbated, well sorted and very fine-grained, made of angular to very angular quartz grains, with small amounts of mica, feldspar, and bioclastic debris (Davies, 1969; Knox et al., 1982). The most common trace fossils are *Thalassinoides, Rhizocorallium, Teichichnus* and *Skolithos* (Bryant et al., 1988). The cemented sandstones are typically less than 0.5 m thick and weather out as ribs in the cliff faces. They contain abundant bivalve shell fragments and scattered fine-grained sand grains set in a matrix of fine-grained ferroan calcite. Small-scale cross- and festoon- bedding occur locally. The bioclastic limestones comprise broken, abraded and bored bivalve fragments, with very minor chamositic or phosphatised ooids and fine-grained sand; typically these rest upon minor erosion surfaces. The formation is regarded as part of a coarsening- and shallowing-upward succession, that commences with the Down Cliff Clay and extends into the Inferior Oolite (Holloway, 1985; Bryant et al., 1988; Hesselbo and Jenkyns, 1995). The sedimentology of the Bridport Sands suggests deposition in a shallow marine environment influenced by storm waves (Davies, 1969; Bryant et al., 1988).

On the Dorset coast, the Bridport Sand Formation belongs mostly to the Upper Toarcian Levesquei Zone, with a thin representative (less than 2 m) of the basal Aalenian Opalinum Zone deposits at the top (Cope et al., 1980; Hesselbo and Jenkyns, 1995). However, farther north in Somerset and the Cotswolds, the onset of Bridport Sand deposition was earlier. The facies gradually extended southwards into Dorset, and is one of the first-documented instances of diachronism (Buckman, 1889). Locally, adjacent to the Bride Fault at the eastern end of Burton Cliff [SY 489 887] and near the Eype Mouth Fault at Shipton Gorge [SY 499 914], Toarcian sandstones contain fissures infilled with younger (Bajocian) faunas, indicative of a phase of synsedimentary fault movement that postdates the Bridport Sand Formation.

Plate 17 Burton Cliff [SY 481 893] showing Bridport Sand Formation (Lias Group) overlain by Inferior Oolite Formation and Fuller's Earth Formation (Great Oolite Group). Height of cliff c. 45 m (P672575).

INFERIOR OOLITE FORMATION

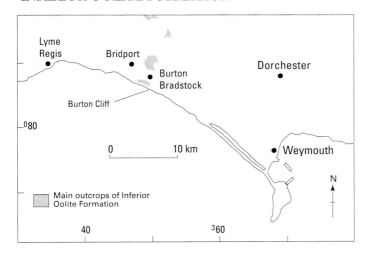

Map 3   Inferior Oolite Formation.

The Inferior Oolite Formation (now regarded as a group throughout England) of south Dorset comprises just a few metres of condensed, mud-rich, shallow water limestone (Plate 17). The beds extend north from the coast near Burton Bradstock in a curved and fragmented belt to Beaminster and Broadwindsor, and form numerous outliers that cap hills in extensively faulted ground. The limestones are predominantly bioclastic or siliciclastic, commonly nodular, and are interbedded with calcareous mudstones, ferruginous and peloidal beds, glauconitic and phosphatic horizons. Richly fossiliferous beds are common.

The Inferior Oolite is approximately 4 m thick on the coast at Burton Bradstock. Progressive northward thickening at depth is demonstrated by thicknesses proved in boreholes, with 18 m at Kimmeridge 5, 21.7 m at Southard Quarry, and 32 m proved at Mappowder, increasing in north Dorset to 44.2 m in the Purse Caundle Borehole [ST 7012 1826] (Barton et al., 1993). Thin successions occur in boreholes north of the Purbeck Monocline, at Bushey Farm (A1 Borehole, 1.8 m), Wareham (2 to 5.5 m) and Wytch Farm (0.2 to 1.2 m). The formation is also attenuated and incomplete in west Dorset and Somerset as a result of major non-sequences. The thin and highly condensed Inferior Oolite seen in south Dorset appears to represent deposition across an intrabasinal structural high (the 'South Dorset Swell' of Callomon and Cope, 1995), in contrast with the offshore limestone ramp that is the likely setting for the thicker successions seen in north Dorset (Sellwood and Jenkyns, 1975; Bristow et al., 1995). In both cases syndepositional faulting caused laterally variable sedimentation and erosion (Callomon and Cope, 1995).

The condensed and laterally variable nature of the Inferior Oolite, and frequency of non-sequences, makes biostratigraphical comparisons the key to understanding the correlation of the various south Dorset successions. The section at Burton Cliff is described by Callomon and Cope (1995) and Cox and Sumbler (2002), where the lower part of the Inferior Oolite (Aalenian) and the upper part (Late Bajocian and earliest Bathonian) are separated by a more broken succession. There are at least five significant biozonal gaps spread through the greater part of the Bajocian (Figure 15a). The succession here contains some distinctively named lithological and faunal horizons (Figure 15b), such as the Scissum Bed near the base of the succession. The bed is named after the unusual abundance of the ammonite *Tmetoceras scissum* (Plate 18), and is a highly calcareous sandstone, similar to the cemented

Figure 15a Comparison of zonal development in the Inferior Oolite Formation for key outcrops in Dorset and the Winterborne Kingston Borehole.

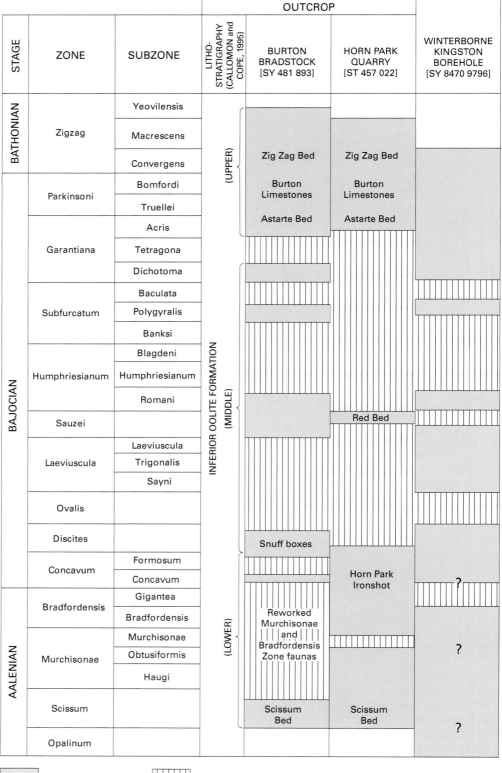

STAGE	ZONE	SUBZONE	LITHO-STRATIGRAPHY (CALLOMON and COPE, 1995)	OUTCROP		WINTERBORNE KINGSTON BOREHOLE [SY 8470 9796]
				BURTON BRADSTOCK [SY 481 893]	HORN PARK QUARRY [ST 457 022]	
BATHONIAN	Zigzag	Yeovilensis	(UPPER)			
		Macrescens		Zig Zag Bed	Zig Zag Bed	
		Convergens		Burton Limestones	Burton Limestones	
BAJOCIAN	Parkinsoni	Bomfordi		Astarte Bed	Astarte Bed	
		Truellei				
	Garantiana	Acris				
		Tetragona				
		Dichotoma	INFERIOR OOLITE FORMATION (MIDDLE)			
	Subfurcatum	Baculata				
		Polygyralis				
		Banksi				
	Humphriesianum	Blagdeni				
		Humphriesianum				
		Romani			Red Bed	
	Sauzei					
	Laeviuscula	Laeviuscula				
		Trigonalis				
		Sayni				
	Ovalis					
	Discites			Snuff boxes		
	Concavum	Formosum	(LOWER)		Horn Park Ironshot	
		Concavum				?
AALENIAN	Bradfordensis	Gigantea		Reworked Murchisonae and Bradfordensis Zone faunas		
		Bradfordensis				?
	Murchisonae	Murchisonae				
		Obtusiformis				
		Haugi				
	Scissum			Scissum Bed	Scissum Bed	?
	Opalinum					

Limestone   Non-sequence

Figure 15b Graphic section of the Inferior Oolite Formation at Burton Cliff, Burton Bradstock [SY 481 893] (adapted from Cox and Sumbler, 2002).

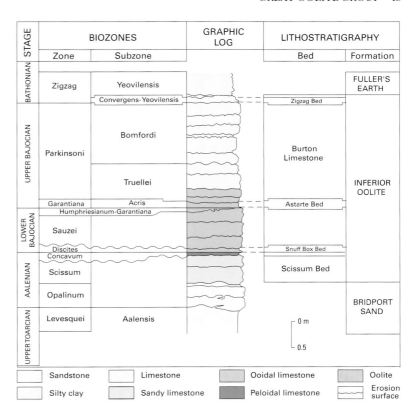

STAGE	BIOZONES		GRAPHIC LOG	LITHOSTRATIGRAPHY	
	Zone	Subzone		Bed	Formation
BATHONIAN	Zigzag	Yeovilensis		Zigzag Bed	FULLER'S EARTH
		Convergens-Yeovilensis			
UPPER BAJOCIAN	Parkinsoni	Bomfordi		Burton Limestone	INFERIOR OOLITE
		Truellei			
	Garantiana	Acris		Astarte Bed	
LOWER BAJOCIAN		Humphriesianum-Garantiana			
	Sauzei			Snuff Box Bed	
	Discites				
AALENIAN	Concavum				
	Scissum			Scissum Bed	
	Opalinum				BRIDPORT SAND
UPPER TOARCIAN	Levesquei	Aalensis			

0 m
0.5

| | Sandstone | | Limestone | | Ooidal limestone | | Oolite |
| | Silty clay | | Sandy limestone | | Peloidal limestone | | Erosion surface |

horizons in the underlying Bridport Sand Formation. The 'Snuff Boxes', also in the lower part of the succession, are discoidal structures, 30 mm to 0.3 m in diameter and up to 80 mm thick, formed by nucleation of calcareous organisms on fossil fragments (Sellwood et al., 1970; Gatrall et al. 1972; Palmer and Wilson, 1990; Hesselbo and Jenkyns, 1995; Plate 19). Material was accreted onto the undersides of the growing snuff boxes, which were periodically over-turned by agitating bottom-currents (Cox and Sumbler, 2002). In the upper part of the succession are the Astarte Bed and Zig Zag Bed, the former containing an abundance of the bivalve *Neocrassina modiolaris* (formerly '*Astarte obliqua*') and the latter characterised by Zig Zag Zone ammonites. The Burton Limestones is a traditional term for the interval of bioclastic limestones and thin calcareous mudstones between the Astarte Bed and Zig Zag Bed. At the eastern end of Burton Cliff, a sliver of Inferior Oolite is caught up in an extension of the Bride Fault and exposed in the upper beach [SY 489 887]. The ammonite fauna indicates the Subfurcatum Zone, Baculata Subzone (Jenkyns and Senior, 1991), not represented in the Burton Cliff itself although known inland in the Purse Caundle Borehole (Barton et al., 1993). Large blocks of Bridport Sand on the foreshore west of the fault trace contain subhorizontal fissures containing out of sequence Inferior Oolite ammonites indicative of the Garantiana Zone, probably Tetragona Subzone (Jenkyns and Senior, 1991).

Inland, the 5 m-thick section at Horn Park Quarry [ST 457 022], near Beaminster, is also described by Callomon and Cope (1995, fig. 10) and Cox and Sumbler (2002). In this section, much more of the Bajocian is missing than at Burton Cliff (Figure 15a), but some of the distinctive horizons can still be recognised, such as the Scissum Bed, the Astarte Bed, the Burton Limestones and the Zig Zag Bed. An exceptionally rich Upper Bradfordensis to Concavum Zone ammonite fauna occurs in the lower part of the succession, in a brown ooidal unit named the Horn Park Ironshot Bed. Between Beaminster and Crewkerne the formation is thin and strata of Levesquei to Subfurcatum zone age are commonly absent.

GREAT OOLITE GROUP

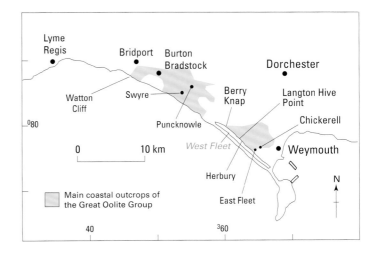

Map 4 Great Oolite Group.

In Dorset, the Great Oolite Group is divided into the **Fuller's Earth**, **Frome Clay**, **Forest Marble** and **Cornbrash** formations (Figure 16). Faulted and discontinuous exposures occur along the west Dorset coast within two belts: north of the Abbotsbury Fault as far as Burton Cliff, and within the axial zone of the Weymouth Anticline, between Shipmore Point [SY 577 836] and West Fleet [SY 624 810].

Fuller's Earth Formation

The basal few metres of Fuller's Earth mudstone is exposed above the Inferior Oolite at Burton Cliff (Plate 17). The formation is not well exposed elsewhere along the Dorset coast because the 5 km-long coastal crop between the Bride and Abbotsbury faults [SY 508 878 to 552 851] is concealed beneath landslipped material. Inland, the formation forms a belt 1 km wide between Shipton Gorge and Broadwindsor, east of and parallel with the outcrop of the Inferior Oolite. The Fuller's Earth shows a progressive southward thickening from typically less than 50 m north of the Mere Fault to more than 200 m south of the major growth faults in south Dorset (Figure 17). In boreholes at Chickerell, Kimmeridge 5 and Hewish the thicknesses are 156 m, 175 m and 219 m respectively, with 113 m present in the Winterborne Kingston Borehole. The thickest successions occur in the Langton Herring Borehole (263 m), and offshore in the Lulworth Banks Borehole (298 m).

The formation comprises two thick mudstone units, the Lower and Upper Fuller's Earth members, separated by a thin limestone member, the Fuller's Earth Rock (Woodward, 1894). This succession is seen in the Shaftesbury area and in the Winterborne Kingston Borehole (Figure 17), but near the coast, the Fuller's Earth Rock is thin or absent, and consequently the formation is not divided. At Burton Cliff, the basal beds are poorly fossiliferous grey, calcareous, silty mudstone, containing the bivalve *Bositra buchii* (Roemer) (Cox and Sumbler, 2002). The highest beds, seen along the shore of the Fleet, comprise grey clay with white limestone nodules and the brachiopod *Rhynchonelloidella smithi* (Davidson). The formation top is taken at the base of a thin argillaceous limestone, the Wattonensis Beds, the basal member of the Frome Clay. The Wattonensis Beds were formerly mapped as Fuller's Earth Rock on Sheet 327 Bridport and the succeeding Frome Clay as Upper Fuller's Earth (White, 1923; Arkell, 1947; Wilson et al., 1958).

Frome Clay Formation

The Frome Clay of Dorset was formerly included with the Upper Fuller's Earth (White, 1923; Arkell, 1947; Wilson et al., 1958), but Penn et al. (1979) showed it to be younger than the Upper Fuller's Earth of the Bath type area and re-named it the Frome Clay. It crops out below the scarp of the Forest Marble along three short stretches of coast: at Watton Cliff (Plate 20) between the Eype Mouth and Mangerton faults, south of Burton Bradstock [SY 493 887 to 507 879], and discontinuously behind the Fleet [SY 593 525 to 610 810] eastward

from Herbury [SY 611 810], within the axial zone of the Weymouth Anticline. Inland, the principal outcrop is an arcuate belt 0.5 km wide between Chilcombe [SY 5290 9105] and Broadwindsor, and there is a narrow, discontinuous, faulted outcrop [SY 620 827] north of Langton Herring. The Frome Clay is typically 60 to 70 m thick in south Dorset (Figure 18), but thins progressively north and north-eastwards. Thick successions occur in boreholes at Kimmeridge 5 (75.5 m), Martinstown (77.5 m) and Hewish (70.18 m), and relatively thin successions in boreholes at Stoborough (43.6 m) and Waddock Cross (48.8 m). Thickness variations in the Fuller's Earth and Frome Clay suggest that the rates of subsidence in the Wessex Basin south of the Mere Fault increased steadily during the Bathonian, favouring the development of a basinal mudstone facies (Bristow et al., 1995).

The Frome Clay consists predominantly of mottled buff and olive-grey, laminated, poorly fossiliferous, calcareous mudstone. The source of the clay is uncertain; it may have been winnowed from argillaceous successions along the western margins of the Wessex Basin (Martin, 1967) or possibly derived from a shelf area between central England and the southern North Sea (Bristow et al., 1995). The base of the Frome Clay is marked by an increase in shell-detritus in calcareous mudstone. A thin limestone-rich interval, the Wattonensis Beds Member, forms the basal unit in Dorset (Figure 16), and has its stratotype locality at Watton Cliff [SY 453 908] (Cox and Sumbler, 2002), where the unit comprises medium olive-grey, bioturbated shell-detrital silty mudstone interbedded with thin (80 to 120 mm thick), pale olive-grey, argillaceous shelly limestones. Each limestone has a sharp, irregular margin, and most have burrowed (*Chondrites*) tops; there are twenty or so limestones at Watton Cliff and typically about five or six in north Dorset. Mudstone beds are approximately 0.3 m thick, with pyritised bivalve and rhynchonellid debris and fossil wood fragments. The Wattonensis Beds have a maximum thickness of 8 m at Watton Cliff; 4.4 m and 2.9 m occur in the Winterborne Kingston and Purse

Plate 18 Some characteristic fossils from the Middle Jurassic of Dorset. Scale bars represent 10 mm (P669426).

1	*Tmetoceras scissum* (Inferior Oolite)	
2	*Parkinsonia parkinsoni* (Inferior Oolite)	
3	*Praeexogyra hebridica* var. *elongata* (Frome Clay)	
4a–b	*Rhynchonelloidella wattonensis* (Frome Clay)	
5	*Praeexogyra hebridica* (Frome Clay)	
6a–b	*Goniorhynchia boueti* (Forest Marble)	
7a–b	*Digonella digona* (Forest Marble)	
8a–b	*Cererithyris intermedia* (Cornbrash)	
9a–b	*Obovothyris obovata* (Cornbrash)	
10	*Neocrassina hilpertonensis* (Cornbrash)	
11	*Trigonia pullus* (Cornbrash)	
12a–b	*Ornithella siddingtonensis* (Cornbrash)	
13a–b	*Macrocephalites dolius* (Cornbrash)	
14a–b	*Clydoniceras discus* (Cornbrash)	

Plate 19 Fallen blocks of limonitic oncoidal limestone ('Snuff Box Bed'), Inferior Oolite Formation, Burton Cliff [SY 481 893] (P672378).

Caundle boreholes, respectively (Penn, 1982; Barton et al., 1993; Bristow et al., 1995).

The Frome Clay belongs to the Upper Bathonian Retrocostatum Zone. The fauna of the Wattonensis Beds includes *Kallirhynchia*, *Rhynchonelloidella wattonensis* (Plate 18), *Bositra buchi*, *Entolium?*, *Gervillella*, *Modiolus?*, ostreids, *Pholadomya?* and *Pinna?*. The fossils listed by Kellaway and Wilson (1941, p. 160) as characteristic of the Wattonensis Beds occur principally in the upper 1 m and in overlying silty mudstone; they include *Acanthothyris powerstockensis*, *Rhynchonelloidella smithi*, *Rugitela* and *Camptonectes*. This unit has yielded ammonites of the Quercinus Subzone in the Weymouth area. The fauna is rather sparse above the Wattonensis Beds, except for two oyster-rich intervals in which *Praeexogyra hebridica* (Plate 18) is abundant. Boreholes near Langton Herring at Herbury [SY 6121 8105] and Seabarn Farm [SY 6263 8054] show that oysters form lumachelles at two levels: the 'Lower Hebridica Lumachelle', or 'Elongata Bed', is 1.1 m thick and occurs immediately above the Wattonensis Beds; the 'Upper Hebridica Lumachelle' is 3.3 m thick and occurs 30 m higher. The upper lumachelle, sometimes referred to as the Hebridica Beds, is seen at Watton Cliff and Langton Hive Point [SY 606 814], and more sparsely in a black fissile mudstone interval in the Winterborne Kingston Borehole at 787.1 to 788.62 m depth (Torrens, 1969; Penn, 1982; House, 1993).

Forest Marble Formation

The Forest Marble is well exposed on the Dorset coast, both at Watton Cliff (Plate 20) near Bridport, and on the shore of the Fleet within the Weymouth Anticline (Cox and Sumbler, 2002), where it crops out as two west–east belts around Langton Herring. Inland exposures are present between the Eype Mouth and Abbotsbury faults, and north of Langton Herring. The formation commonly forms a prominent scarp and an irregular topography is associated with the extremely varied lithology. It is typically 40 to 55 m thick in south Dorset (Figure 18), and reaches a maximum of 66.4 m in the Hewish Borehole. Relatively thick successions also occur in boreholes at Lulworth Banks (64.9 m), Winterborne Kingston (52.5 m) and Kimmeridge 5 (52 m).

Although the formation name suggests a predominance of limestone, the principal lithology in Dorset is a greenish grey, brownish grey-weathering, sandy, more or less calcareous mudstone. Thin wisps, lenses and laminae of calcareous sandstone, thick bodies of reddish orange sand and numerous laterally impersistent units of limestone and sandstone occur throughout the succession. These vary vertically and laterally, from flaggy, cross-bedded, sparsely ooidal, shell-detrital, oyster-rich limestones, commonly with mud clasts and abundant lignite debris in their basal part, to laminated, cross-bedded calcareous sandstones. The sedimentology and fauna suggest deposition in a shallow-marine or brackish water environment that was periodically affected by storms (Bristow et al., 1995).

The formation base is taken at the base of the Boueti Bed (Figure 16), a yellowish grey, argillaceous shelly micritic limestone, up to 1 m thick that overlies the Frome Clay non-sequentially. It is especially well developed in low cliffs at the northern end of the Herbury peninsula, east of Herbury [SY 6202 8145; 6212 8152; 6222 8169; 6210 8190] and at Watton Cliff (Plate 20) (Cox and Sumbler, 2002); it commonly contains a rich and varied fauna that includes the eponymous brachiopod *Goniorhynchia boueti* (Plate 18). A second, similar shell bed with a burrowed base, the Digona Bed, also occurs on the Herbury Peninsula, about 18 m above the formation base (Figure 16). It is a 1.5 m-thick interval of pale-grey and cream-coloured limestone and calcareous mudstone, and is also characterised by a brachiopod fauna dominated by terebratulids including *Digonella digona* after which the bed is named (Plate 18); *Avonothyris bradfordensis* and *Rhynchonelloidella curvivarians* also occur, together with the bivalves *Nuculana*, *Oxytoma* and *Plagiostoma* and common ossicles of the crinoid *Apiocrinites*. At Watton Cliff, the characteristic

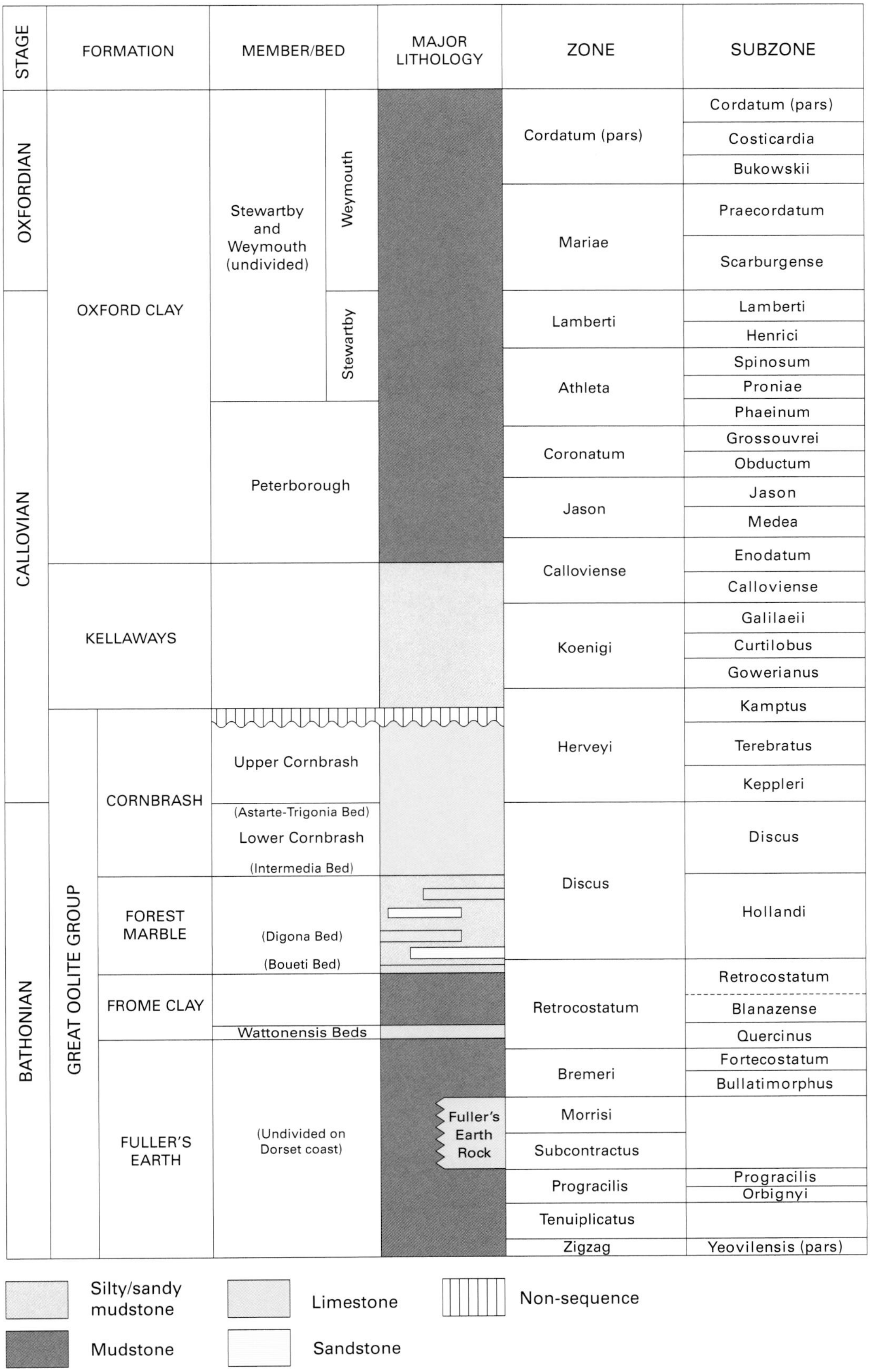

Figure 16
Biostratigraphical summary of the Fuller's Earth, Frome Clay, Forest Marble, Cornbrash, Kellaways and Oxford Clay formations. Not to scale.

STAGE	FORMATION	MEMBER/BED		MAJOR LITHOLOGY	ZONE	SUBZONE
OXFORDIAN	OXFORD CLAY	Stewartby and Weymouth (undivided)	Weymouth		Cordatum (pars)	Cordatum (pars)
						Costicardia
						Bukowskii
					Mariae	Praecordatum
						Scarburgense
CALLOVIAN			Stewartby		Lamberti	Lamberti
						Henrici
		Peterborough			Athleta	Spinosum
						Proniae
						Phaeinum
					Coronatum	Grossouvrei
						Obductum
					Jason	Jason
						Medea
	KELLAWAYS				Calloviense	Enodatum
						Calloviense
					Koenigi	Galilaeii
						Curtilobus
						Gowerianus
BATHONIAN	GREAT OOLITE GROUP	CORNBRASH	Upper Cornbrash		Herveyi	Kamptus
						Terebratus
						Keppleri
		(Astarte-Trigonia Bed) Lower Cornbrash (Intermedia Bed)			Discus	Discus
		FOREST MARBLE	(Digona Bed)			Hollandi
			(Boueti Bed)			
		FROME CLAY			Retrocostatum	Retrocostatum
						Blanazense
			Wattonensis Beds			Quercinus
		FULLER'S EARTH	(Undivided on Dorset coast)	Fuller's Earth Rock	Bremeri	Fortecostatum
						Bullatimorphus
					Morrisi	
					Subcontractus	
					Progracilis	Progracilis
						Orbignyi
					Tenuiplicatus	
					Zigzag	Yeovilensis (pars)

Silty/sandy mudstone   Limestone   Non-sequence

Mudstone   Sandstone

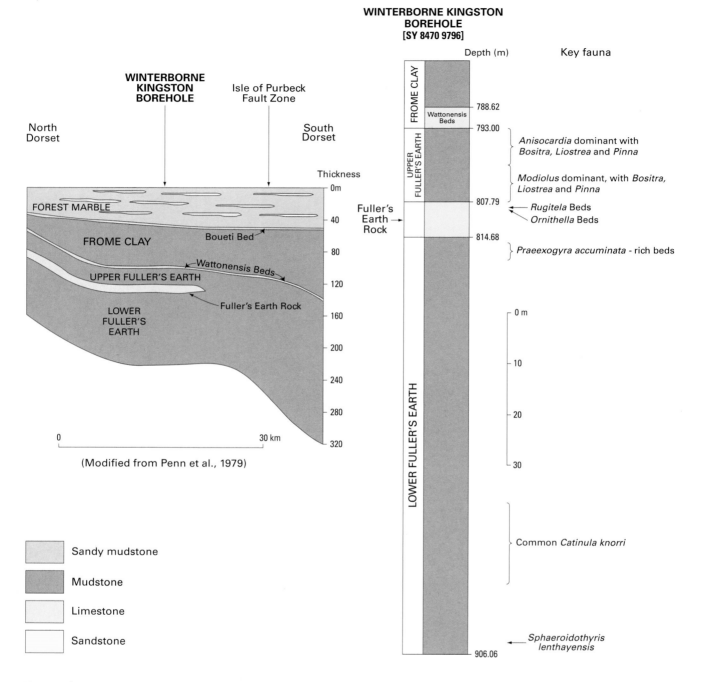

WINTERBORNE KINGSTON BOREHOLE
[SY 8470 9796]

Depth (m)   Key fauna

FROME CLAY

788.62

Wattonensis Beds

793.00

UPPER FULLER'S EARTH

Anisocardia dominant with *Bositra, Liostrea* and *Pinna*

Modiolus dominant, with *Bositra, Liostrea* and *Pinna*

807.79

Fuller's Earth Rock

Rugitela Beds
Ornithella Beds

814.68

Praeexogyra accuminata - rich beds

LOWER FULLER'S EARTH

0 m

10

20

30

Common *Catinula knorri*

Sphaeroidothyris lenthayensis

906.06

WINTERBORNE KINGSTON BOREHOLE

Isle of Purbeck Fault Zone

North Dorset

South Dorset

Thickness

0m

FOREST MARBLE

40

FROME CLAY

Boueti Bed

80

Wattonensis Beds

120

UPPER FULLER'S EARTH

Fuller's Earth Rock

160

LOWER FULLER'S EARTH

200

240

280

0   30 km

320

(Modified from Penn et al., 1979)

Sandy mudstone

Mudstone

Limestone

Sandstone

Figure 17 The Fuller's Earth and Frome Clay formations in the Winterborne Kingston Borehole, and their lateral variation between this borehole and the south Dorset coast.

fauna of the Digona Bed is lacking, although abundant pectinid bivalves, oysters, shark teeth and fossil wood are present (Callomon and Cope, 1995). The top of the Forest Marble Formation is taken at the first appearance of thickly bedded, micritic limestones of the Cornbrash, which commonly form well-featured ground inland.

The Forest Marble Formation is assigned to the late Bathonian Hollandi Subzone of the Discus Zone (Torrens,

1980b; Figure 16). Although richly fossiliferous with brachiopods and bivalves, the rarity of ammonites (typically small *Delecticeras*) makes further biostratigraphical refinement difficult. Fallen blocks of Forest Marble at Watton Cliff contain mammalian teeth (Freeman, 1976), and Ensom (1977) recorded a tooth of a mammal-like reptile from the same locality. Shark and crocodile teeth also occur in the formation (Freeman, 1976; Callomon and Cope, 1995).

Forest Marble Formation

Frome Clay Formation

Plate 20   Frome Clay and Forest Marble formations, Watton Cliff [SY 451 908]. The Boueti Bed, the basal bed of the Forest Marble, is a conspicuous white micrite near the top of the cliff. Height of cliff c. 50 m (P672028).

Cornbrash Formation

The Cornbrash, an old Wiltshire term for stony ground suitable for cereal growth, is a thin limestone unit. Dip-slopes of up to 1 km give a wide outcrop in the Bridport district, south of the Bride Fault around Puncknowle [SY 5370 8865], and in the southern limb of the Weymouth Anticline around Chickerell [SY 645 805]. The principal coastal exposures are at Shipmoor Point [SY 577 836] and Berry Knap [SY 585 830] (Cox and Sumbler, 2002) in the northern fold limb, where the formation is repeated by strike faulting. In south Dorset, the formation is typically about 10 m thick (Figure 18), as proved by boreholes at Arne (G1 Borehole, 10.1 m), Bushey Farm (A1 Borehole, 10.3 m), Waddock Cross (12.2 m), and Wytch Farm (7.3–9.8 m). There is progressive thickening offshore, with 16.5 m and 19 m in boreholes at Lulworth Banks and Kimmeridge 5. Inland the succession thins to about 6 to 8 m in north Dorset.

The formation is traditionally divided, into the Lower and Upper Cornbrash (Berry and Fleet members of Page, 1989, of Upper Bathonian and Lower Callovian ages, respectively; Figure 16). The limestones of the Lower Cornbrash are typically pale cream, sparsely ooidal and peloidal micrite, locally very shelly or with thin, shelly mudstone partings and pseudonodular appearance. Three principal units were recognized by Douglas and Arkell (1928) and Page (1989): a basal unit of micritic limestone with abundant *Cererithyris intermedia* ('Intermedia Bed'): a median, or upper, unit that consists either

of shell-detrital and sparsely fossiliferous limestones or argillaceous pseudonodular limestone with *Obovothyris obovata*: and locally, an upper micrite that is exceptionally fossiliferous and characterised by the association of bivalves *Neocrassina hilpertonensis* and *Trigonia* ('Astarte-Trigonia Bed'; Figure 16; Plate 18). Douglas and Arkell (1928) recorded these strata in a former quarry between Swyre [SY 528 882] and Burton Bradstock [SY 5123 8850].

The Upper Cornbrash of Dorset is predominantly cream-coloured sandy biomicrite with the brachiopods *Ornithella* [*Microthyridina*] *siddingtonensis* in the lower part ('Siddingtonensis Beds') (Plate 18) and *Ornithella* [*Microthyridina*] *lagenalis* in the upper part, together with calcareous sandstone and subordinate sparsely sandy, peloidal and bioclastic limestone. Numerous non-sequences are suggested by the combination of erosional contacts and local accumulations of sand and bioturbated shell debris, but biostratigraphical correlations based on ammonite faunas are hampered by lack of material. The junction between the Lower and Upper Cornbrash can be seen at Berry Knap, near Abbotsbury, the type section for the Berry and Fleet members of Page (1989). Small coastal exposures west of East Fleet [west of SY 634 799] show only parts of the Upper Cornbrash, and comprise sparsely fossiliferous sandy limestones.

Just two genera of ammonites occur in the Cornbrash (Callomon and Cope, 1995; Plate 18): *Clydoniceras* in the Lower Cornbrash indicates the upper Discus Zone (Discus Subzone) and *Macrocephalites* in the Upper Cornbrash indicates the Herveyi Zone (Keppleri and Terebratus

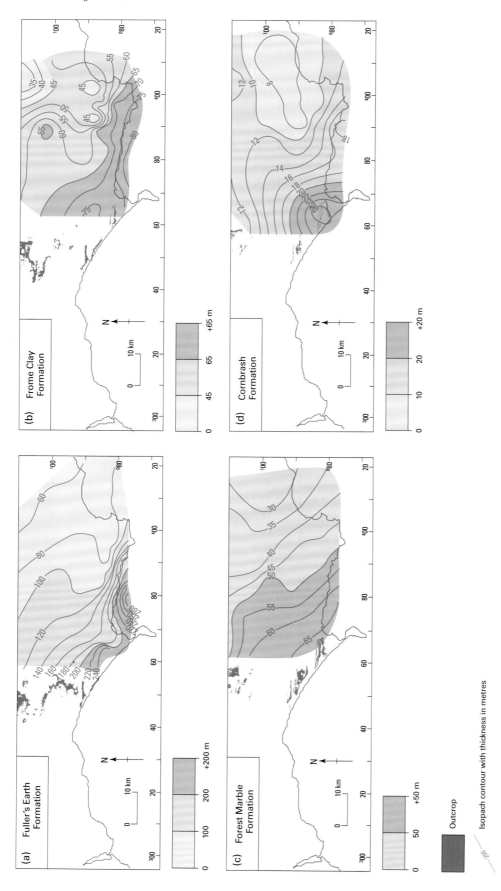

Figure 18   Generalised isopach maps for selected Middle Jurassic formations in Dorset.

subzones). The top of the formation is a non-sequence at which the lower part of the succeeding (Kamptus) subzone of the Herveyi Zone is missing (Page, 1989; Figure 16). The Cornbrash also has an abundant and diverse fauna of brachiopods that can be used for zonation (Douglas and Arkell, 1928, 1932). Bivalves (including *Meleagrinella*) and echinoids are also common, and the sedimentology and fauna of the formation suggest that deposition occurred in a warm, shallow sea in which there was repeated sediment reworking and negligible clastic input from neighbouring land areas (House, 1989; Callomon and Cope, 1995).

KELLAWAYS FORMATION

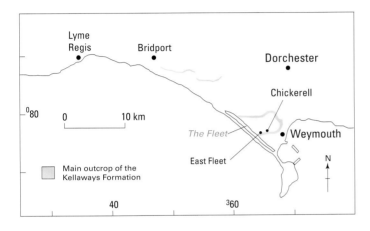

Map 5   Kellaways Formation.

The Kellaways Formation is poorly exposed on the Dorset coast, and is restricted to a short section along the shore of the Fleet lagoon, near East Fleet [SY 638 802]. However, the formation is mapped around the closure of the Weymouth Anticline as a series of faulted blocks above the Cornbrash. It also occurs as two partially fault-bounded blocks near Bridport [SY 520 910; 560 890] and near Rampisham [SY 555 035]. The thickness of the formation is typically in the range 32 to 43 m, with 32.6 m in the Combe Throop Borehole, about 35 m in boreholes at Mappowder, Wareham and Kimmeridge, and 40 to 43 m in boreholes at Arne (Borehole G1), Bere Regis and Encombe. Offshore, the formation is 51.5 m thick in the Lulworth Banks Borehole.

The predominant lithology comprises sandy mudstone and muddy sandstone with some small cementstone nodules, and a distinctive bed of calcareous sandstone near the base. Formerly, one of the best exposures of the Kellaways Formation in southern England was at the Putton Lane Brickpit [SY 650 799], Chickerell, where Arkell (1947, p. 27) recorded a section of about 5 m. Wilson et al. (1958) recorded 6.3 m in the brick pit at Bothenhampton [SY 484 914], which has subsequently been backfilled.

The original geological survey of the Weymouth district included the Kellaways Formation within the Oxford Clay. Both formations have similar weathering profiles, and deep auger holes are required to differentiate the two at surface. The lower part of the Kellaways Formation weathers to a yellow or orange-brown clayey sand with a little granular gypsum. The middle and upper parts weather deeply to a mottled orange, brown and pale yellow, jarositic (a hydrated iron-rich sulphate) sandy clay and clayey sand. The top of the Kellaways Formation is marked by a sharp change from sandy clay to uniform silty clay of the basal Oxford Clay Formation. Previously, the formation has been subdivided into a lower Kellaways Clay Member, overlain by the Kellaways Sand Member (Callomon and Cope, 1995), but distinction between these units can be problematic. No formal lithostratigraphical subdivision of the formation has been attempted in south Dorset, but it seems probable that the whole succession should be assigned to the Kellaways Clay Member, the succeeding Kellaways Sand being very poorly developed in this area.

The Kellaways Formation ranges from the lower Callovian Herveyi Zone (top Kamptus Subzone), through the Koenigi Zone (Gowerianus, Curtilobus and Galilaeii subzones) to the lower Calloviense Zone (Calloviense Subzone and Enodatum Subzone (pars)) (Callomon, 1964; Page, 1989; Figure 16). A more refined scheme of ammonite faunal 'horizons' is also available for this interval (Callomon et al., 1989). The characteristic ammonites are species of *Proplanulites*, *Kepplerites* and *Sigaloceras* (Plate 21). Oysters characterise different levels in the succession, the small *Nanogyra nana* occurring in the basal part, with *Catinula alimena* higher up, and *Gryphaea* (*Bilobissa*) *dilobotes* (Plate 21), near the top, marking the base of the Calloviense Zone and Subzone (Callomon and Cope, 1995). Page (1989) recorded a variably developed bivalve fauna through the Kellaways Formation, that of the basal beds being of rather low diversity, and dominated by *Meleagrinella braamburiensis*, *Modiolus bipartitus* and *Nuculana*. More diverse faunas, including *Myophorella*, *Thracia*, *Oxytoma*, *Pleuromya*, *Modiolus* and *Grammatodon* occur higher up, but there is a return to a low-diversity fauna, characterised by *Catinula alimena* or *Gryphaea* (*Bilobissa*) *dilobotes*, with *Oxytoma* at the top of the succession.

OXFORD CLAY FORMATION

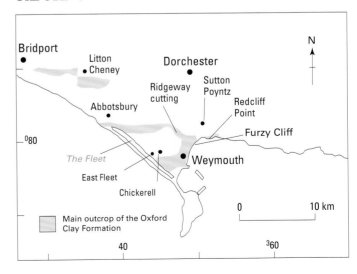

Map 6   Oxford Clay.

The principal coastal exposures of the Oxford Clay are in the northern limb of the Weymouth Anticline, south of Abbotsbury [SY 560 846 to 670 830], and as a wide outcrop on the southern limb, between the Fleet (Plate 22) and Weymouth Bay [SY 640 790 to 680 790] (including the anticlinal inlier [SY 715 818] east of Redcliff Point). In addition, small outcrops of Oxford Clay are present adjacent to the Eype Mouth [SY 480 915 to 534 910] and Litton Cheney [SY 537 895 to 580 893] faults, and in the structurally complex area [SY 672 854 to 722 839] between the Ridgeway railway cutting and Sutton Poyntz. The formation is divided into the **Peterborough**, **Stewartby** and **Weymouth** members; formerly these were known respectively as the Lower, Middle and Upper Oxford Clay (Cox et al., 1993; Figure 16). The base of the Weymouth Member corresponds with the base of the Upper Jurassic. The formation has been proved in many deep boreholes in the district (Figure 19), although at Waddock Cross and Martinstown it has been removed by pre-Cretaceous erosion. Geophysical logs indicate thickness in boreholes as follows: Bere Regis 111 m; Creech 126 m; Kimmeridge 5, 101 m; Osmington 133 m; Spetisbury 125.3 m; Stoborough 111.8 m; Wareham 3 115.8 m; Winterborne Kingston 134.5 m. The exceptionally thick 177 m of Oxford Clay proved in the Coombe Keynes Borehole may be the result of structural complication associated with the Purbeck Monocline.

Data from the lower part of the Oxford Clay suggest that it was deposited in a warm (about 20°C), shallow sea, with occasionally poorly oxygenated water occurring at the sea bed (Martill and Hudson, 1991). The formation spans the upper Callovian and lower Oxfordian (Callomon and Cope, 1995; Figure 16), and is richly fossiliferous with ammonites (especially *Kosmoceras*) and bivalves (including *Gryphaea*; Plate 21); fish and dinosaur remains are relatively common in the lower beds, although these are poorly exposed in Dorset (Hudson and Martill, 1991; Callomon and Cope, 1995).

Peterborough Member

The Peterborough Member (Kosmoceras Shales of Arkell, 1947) is the most distinctive part of the Oxford Clay. The mudstones characteristically include brownish grey to chocolate-brown (Plate 22), fissile, shelly and organic-rich ('bituminous') units, and contain abundant ammonites, particularly *Kosmoceras*, many preserved as crushed aragonitic shells (Callomon and Cope, 1995). The member also has a characteristic benthonic mollusc fauna comprising abundant nuculacean bivalves *Meleagrinella*, *Oxytoma* and *Gryphaea* (the last particularly in the basal part), and the gastropod *Cerithium* (Cox et al., 1993; Callomon and Cope, 1995). The member belongs to the Calloviense (pars), Jason, Coronatum and Athleta (pars) zones (Figure 16) and varies in thickness across the district from 23 m in the Arne G1 Borehole to 44.8 m in the Encombe Borehole, but is mostly in the range of 30 to 35 m. Thicker successions occur in boreholes at Hewish (59.5 m) and Kimmeridge 5 (52.5 m). The best exposure of this interval is at Chickerell (Crookhill)

Brickpit [SY 644 798], where 19 m of Peterborough Member is overlain by 8 m of Stewartby Member (Smith *in* Torrens, 1969; Cox and Sumbler, 2002). The member is intermittently exposed south-east of East Fleet, where the shales are highly bituminous, and large flattened cementstones were formerly collected for making ornamental table tops.

Stewartby and Weymouth members

The mudstones of the Stewartby (Tidmoor Point Clays of Arkell, 1947) and Weymouth (Furzedown Clays, Jordan Cliff Clays and Red Nodule Beds of Arkell, 1947) members are typically pale grey, calcareous and relatively poorly fossiliferous. The Lamberti Limestone, at the top of the Stewartby Member throughout most of England, is absent in Dorset, and the members are not separable in field mapping. In boreholes, the combined Stewartby and Weymouth members vary irregularly in thickness across the district, with 78 m at Bere Regis, 83 m in Wareham 3, 93 m at Creech, 98.5 m at Winterborne Kingston, 114 m in the Bushey Farm A1 Borehole, and 131 m at Coombe Keynes.

The members belong to the upper Callovian Athleta (pars) and Lamberti zones and the lower Oxfordian Mariae and Cordatum (pars) zones (Figure 16). Along the coast east of Weymouth to Redcliff Point [SY 713 817], there is one of the thickest and most unbroken successions across the Callovian–Oxfordian boundary (Callomon and Cope, 1995; Cox and Sumbler, 2002), although the strata are not generally well exposed. Fossils are rather sparse in the lower (Stewartby Member) part, and the ammonites, which are mainly *Kosmoceras* and *Quenstedtoceras*, are preserved as uncrushed pyritic specimens, some associated with sideritic mudstone nodules, rather than the aragonitic impressions found in the underlying Peterborough Member (Cox et al., 1993; Callomon and Cope, 1995). Exceptionally well-preserved ammonites of the Lamberti Zone occur at Tidmoor Point [SY 644 786], behind East Fleet. Belemnites and *Gryphaea* are also characteristic fossils, *G. lituola* occurring

Plate 21 Some characteristic fossils from the Kellaways Formation, Oxford Clay Formation and Corallian Group of Dorset. Scale bars represent 10 mm (P669423).

1	*Gryphaea (Bilobissa) dilobotes* (Kellaways)
2a–b	*Kepplerites (Gowericeras) gowerianus* (Kellaways)
3a–b	*Sigaloceras calloviense* (Kellaways)
4	*Kosmoceras (Lobokosmoceras) phaeinum* (Oxford Clay)
5	*Gryphaea dilatata* (Oxford Clay)
6a–b	*Cardioceras scarburgense* (Oxford Clay)
7	*Gryphaea lituola* (Oxford Clay)
8a–b	*Aspidoceras perarmatum* (Corallian)
9a–b	*Quenstedtoceras lamberti* (Oxford Clay)
10	*Thamnasteria arachnoides* (Corallian)
11	*Myophorella clavellata* (Corallian)
12a–b	*Ringsteadia anglica* (Corallian)
13a–b	*Perisphinctes (Arisphinctes) helenae* (Corallian)
14a–b	*Goliathiceras capax* (Corallian)
15	*Pinna* (Corallian)

Plate 22 Brown fissile mudstones ('Kosmoceras Shales') of the Peterborough Member, Oxford Clay Formation, south-east of East Fleet village [SY 638 791]. Height of cliff c. 4 m (P672073).

in the lower part of the succession and large *G. dilatata* dominating the higher (Weymouth Member) part and occurring in conspicuous concentrations in the cliff exposures at Redcliff Point, and on the foreshore behind East Fleet [SY 6485 7800] (Callomon and Cope, 1995). *Cardioceras* and *Quenstedtoceras* occur in the Weymouth Member at Furzy Cliff [SY 700 818], with locally abundant specimens of the bivalves *Isognomon* and *Modiolus*, and part of the same interval forms a steeply south-dipping fault sliver in the overgrown Ridgeway railway cutting [SY 6727 8540].

CORALLIAN GROUP

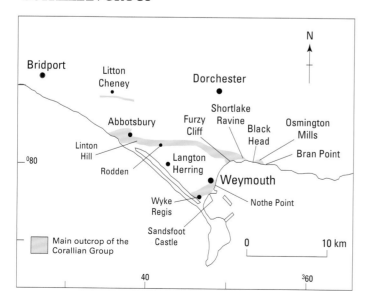

Map 7 Corallian Group.

The Corallian Group of Dorset is a succession of shallow-marine limestones, mudstones and sandstones formed during a regression that followed the mudstone deposition of the Oxford Clay (Figure 20). The sediments accumulated on a relatively low-relief ramp-type margin that dipped westward from the Hampshire–Dieppe High into the Channel Basin. The outcrop forms two approximately east–west orientated tracts on the limbs of the Weymouth Anticline. The southern tract, extending from Wyke Regis [SY 657 774] to Weymouth, is poorly exposed. The northern tract extends from Abbotsbury to Weymouth Bay, intersecting the coast between Bowleaze Cove [SY 730 819] and Ringstead Bay [SY 758 814] where the group is exposed in spectacular cliff sections. There is also a small, fault-bounded inlier south of Litton Cheney [SY 550 902]. At its type section, near Osmington Mills (Figure 21; Plate 23), the group is 67.6 m thick (Wright and Cox, 2001; Figure 19). Thicker successions occur to the west, with 118.2 m at Hewish and 157 m at Abbotsbury, and to the east, with 97 m at Kimmeridge 5 and 101.8 m at Encombe (Figure 19). The thickening, relative to the type section, is largely due to the development of sandstones and ironstones of early Kimmeridgian age, which are included as part of the Corallian Group. North of the Abbotsbury–Ridgeway and Purbeck faults, the group has been extensively removed by Early Cretaceous erosion.

The group ranges from the base of the Lower Oxfordian Cordatum Zone and Subzone to (locally) the Lower Kimmeridgian Cymodoce Zone (Arkell, 1947; Coe, 1995; Newell, 2000). Although relatively rare, ammonites provide the basis for age determination and were among the first to be studied by Arkell (1935–48). However, strong provincialism affects ammonite faunas in the Oxfordian, such that three different ammonite zonal schemes apply to different geographical areas

(Cope et al., 1980; Bristow et al., 1995). In this account, reference is mainly made to the Sub-Boreal scheme, but Figure 20 shows the relationship to the standard Boreal scheme of Wright and Cox (2001). The dominant macrofossils are bivalves; different associations indicate different environmental parameters, the nature of the substrate probably being the most important influence (Fürsich, 1976, 1977).

The basic stratigraphical subdivisions of the 'Corallian' are largely those detailed in Arkell (1933; 1936a; 1947), following the earlier work of Blake and Hudleston (1877). Wright (1986) formalised this scheme promoting the Corallian to group status and dividing it into six formations. During the present resurvey, five formations were recognised and two of these are further subdivided. New borehole data are available from the Abbotsbury area, where the BGS boreholes Abbotsbury 1 [SY 5847 8533] and 2 [SY 5851 8505] were drilled in 1997 (Newell, 1998; 2000; Figure 22). A stratigraphical summary of the group is given in Figure 21. Recent revisions to Corallian lithostratigraphical nomenclature (Wright and Cox, 2001) postdate the BGS mapping in Dorset, but are referred to below.

Nothe Formation

The Nothe Formation, renamed Redcliff Formation by Wright and Cox (2001), comprises a succession of sandstone and mudstone at the base of the Corallian Group. The formation is 18 to 30 m thick with 23 m in the Hewish Borehole (Figure 22). The formation includes the **Nothe Grit**, **Nothe Clay** and **Bencliff Grit** members. In the succession seen north of Langton Herring, none of these divisions can be distinguished, because of an apparent overall westward fining in grain-size. The boundary with the underlying Oxford Clay is more subtly marked (by a slight upwards increase in the sand content of mudstones) than on the coast.

The Nothe Formation is assigned to the top Cordatum Zone (Cordatum Subzone) and lower Plicatilis Zone (Vertebrale Subzone), at the junction of the Lower and Middle Oxfordian (Coe, 1995). In south Dorset, there is a non-sequence between the top of the Cordatum Zone and base of the Plicatilis Zone, within the Nothe Grit Member (Wright, 1986). The fauna mostly comprises ammonites and bivalves, and is conspicuously bioturbated in parts with *Ophiomorpha*, *Rhizocorallium*, *Thalassinoides* and *Chondrites* (Wright, 1986; Coe, 1995).

Nothe Grit Member

The Nothe Grit comprises up to 15 m of alternating moderately and weakly cemented sandstone that is fine grained, clayey and locally calcareous. The formation is pervasively bioturbated and so few primary sedimentary structures remain; *Thalassinoides* and *Rhizocorallium* are the dominant trace fossils, and can be seen weathering out on the wave-cut platform at Nothe Point [SY 685 786]. Sponge spicules can make up almost 50 per cent of the grains in the moderately well-cemented sandstones. The upper part of the Nothe Grit, designated 'Preston Grit Member' by Wright (1986), is about 1.8 m thick, and comprises a lower argillaceous sandstone overlain by a bioclastic, calcareous sandstone (Sun, 1989); the basal contact is an erosion surface, coincident with the Cordatum–Vertebrale zonal boundary.

Arkell (1947) provided a full account of the fauna. This is relatively sparse in the lower part, comprising serpulids, oysters (e.g. *Lopha*, *Gryphaea dilatata*) and ammonites (*Cardioceras* spp.). The higher part of the member has a more abundant and diverse fauna, dominated by the bivalves *Chlamys fibrosus* and *Pleuromya uniformis*, and also including the ammonites *Goliathiceras* spp., *Perisphinctes*, and *Aspidoceras* (Plate 21). The succession contains an indurated bed with abundant sponge spicules, and at Osmington Mills [SY 735 816], there is a concretionary horizon with common specimens of the bivalve *Isognomon* cf. *cordati* (Wright, 1986; Coe, 1995).

Nothe Clay Member

The Nothe Clay, up to 20 m thick, has a gradational junction with the underlying Nothe Grit. The member is dominated by grey mudstone but contains eight limestone beds in the lower part, including nodular, micritic, sideritic and ooidal types (Wright, 1986). The top of the Nothe Clay consists of mudstone with scattered lenses of sandstone. Epifaunal bivalves are characteristic of the fauna, including *Isognomon*, *Liostrea*, *Nanogyra nana* and *Modiolus bipartitus* (Wright, 1986). Rare ammonites include *Scoticardioceras*, *Goliathiceras* spp. and *Perisphinctes*. The higher part of the member contains common fossil wood and charcoal, and the U-shaped trace fossil *Diplocraterion*; ammonites and other marine fossils are sparse, and the ostracod and foraminifera faunas include freshwater-tolerant species, and records of rootlets and plant material at Bran Point [SY 741 814 to 744 814] are consistent with a turbulent, nearshore environment (Coe, 1995).

Bencliff Grit Member

The Bencliff Grit Member, up to 7 m thick, forms a continuous outcrop in the exposed southern limb of the Weymouth Anticline and in outliers in the northern limb, west of Preston [SY 705 830]. The member comprises four buff-coloured, fine-grained sandstone beds, locally with large concretions or 'doggers' several metres in diameter, separated by thin discontinuous beds of sandy mudstone (Goldring et al., 1998). The sandstone beds contain 'swaley' cross-stratification (Allen and Underhill, 1989; Sun 1989), while the intervening mudstone beds contain ripple-cross laminated sand and are extensively bioturbated with *Diplocraterion habichi* and *Diplocraterion parallelum* (Goldring et al., 1998). The fauna includes freshwater-tolerant ostracods and foraminifera, but ammonites are correspondingly rare (Talbot, 1973), consistent with a near-shore environment.

Osmington Oolite Formation

The Osmington Oolite Formation consists predominantly of coarse-grained shelly oolites, and is typically 30 to 40 m thick, although 46.4 m was proved in the Abbotsbury 2 Borehole. The formation is mapped undivided although Wright (1986) named three subdivisions: Upton, Shortlake and Nodular Rubble members, recognisable in the coastal outcrop (Plate 23) and also in the cored succession at Abbotsbury. The Upton Member, at the base of the succession, comprises calcareous sandstone, argillaceous limestone and mudstone. Cross-bedded, ooidal limestones interbedded with calcareous mudstones are the characteristic lithologies of the overlying Shortlake Member, and the formation is capped by nodular micritic limestones and calcareous mudstones of the Nodular Rubble Member. At Abbotsbury, these different lithologies constitute three upward-coarsening cycles. On the foreshore between Shortlake Ravine [SY 7201 8199] and Osmington Mills, the Osmington Oolite is about 3 m thicker than at Bran Point [SY 744 814], and Arkell (1947) also reported that it becomes less ooidal and more marly eastwards.

The sparse fauna of the Osmington Oolite includes the bivalve *Nanogyra nana* (abundant in a limestone in the lower part of the succession), scattered *Nautilus* and the ammonites *Cardioceras* spp. and *Perisphinctes* spp. (Wright, 1986; Coe, 1995). At the base of the member, the upper Vertebrale Subzone is cut out by a non-sequence at the junction with the underlying Nothe Clay Member, and another non-sequence within the Osmington Oolite cuts out the top of the Antecedens Subzone (Wright, 1986; Figure 20). Trace fossils are locally common, and nine different ichnospecies have been recognised in the lower part of the succession. In the higher part, where *Thalassinoides* is extensively developed, the burrows are cemented to produce the nodular texture characteristic of the Nodular Rubble Member (Coe, 1995). Some unusual associations of trace fossils appear to be connected with the development of unconformities (Coe, 1995).

Clavelleta Formation

The Clavellata Formation is made up of coarsely bioclastic limestone with muddy partings; *Myophorella clavellata* (from which the formation takes its name; Plate 21) is

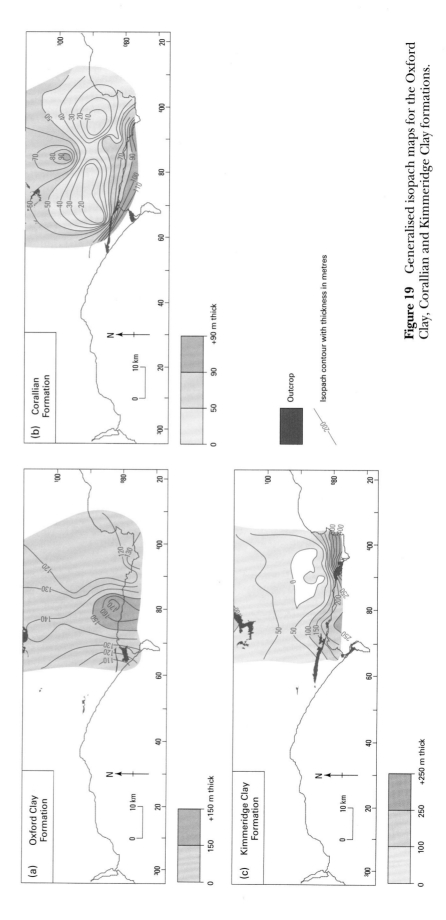

Figure 19 Generalised isopach maps for the Oxford Clay, Corallian and Kimmeridge Clay formations.

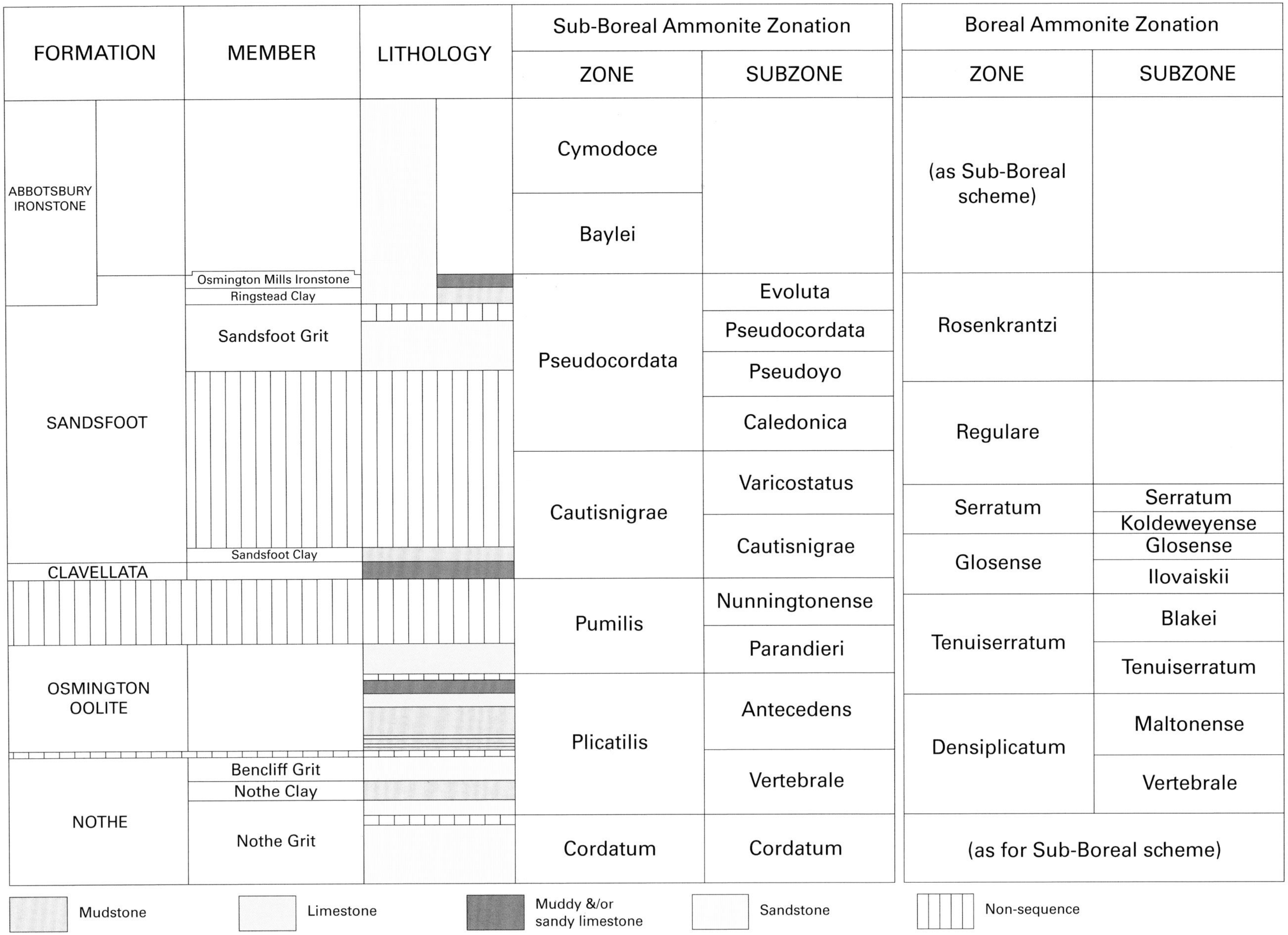

Figure 20 Stratigraphy of the Corallian Group of south Dorset.

Figure 21 Log of the Corallian Group at Osmington [SY 697 816 to SY 752 813], and its lithostratigraphcial classification (based on figures by Sun, 1989 and Wright and Cox, 2001).

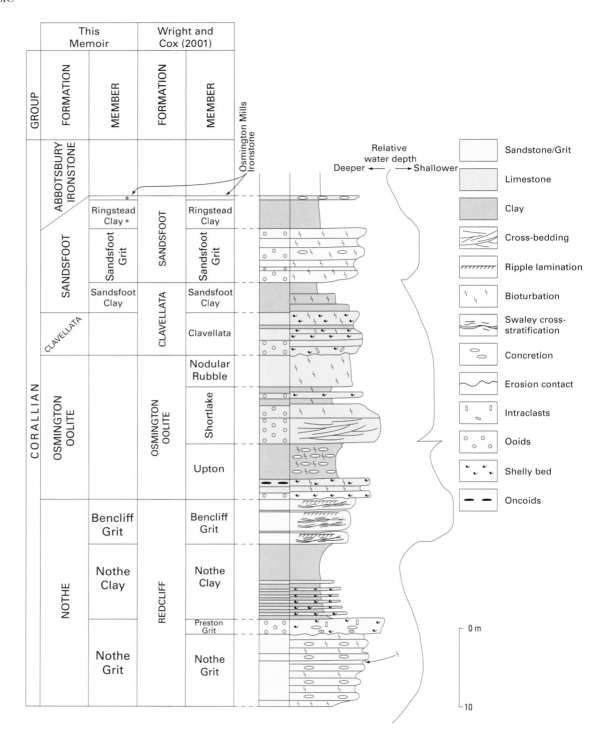

very abundant in the middle part of the succession, and is usually concentrated into several shell-rich beds (Coe, 1995). The formation is readily recognisable, on the coast around Osmington, and inland at Abbotsbury, in borehole core and at outcrop on Linton Hill [SY 5841 8463]. Like the Osmington Oolite, the Clavellata Formation was mapped undivided, although informal subdivisions have been recognised and named on the coast

(Wright, 1986). In ascending stratigraphical order these are the Sandy Block, Chief Shell Beds, Clay Band and Red Beds. The formation thickness is generally in the range 6 to 12 m, with 12.8 m proved in the Abbotsbury 2 Borehole.

Pervasively bioturbated, sandy bioclastic limestones, muddy limestones and dark argillaceous bioturbated sandstones with discontinuous wavy mudstone laminae

Plate 23   The Corallian Group
at Osmington Mills [SY 741 814].
Buff sandstones of the Bencliff Grit
Member at the base of the section,
sharply overlain in turn by grey
mudstones and limestones of the
Upton and Shortlake members. The
Nodular Rubble Member is seen at
the top of the section. Height of cliff
c. 35 m (P672350).

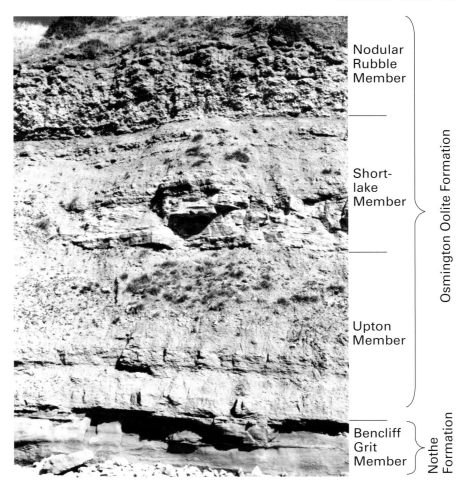

in the lower part of the formation (Sandy Block) pass upwards into clean bioclastic limestones with shell beds dominated by *Myophorella clavellata* (Chief Shell Beds). Above this is sandy bioturbated mudstone (Clay Band), overlain by shelly oolite with an argillaceous matrix, interbedded with dark yellowish orange sideritic limestones (Red Beds). The junction with the subjacent Osmington Oolite Formation is an undulating nodular surface, which marks an important non-sequence (Figure 20); most of the higher part of the Pumilus Zone (upper Parandieri Subzone and Nunningtonense Subzone (pars)) is missing. Wright (1986) recorded *Amoeboceras transitorium* and *Decipia*, which are characteristic of the Nunningtonense Subzone, and there is a solitary record of *Perisphinctes* (*Pseudarisphinctes*) aff. *shortlakensis* (Wright, 1986; Coe, 1995).

Sandsfoot Formation

The Sandsfoot Formation is a succession of ferruginous mudstone and sandstone, divisible into the Sandsfoot Clay Member overlain by the Sandsfoot Grit Member in the gentle, south-dipping southern limb of the Weymouth Anticline. In a recent stratigraphical revision, Wright and Cox (2001) included the Sandsfoot Clay in the top of the Clavellata Formation, and expanded the

Sandsfoot Formation to include the Ringstead Clay and Osmington Mills Ironstone members of Wright (1986). These members have been mapped with the Kimmeridge Clay Formation because of poor exposure and landslipping, but are correctly included within the Corallian Group and are herein described as part of the Sandsfoot Formation.

The **Sandsfoot Clay Member**, about 4 m thick near Sandsfoot Castle [SY 676 773] in Portland Harbour and 6.8 m thick in the Abbotsbury 2 Borehole, is a unit of soft, interbedded, calcareous mudstone and muddy siltstone with some lenses of sandstone (Coe, 1995). The base of the member is gradational, with a progressive decrease in bioclastic debris and an increase in mud and silt above the Clavellata Formation. The member contains a rather impoverished fauna (*Perisphinctes* sp., *Deltoideum delta*, *Astarte* and serpulids) compared with coeval deposits elsewhere in the UK, which might suggest a low salinity palaeo-depositional environment (Wright, 1986). In contrast, the **Sandsfoot Grit Member** consists predominantly of bioturbated sandstone that is locally muddy or ferruginous; it is up to 10.6 m thick in the Abbotsbury 2 Borehole. In the upper part of the member, closely spaced erosion surfaces are overlain by shell debris, fish teeth and rounded phosphate pebbles, and there is a sharp and erosive junction with the overlying Abbotsbury Ironstone.

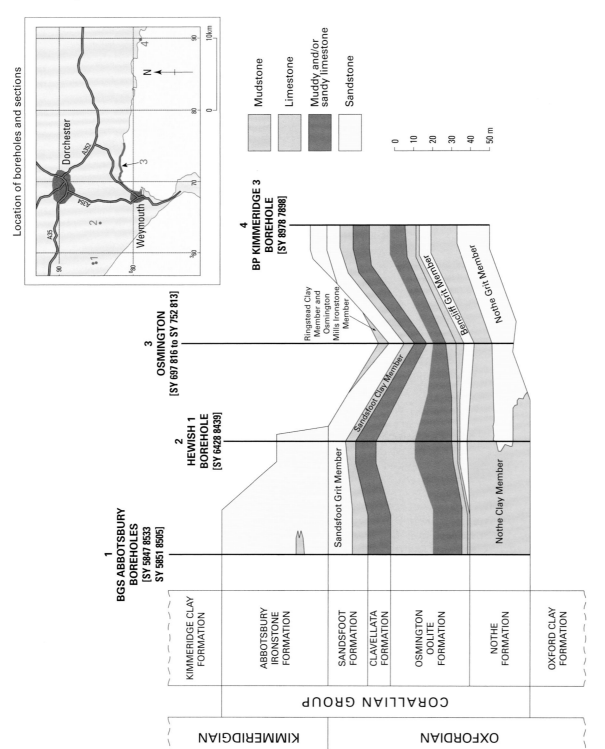

Figure 22 Stratigraphical correlation of the Corallian Group in key boreholes and outcrops along the south Dorset coast (based on a figure by Newell, 2000).

A low diversity fauna, dominated by the bivalves *Pinna* and *Chlamys*, also includes locally common oysters (*Deltoideum delta*) and the ammonites *Ringsteadia* and *Microbiplices*. In Fürsich's (1977) palaeoecological analysis of the Corallian Group, the '*Pinna* Association' of bivalves in the Sandsfoot Grit comprises many specimens preserved in life position and horizons with numerous flat-lying shells; it may reflect more-or-less continuous sedimentation, with episodic current scour that excavated shells from the supporting sediment.

The youngest part of the Corallian Group at some south Dorset localities (e.g. Osmington [SY 697 816 to 752 813], east of Weymouth) is represented by a thin and condensed succession of smooth-textured calcareous mudstones and ironstones, forming the **Ringstead Clay Member** and overlying **Osmington Mills Ironstone Member**. These deposits are coeval with the Abbotsbury Ironstone Formation (see below), which forms the youngest Corallian Group elsewhere in south Dorset. Up to 5 m of Ringstead Clay occurs in the coastal succession between Sandsfoot and Osmington Mills, characterised by common, lensoidal, orange-weathering ferruginous concretions in silty mudstone (Brookfield, 1978; Wright, 1986). The impoverished fauna of the Ringstead Clay is dominated by small fossils such as the bivalves *Palaeonucula menkii* and *Corbula prora* and the echinoid *Pseudodiadema* (Brookfield, 1978). The Osmington Mills Ironstone consists of a thin, limonite-oolite calcareous mudstone or, locally, impure limestone. The type locality is Osmington Mills, where the bed is 0.48 m thick, and it is also seen at East Fleet [SY 660 766], where is it 0.37 m thick. The member is much more fossiliferous than the Ringstead Clay, with abundant bivalves, gastropods and serpulids and, locally in Ringstead Bay [SY 748 813 to 755 813] and at Black Head [SY 7300 8090], common specimens of the coral *Thamnasteria arachnoides* form the Ringstead Coral Bed (Wright, 1986; Coe, 1995; Plate 21).

Abbotsbury Ironstone Formation

The Abbotsbury Ironstone is a succession of up to 57 m of ironstone and ferruginous sandstones, which occurs between the Sandsfoot and the Kimmeridge Clay formations. The ironstone is thickest around Abbotsbury where it was formerly worked for iron, but has been detected at outcrop to the north at Litton Cheney [SY 552 908] (Cope, 1971) and to the east as far as Rodden [SY 612 842], beyond which the succession no longer forms a mappable topographic feature. The lower part of the formation belongs to the Upper Oxfordian Pseudocordata Zone (Evoluta Subzone pars), but the greater part lies within the basal Kimmeridgian Baylei and Cymodoce zones (Arkell, 1947; Newell, 2000), and because of this has been included in the Kimmeridge Clay of many earlier accounts (Figure 20).

In the Abbotsbury boreholes (Figure 22), the formation is divided into two parts by a 3 m-thick mudstone (Newell, 2000). The lower ironstone unit is 13 m thick, including a 4.5 m-thick dark yellowish brown, ferruginous ooid grainstone at the base, with clayey burrow fills and

bioclastic debris; above this much sandier, bioclastic ironstones occur, interbedded with sandstones. The upper unit is 41 m thick and comprises ooidal ironstones, clayey sandstones and mudstones. The ironstones are mainly massive, bioturbated and greenish grey, although some are oxidised to reddish brown. They differ from those at the base in being thinner, extremely sandy, and dominated by oocasts (voids left by leached-out ooids). Other components include bioclastic material, wood debris and well-rounded 'lydite' (i.e. black chert) granules. This unit compares closely with the description of the Abbotsbury Ironstone at outcrop given by Brookfield (1973), and is overlain by 12.4 m of sandstone and muddy sandstone that passes up into the overlying Kimmeridge Clay.

The fauna from the Abbotsbury Ironstone was listed by Brookfield (1978), and includes a rich and varied assemblage of brachiopods (e.g. *Rugitela, Kutchithyris, Lingula, Ornithella, ?Septaliphoria*) and age-diagnostic species of the ammonite genus *Rasenia* (Wright and Cox, 2001). The development of the Abbotsbury Ironstone Formation has been related to the interplay of eustatic sea-level changes and the geometry and synsedimentary movement of the Abbotsbury–Ridgeway Fault (Newell, 2000). The Weymouth Bay area, where the Abbotsbury Ironstone is absent, is inferred to have been the site of a fault ramp, down which material was swept to more rapidly subsiding regions of sediment accumulation (e.g. Abbotsbury).

KIMMERIDGE CLAY FORMATION

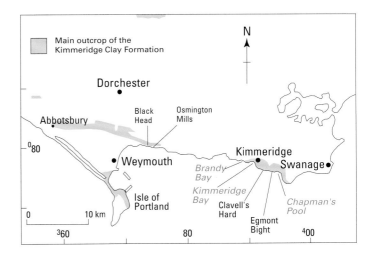

Map 8   Kimmeridge Clay Formation.

The Kimmeridge Clay Formation is a thick succession of more or less calcareous and organic-rich mudstone. In the North Sea, the formation is of great economic importance and forms the principal source rock for oil (Cornford, 1984). However, the Kimmeridge Clay in Dorset differs somewhat from the formation as developed in the North Sea (Wignall, 1994), and in the Wessex Basin the formation has never achieved sufficient burial depths to allow oil generation. The Kimmeridge Clay was deposited in a marine environment under oxygen deficient or anoxic conditions. The presence of storm-beds suggests a maximum water depth of around 50 m (Wignall, 1994). Alternations of oxic and anoxic sea-floor environments, as evidenced from palaeoecological studies, may be due to climatic control, perhaps reflecting Milankovitch cyclicity (House, 1985).

The best-known exposure of Kimmeridge Clay in south Dorset is the classic coastal type section between Brandy Bay [SY 893 792] and Chapman's Pool [SY 955 771] near Kimmeridge village. It is the thickest argillaceous formation in the British onshore Jurassic, reaching more than 500 m in parts of south Dorset. South of the Purbeck Monocline, the Southard Quarry [SZ 0234 77750] and Encombe boreholes [SZ 9712 7831] proved 444 m and at least 541 m of Kimmeridge Clay, respectively; more than 234 m are present in the Kimmeridge 5 Borehole. However, north of the Purbeck Monocline and across the South Dorset High, the formation is thin or absent (Figure 19), because of early Cretaceous erosion. Reduced thicknesses of 47.7 m and 42.4 m occur in boreholes at Winterborne Kingston and Spetisbury, respectively.

The Kimmeridge Clay comprises at least seven main lithologies:

- *mudstone*   pale to dark grey, clay minerals are predominantly illite and kaolinite with minor amounts of smectite and chlorite; beds 0.5 to 2 m thick
- *calcareous mudstone*   pale grey to grey, highly calcareous, beds mostly 3 to 4 m, but may reach 19 m thick
- *bituminous mudstone*   medium grey to black, laminated, total organic carbon up to 30 per cent, beds 0.1 to 2 m thick
- *'oil shale'*   black, laminated, pyrite nodules, total organic carbon up to 60 per cent; beds 0.1 to 0.8 m thick
- *silty mudstone*   pale to dark grey, structureless or cross-laminated, silt-grade material dominated by quartz
- *coccolith limestone*   white, composed almost entirely of layers of coccoliths, beds generally less than 0.2 m thick
- *concretionary carbonate*   grey to mustard yellow, variable composition of ferroan dolomite and calcite, bed thickness generally less than 0.2 m

These lithologies are typically organised into rhythmic successions, which vary in scale from 0.5 m to tens of metres thick (Plate 24). Many of the individual small-scale rhythms can be correlated over distances of tens of kilometres. The larger scale rhythms can be correlated throughout much of the Kimmeridge Clay outcrop and subcrop.

Ammonites are abundant, and provide the means for regional subdivision and correlation of the Kimmeridge Clay. They are usually preserved as crushed aragonitic shells in the mudstones and commonly have a beautiful iridescent sheen. The long-established zonal scheme is based on species of *Pictonia, Rasenia, Aulacostephanus, Pectinatites, Pavlovia* (Plate 25) and *Vigatopavlovia* (Arkell, 1947). These rich faunas show that the base of the Kimmeridge Clay mudstone in Dorset is diachronous, occurring at the base of the Kimmeridgian Stage and Baylei Zone on the coast at Black Head [SY 7258 8200] (Cox and Gallois, 1981), and within the succeeding Cymodoce Zone in the Abbotsbury area, where most of the underlying Abbotsbury Ironstone (Corallian Group) is Kimmeridgian. The top of the Kimmeridge Clay Formation is at the top of the Fittoni Zone (Cope, 1980). The remains of marine reptiles also occur in the formation, including plesiosaurs, ichthyosaurs, crocodiles, turtles and pterosaurs (Taylor and Benton, 1985). At Egmont Bight, on the Isle of Purbeck, a rare specimen of *Kimmerosaurus* has been found, which is suggested to have used its distinctively slender and recurved teeth to filter small fish and crustaceans from the water (Taylor and Benton, 1985). Even rarer is the find of a jaw bone of a large bipedal carnivorous dinosaur, associated with Autissiodorensis Zone ammonites, dredged up from the sea off the Isle of Portland (Powell, 1987).

Conventionally the Kimmeridge Clay is divided into 'Lower Kimmeridge Clay' and 'Upper Kimmeridge Clay', respectively of Lower and Upper Kimmeridgian age. These terms have no formal status but have proved useful for general descriptive purposes. Standard stage nomenclature for the Kimmeridge Clay has proved contentious since d'Orbigny's (1842–1851) ambiguous definition of his Kimmeridgian and Portlandian Stages (see Cox and Gallois, 1981). British workers have traditionally equated the Kimmeridgian Stage with the Kimmeridge Clay Formation, extending from the Baylei to Fittoni zones, and this scheme is followed in the present account. However, mainland European geologists limit the Kimmeridgian Stage to the Baylei to Autissiodorensis zones, and lower the Portlandian Stage boundary to the base of the Elegans Zone. Cope (1993), following Blake (1880), proposed that the controversial Late Kimmeridgian interval (Elegans to Fittoni Zones) should be placed in a separate Bolonian Stage.

Cox and Gallois (1981) further divided the Kimmeridge Clay into 49 distinctive units ('Beds') on the basis of a combination of lithological and macrofaunal

Plate 24   Some characteristic fossils from the Upper Jurassic of Dorset. Scale bars represent 10 mm (P669421).

1a–b	*Torquirhynchia inconstans* (Kimmeridge Clay)
2a–b	*Rasenia* sp. (Kimmeridge Clay)
3	*Pectinatites* aff. *wheatleyensis* (Kimmeridge Clay)
4	*Aulacostephanus autissiodorensis* (Kimmeridge Clay)
5	*Solenopora* (Portland Gp.)
6	*Neocrassina extensa* (Kimmeridge Clay)
7	*Pavlovia rotunda* (Kimmeridge Clay)
8	*Progalbanites albani* (Portland Gp.)
9	*Myophorella* (Portland Gp.)
10	*Aptyxiella portlandica* (Portland Gp.)
11	*Laevitrigonia* (Portland Gp.)
12	*Titanites giganteus* (Portland Gp.)

Plate 25 Kimmeridge Clay Formation showing rhythmic interbedding of blocky, organic-poor mudstone and fissile, organic-rich shale; Kimmeridge Bay [SY 906 792]. Height of cliff c. 10 m (P669972, left; P669971, right).

characters; Gallois (2000) extended this scheme to 63 'Beds' to encompass new units at the top of the formation (Figure 23). Some of these units, notably calcareous beds, oil shales and thin siltstones form distinctive markers in the succession (Blake, 1875; Arkell, 1947; Cox and Gallois, 1981; Figures 23; 24). Decimetre- to metre-thick beds of dolomite and coccolith-rich limestone (generally termed 'stone bands') are particularly prominent at coastal outcrop, where they form the 'Kimmeridge Ledges'.

In the lower part of the Kimmeridge Clay (Beds 1–28 of Cox and Gallois, 1981; 158 m thick in the Metherhills 1 Borehole), best seen in the steeply dipping section at Black Head [SY 7258 8200], the main lithology is mudstone with subordinate muddy siltstones, and concretionary limestones. The Inconstans Bed, which marks the base of the Kimmeridge Clay, is a 0.5 m thick mudstone with abundant *Torquirhynchia inconstans* (Plate 25). This is overlain by a thick mudstone succession that contains several marker beds. Two ripple-cross laminated siltstones (Wyke Siltstone and Blackhead Siltstone) occur in the Cymodoce Zone, and can be recognised in coastal sections east of Blackhead at Osmington Mills [SY 7348 8173] and Ringstead Bay [SY 7606 8141], and farther west at Wyke Regis [SY 659 767 to 667 763] and Sandsfoot [SY 669 765 to 672 772]. Their correlation demonstrates substantial thickening of the upper part of the Baylei Zone at Wyke Regis and Sandsfoot (Wright and Cox, 2001). Towards the top of the Mutabilis Zone is the Supracorallina Bed, a mudstone crowded with *Neocrassina extensa* (a bivalve formerly known as *Astarte supracorallina*) [seen at SY 7258 8200 at Black Head and at SY 7336 8186 near Osmington Mills]. These sections also expose the North Wootton Siltstone, a shelly and sandy siltstone with a basal erosion surface that marks the base of the Eudoxus Zone.

The middle part of the Kimmeridge Clay (beds 29–38 of Cox and Gallois, 1981; about 150 m thick in the Swanworth Quarry 1 Borehole) is marked by an increase in the proportion of bituminuous mudstone and 'oil shale', interbedded with mudstone and calcareous mudstone. Above this (beds 39–58 of Cox and Gallois, 1981; about 187 m thick in the Swanworth Quarry 1 Borehole), up to 19 m of highly calcareous and sparsely fossiliferous mudstones are developed. The Blackstone (within Bed 42), with up to 60 per cent total organic carbon and containing pyritised plates of the pelagic crinoid *Saccocoma*, forms a distinctive marker at the Wheatleyensis–Hudlestoni zonal boundary (Wright and Cox, 2001). This is the 'Kimmeridge Coal' that was formerly worked as a fuel from adits at Clavell's Hard [SY 920 777] and Portesham [SY 610 853] during the 17th to 19th centuries. Calcareous mudstones interbedded with bituminuous mudstone and three well-developed coccolith limestones (White Stone Band, Middle White Stone Band and Freshwater Steps Stone Band) occur above the Blackstone, but higher in the succession, between the Freshwater Steps Stone Band and base of the Lower Hounstout Silt, 'oil shales' and bituminuous mudstones decrease markedly in frequency. Westward thinning of this part of the succession occurs between Kimmeridge Bay (where the interval from the Blackstone to Freshwater Stone Band is 71 m) and Ringstead (where the same interval is just 17 m thick) (Cox and Gallois, 1981).

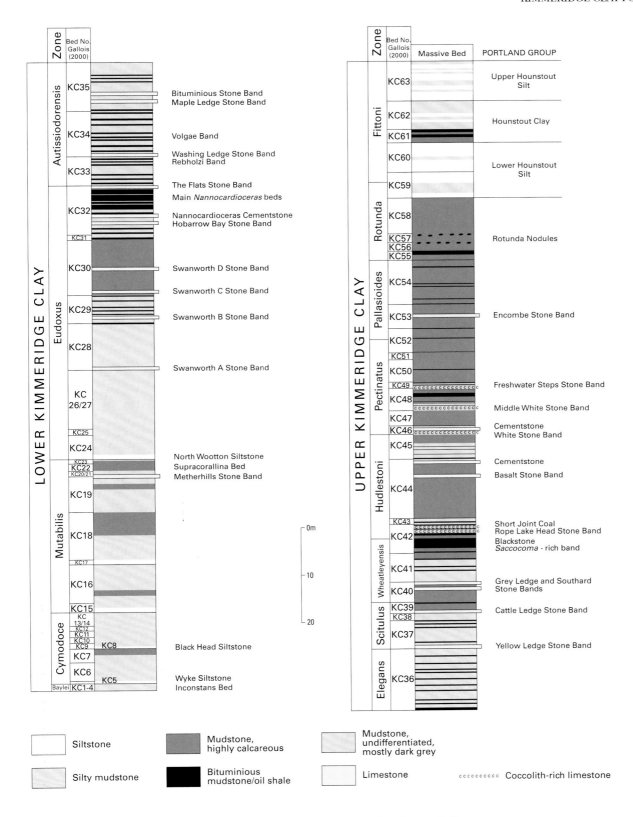

Figure 23   The stratigraphy of the Kimmeridge Clay Formation in south Dorset, based on boreholes and outcrops (from Gallois, 2000).

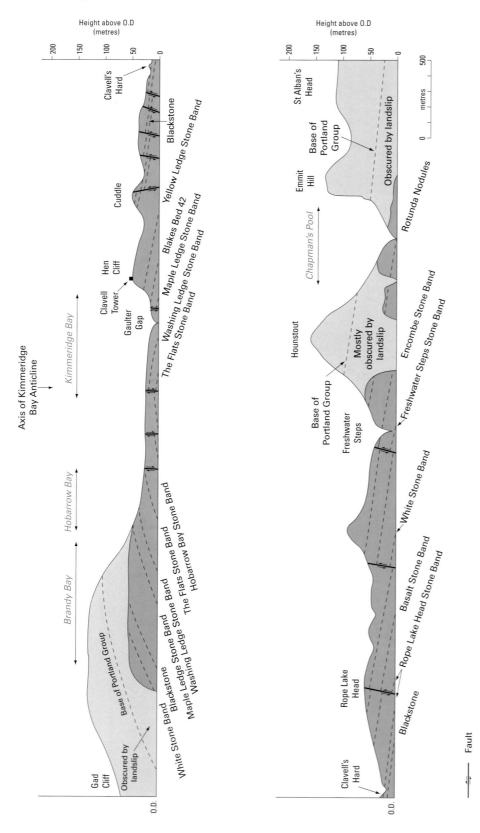

Figure 24   Geological sketch sections of the Kimmeridge Clay exposed in the cliffs between Brandy Bay and Chapman's Pool (based on Cox and Gallois, 1981, fig. 8; Gallois, 2000, fig. 2; and Wright and Cox, 2001, figure 2.26).

Plate 26 Portland Sand and Portland Stone formations at Mutton Cove [SY 680 710]. The Portland Sand, largely obscured by scree, forms steeply sloping ground beneath precipitous cliffs of Portland Stone. Height of cliff c. 75 m (P672835).

Portland Stone Formation

Portland Sand Formation

The uppermost Kimmeridge Clay (beds 59–63 of Gallois, 2000; 58 m thick in the Swanworth Quarry 1 Borehole) is composed of fine-grained sand and silt. These strata equate with the Lingula Shales, Rhynchonella Marls and Hounstout Marl of Arkell (1933), and with the Lower Hounstout Silt, Hounstout Clay and Upper Hounstout Silt members of Gallois (2000). A group of three thin 'bituminous' mudstones form a marker at the base of the Hounstout Clay (Wright and Cox, 2001). The top of the Kimmeridge Clay Formation is marked by a prominent cemented bed of very fine-grained sand and silt, named the 'Massive Bed' on the Isle of Purbeck and the 'Black Nore Sandstone' on the Isle of Portland.

PORTLAND GROUP

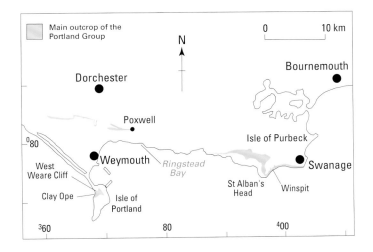

Main outcrop of the Portland Group

0   10 km

N

Dorchester

Bournemouth

Poxwell

Isle of Purbeck

0 80

West Weare Cliff

Weymouth   *Ringstead Bay*

Swanage

Clay Ope   Isle of Portland

St Alban's Head   Winspit

360   80   400

Map 9 Portland Group.

The Portland Group of Dorset comprises shallow marine shelf dolomitic sandstones and massive limestones formed during a regression that followed the mudstone deposition of the Kimmeridge Clay. During the recent BGS resurvey, four well-established lithostratigraphical divisions have been mapped (Figure 25): the **Portland Sand Formation** and the **Portland Stone Formation**, the latter divided into the **Portland Chert Member** and the **Portland Freestone Member**. The formations have been informally subdivided into a series of beds; those in the thicker Isle of Purbeck succession can be correlated in part with locally named beds on the Isle of Portland. The differing names across Dorset reflect partly the lateral lithological variations in the group.

In its type area, between Weymouth and Swanage, the Portland Group has a fragmented outcrop, but it is exposed spectacularly on the coast in cliff-sections around the Isle of Portland (Plate 26), including Clay Ope, West Weare Cliff [SY 680 719], and along the southern coast of the Isle of Purbeck, including St Alban's Head [SY 960 754] and Winspit [SY 977 761]. The main inland outcrops are on the Isle of Portland, and in the areas north of Weymouth and Kimmeridge, where the Portland Stone is exposed in numerous building stone quarries. In Dorset, the group is 50 to 80 m thick, with about 52 m recorded in exposures on the Isle of Portland (Coe, 1996) and in the Chaldon Herring G3 Borehole, and about 75 to 80 m in the Swanage district where it is 76.2 m thick in the Southard Quarry Borehole. The near complete succession seen at Ringstead is much thinner, totalling 27 m (Figure 26). The group has been removed by Early Cretaceous erosion north of the Purbeck Monocline and is absent across the Cranborne–Fordingbridge High in central and north Dorset. Offshore oil wells suggest that the thicker succession on the Isle of Purbeck forms part of a major basin,

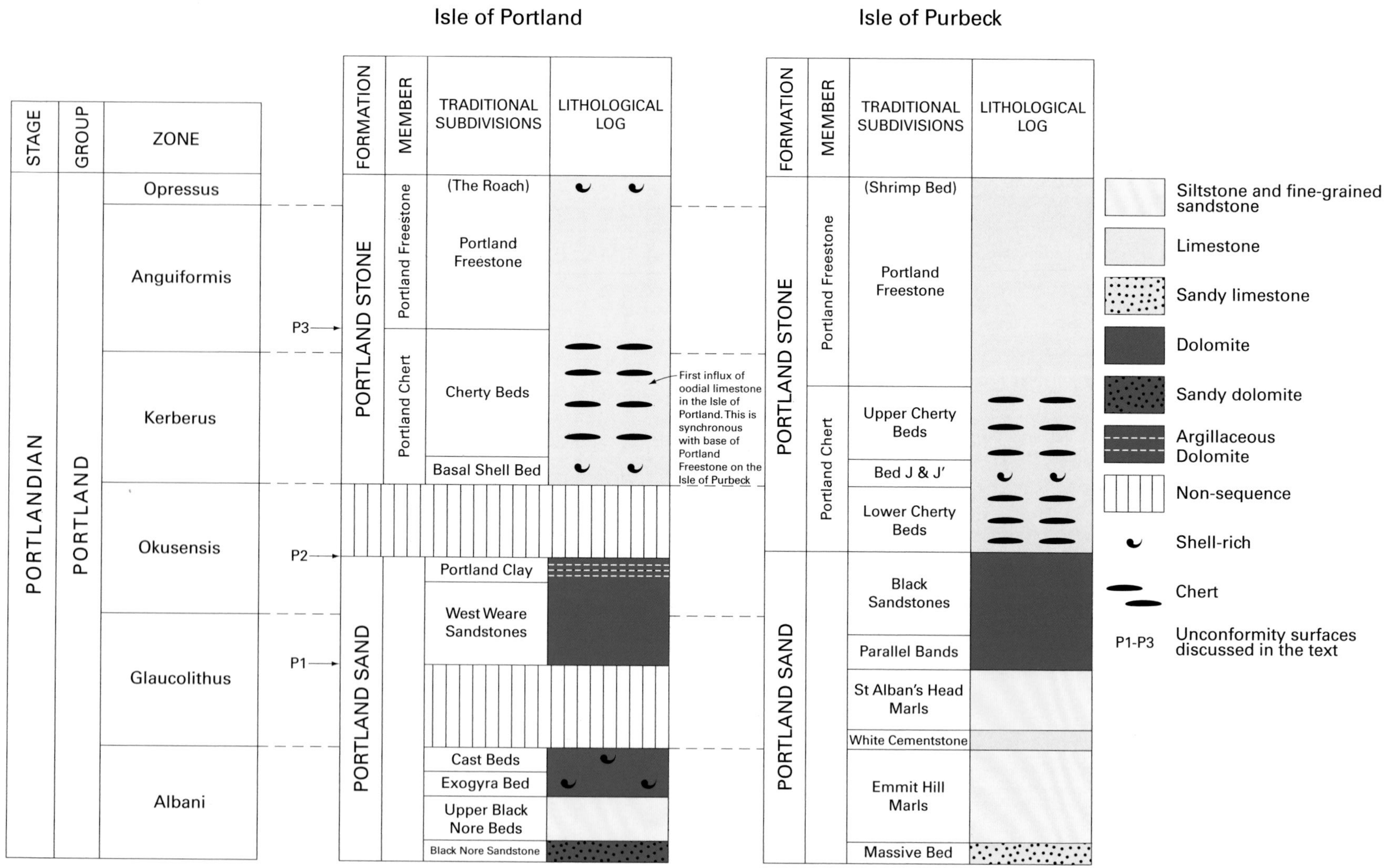

Figure 25   Stratigraphy and correlation of the Portland Group on the Isle of Portland and the Isle of Purbeck (based on a figure by Coe, 1996).

Figure 26 Lithostratigraphical correlation of key sections in the Portland Group based on data from Coe (1996).

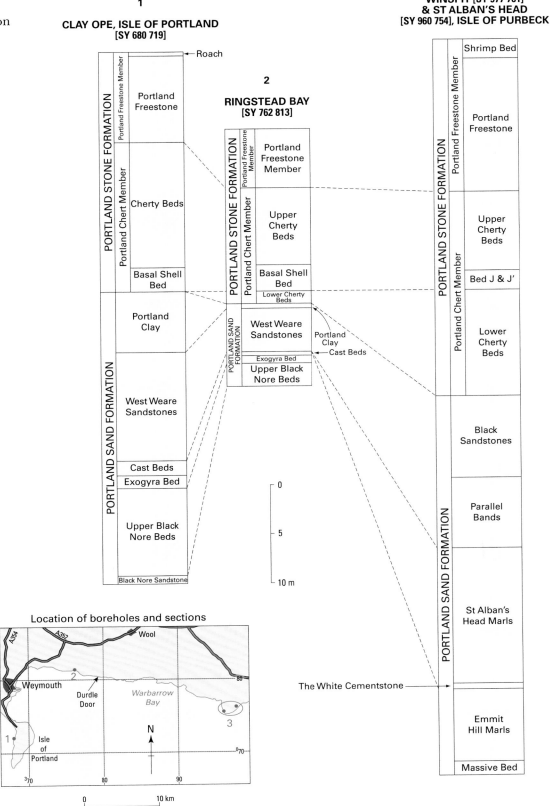

elongate east–west, extending offshore to the south and east for some 10 km (Ainsworth et al., 1998).

The Portland Group encompasses the Albani to the Anguiformis zones of the Portlandian Stage (Callomon and Cope, 1995; Figure 25), and is famous for its large ammonites, with some species of *Titanites* reaching a diameter of nearly a metre (Wimbledon and Cope, 1978; Plate 25). Bivalves and gastropods are also abundant, especially large, robust forms such as oysters and trigoniid bivalves. Crustacean remains are locally abundant at the top of the group on the Isle of Purbeck (Callomon and Cope, 1995). Locally, in the upper part of the group, there are small patch-reefs built around large laminated masses of the calcareous red alga *Solenopora*, to which numerous oysters and other bivalves became attached (Fürsich et al., 1994). However, despite this profusion, Ager (1976) pointed out that the fauna is of quite low diversity, and is particularly lacking in corals, brachiopods, echinoids, belemnites and nautiloids. These absences form part of a general picture of progressive depletion of faunas in Upper Jurassic formations in Dorset, which seems best explained by an increasing trend towards hypersalinity (Ager, 1976), culminating in the formation of evaporites at the base of the overlying Purbeck Group. Although much rarer than other macrofossils, the Portland Group in Dorset has also furnished a variety of marine, littoral/freshwater and terrestrial reptiles that includes turtles, crocodiles, pterosaurs and dinosaurs (Delair and Wimbledon, 1993).

Coe (1996) attempted to increase the resolution of stratigraphical correlation by identifying sequence boundaries (regional unconformities formed during relative sea-level fall). The stratigraphical position of the lowest two boundaries ('P1' and 'P2' of Coe, 1996) on the Isle of Portland are associated with apparently large stratal gaps when compared with the Isle of Purbeck where there is a more complete Portlandian succession than is found elsewhere in Dorset (Figure 25). Underhill (2002) argued that these variations relate to localised synsedimentary fault movement on the Abbotsbury–Ridgeway–Purbeck–Wight structures.

Portland Sand Formation

A number of informal divisions can be recognised in the Portland Sand Formation. The succession is described by reference to representative sections on the Isle of Portland at Clay Ope (West Weare Cliff [SY 680 719]), at Ringstead Bay [SY 762 813] and on the Isle of Purbeck at Winspit [SY 977 761] and St Alban's Head [SY 960 754] (Coe, 1996, figs. 7; 8; Figures 25; 26).

On the Isle of Purbeck, the formation base is marked by the **Massive Bed**, a well-cemented sandy limestone about 1.8 m thick. In areas of poor exposure, this produces a strong scarp feature and spring line above the more gently sloping ground that is underlain by Kimmeridge Clay. The Massive Bed is overlain by the **Emmit Hill Marls** and **St Alban's Head Marls**, which comprise 9.1 m and 13.7 m, respectively, of siltstone and fine-grained sandstone with variable amounts of calcite and dolomite, separated by the **White Cementstone**,

about 0.7 m thick. At the top of the formation are 13 m of finely crystalline dolomites, the **Parallel Bands** and the **Black Sandstones**.

On the Isle of Portland, the base of the Portland Sand Formation is marked by the **Black Nore Sandstone**, a well-cemented feature-forming sandy, dolomitic limestone up to 0.7 m thick, overlain by the **Upper Black Nore Beds**, 8.5 m of siltstone and fine-grained sandstone with variable amounts of calcite and dolomite. At their top, are two further feature-forming units, the **Exogyra Bed** (Arkell, 1947) and the **Cast Beds**, a shell-rich interval up to 2.5 m thick, comprising disarticulated shells of the oyster *Nanogyra nana*, plus other bivalves, serpulids and sponge spicules (Coe, 1996). These beds are disconformably overlain (the 'P1' sequence boundary of Coe, 1996), by 11 m of finely crystalline dolomite of the **West Weare Sandstones** and 6 m of argillaceous dolomite of the **Portland Clay**. The succession at Ringstead Bay is similar, but much thinner (Figure 26).

The Portland Sand Formation belongs to the Albani Zone, Glaucolithus Zone and lower Okusensis Zone (Wimbledon, 1980). The Albani Zone is characterised by species of the ammonites *Progalbanites* and *Pavlovia* (Callomon and Cope, 1995; Plate 25). Faunal abundance and diversity progressively increase above the base of the Albani Zone, culminating near the top of the Zone (on the Isle of Portland) in the Exogyra Bed, containing the ammonite *Epivirgatites* in addition to those listed above (Callomon and Cope, 1995). This acme of faunal abundance and diversity at the top of the Albani Zone was interpreted by Coe (1996) as a maximum flooding surface formed at a time of relative sea-level rise. The succeeding Glaucolithus Zone is characterised by *Glaucolithites*, represented by *G. caementarius* at Hounstout Cliff on the Isle of Purbeck (Wimbledon and Cope, 1978). A non-sequence ('P1' of Coe, 1996; see above) in the lower part of the Glaucolithus Zone on the Isle of Portland represents the lowest of three sequence boundaries in the Portland Group formed by relative falls of sea level. In the upper part of the Portland Sand Formation (Okuensis Zone) fossils are generally rare, although ammonites are locally common at the top of the formation (e.g. *Galbanites okusensis* and *Crendonites gorei*; Callomon and Cope, 1995) (Coe, 1996). A second non-sequence ('P2' of Coe, 1996) on the Isle of Portland omits the upper Okusensis Zone and separates the Portland Sand and Portland Stone formations (Figure 25).

Portland Stone Formation

The Portland Stone Formation is divided into the Portland Chert and Portland Freestone members, based on the presence or absence of common black nodular chert in massive micritic limestone (Figure 25). A topographic feature break approximately coincides with the junction between the two units.

Portland Chert Member

The Portland Chert Member comprises pale brown or grey bioturbated biomicrites with peloids, sponge spicules and some shell material and common black nodular cherts. On Portland, the **Basal Shell Bed**, 2.7 m thick, rests disconformably on the Portland Clay (Coe, 1996; see above). On the Isle of Purbeck, the member is divided into the **Lower Cherty Beds** and **Upper Cherty Beds** by a median, more shelly, interval (**Bed J and J¹**), that is correlative with the Basal Shell Bed on the Isle of Portland. The member is 17 m and 32 m thick on Portland and the Isle of Purbeck, respectively. The Portland Chert Member seen at Ringstead Bay is 12 m thick, and similar to that on the Isle of Purbeck, with a thin representative of the Lower Cherty Beds below the Basal Shell Bed and Upper Cherty Beds (Figure 26).

The base of the Portland Chert Member, coincident with the base of the Portland Stone Formation, is diachronous from the upper Okusensis Zone on the Isle of Purbeck, to the base of the Kerberus Zone on the Isle of Portland (Wimbledon, 1980). The remainder of the member belongs mainly to the Kerberus Zone (Isle of Purbeck), but on the Isle of Portland it also extends into the Anguiformis Zone (Wimbledon, 1980). The chert that is the distinguishing feature of this member is derived from the spicules of siliceous sponges (mainly *Rhaxella*) and, locally on the Isle of Purbeck, can be seen to be replacing *Thalassinoides* burrows (Coe, 1996) in a manner similar to flints in the Upper Cretaceous Chalk Group (Clayton, 1986). The Basal Shell Bed on Portland is strongly bioturbated, with *Thalassinoides* occurring at two or three horizons, and a fauna dominated by bivalves (55 species) and gastropods (17 species), but also including abundant tubes of the serpulid worm *Glomerula gordialis*, and rarer ammonites, brachiopods, echinoids and asteroids (Cox, 1925). Coe (1996) noted that large *Titanites* (including *T. giganteus*, *T. titan*, *T. bononiensis*, *T. pseudogigas*, *Kerberites kerberus*, *K. audax* and *Crendonites* spp.; Callomon and Cope, 1995), commonly encrusted with the oyster *Nanogyra* and serpulids, were locally abundant in the top of the unit. Eastwards, the Basal Shell Bed equates with a closely spaced pair of fossiliferous beds ('J' and 'J¹' of Arkell, 1947) that occur above the Lower Cherty Beds on the Isle of Purbeck (Coe, 1996). They are intensely bioturbated with *Thalassinoides*, packed with broken bivalves and serpulids and locally, at Dancing Ledge [SY 9980 7685], have abundant ammonites encrusted with *Nanogyra* and sepulids. At Ringstead Bay [SY 7600 8140], the equivalent of the Basal Shell Bed is rich in the serpulid *Glomerula gordialis*. The abundance of fauna at this level is interpreted as evidence of a transgressive horizon, formed at a time of relative sea-level rise. Above the Basal Shell Bed there are just a few shelly horizons in the remainder of the Portland Chert Member on the Isle of Portland, implying a rapid increase in water depth.

Portland Freestone Member

The Portland Freestone Member on the Isle of Portland is a thick-bedded, laminated to massive, ooidal, shell-rich micrite that forms the face of a well-defined escarpment. Many units have been named by local quarrymen (see Arkell, 1947). In comparison, the 'freestones' on the Isle of Purbeck are more thinly bedded and contain more bioclastic debris. The member is about 9 m and 13 m thick on Portland and at St Alban's Head, respectively, and 6 m thick at Ringstead Bay (Figure 26). The contact with the overlying Purbeck Limestone Group can be seen in a quarry [SY 7432 8356] just south of Poxwell, and on the north side of Ringstead Bay [around SY 7616 8157].

The Portland Freestone Member belongs to the upper Kerberus, Anguiformis and basal Opressus zones (Coe, 1996). On the Isle of Portland, the base of the member belongs to the lower Anguiformis Zone, and is separated from the underlying Portland Chert Member by an unconformity ('P3' sequence boundary of Coe, 1996) marked by a sharp, locally burrowed surface overlain by a shell lag. Eastwards, in the Isle of Purbeck, the succession is unbroken, and the base of the Portland Freestone is slightly older, belonging to the upper Kerberus Zone (Coe, 1996; Figure 25). The ammonites of the Portland Freestone are dominated by more densely ribbed species of *Titanites* (especially *Titanites anguiformis*) than are seen at older levels in the group (Callomon and Cope, 1995). In outcrops east of the Isle of Portland, Townson (1975) recorded locally bioturbated and shell-rich horizons with concentrations of gastropods and bivalves. In these successions, an ostracodal stromatolitic limestone occurs widely at the top of the Portland Freestone. Locally in east Purbeck, Townson (1975) also described an oyster-rich interval in the top of the Portland Freestone (the Tilly Whim Oyster Bed of Arkell, 1947) comprising up to 3 m of limestone containing abundant bivalve shells, particularly *Nanogyra nana*.

In the highest 3 to 4 m of the Portland Freestone Member on the Isle of Portland there are small patch-reefs, formed by masses of oysters and bryozoans cemented around a massive calcareous laminated framework built up by the red alga *Solenopora* (Townson, 1975; Fürsich et al., 1994). The topmost horizon is a particularly fossiliferous interval, up to 1 m thick, known as the 'Roach' . In this bed the shells are mostly dissolved out to leave a rock full of the moulds of gastropods and bivalves (Arkell, 1947). The characteristic fossils are the bivalves *Myophorella* and *Laevitrigonia* and the gastropod *Aptyxiella portlandica* (Fürsich et al., 1994; Plate 25), many encrusted by bryozoans and oysters. The high proportion of articulated bivalves may indicate catastrophic burial by storm events, and the subsequent leaching of shells could indicate percolation of acidic groundwaters associated with the freshwater deposits of the Purbeck Limestone Group (Fürsich et al., 1994). The top bed of the member on the Isle of Purbeck is a porcellanous micrite, the 'Shrimp Bed' (Figure 25), which yields remains of *Callianassa*, bivalves (including *Trigonia*, *Protocardia* and *Isognomon*) and the ammonite *Paracraspedites opressus* (Arkell, 1947; Callomon and Cope, 1995).

Overlying the Portland Group is the **Purbeck Group**, for which new age data show that only the basal strata belong to the Jurassic, and so for convenience, the Purbeck Group is described in the next chapter (Lower Cretaceous).

FOUR

Lower Cretaceous

The strata described in this chapter crop out in a series of discontinuous coastal exposures on the Isle of Purbeck, between Lulworth Cove and Swanage Bay. The succession comprises a basal limestone unit overlain by alternating mudstone and sandstone. The lower part of the succession (**Purbeck Group** and **Wealden Formation**) was deposited mostly in freshwater or marginal marine conditions and there is also evidence that part of Dorset was land at this time. Marine conditions were re-established across the region when the upper part of the succession was deposited (**Lower Greensand**, **Gault** and **Upper Greensand** formations).

The thickness of Lower Cretaceous strata in Dorset is extremely variable. North of the Abbotsbury–Ridgeway and Purbeck faults, and across the Cranborne–Fordingbridge High, Lower Cretaceous strata are largely absent, removed by erosion during Miocene Alpine tectonism. However, thick successions are present in south Dorset, with at least 900 m in the Swanage area. There is a rapid westward thinning across the Isle of Purbeck with about 525 m at Worbarrow Bay [SY 865 802], 300 m at Mupe Bay [SY 845 800], 200 m at Lulworth [SY 826 798], and 100 m at Durdle Cove [SY 805 802].

Ammonites, the most useful fossils for biostratigraphy, are absent from the basal part of the succession as a result of the environmental conditions that occurred during deposition of the Purbeck Group. However, fossil vertebrates are common including dinosaurs (*Iguanodon* and *Megalosaurus*), crocodiles, fish, turtles and pterosaurs, as well as mammals. These strata also contain evidence of wooded land areas, seen in the 'fossil forest' at Lulworth Cove and elsewhere (Plate 27). Few macrofossils occur in the overlying Wealden Formation, and so age data is based on ostracods and palynology. However, the reappearance of ammonites in the marine strata that form the Lower Greensand, Gault and Upper Greensand formations greatly improves correlation within these successions.

JURASSIC–CRETACEOUS BOUNDARY

The precise position of the Jurassic–Cretaceous boundary in the Dorset succession has long been a matter of debate, principally because Late Jurassic and Early Cretaceous environments in southern England were unfavourable for ammonites, which provide the best means for age determination and correlation.

Arkell (1933) placed the base of the Cretaceous at the base of the Wealden Formation in Dorset, and later Casey (1963) suggested that the 'Cinder Bed' (basal Stair Hole Member, Purbeck Group) equated with the basal Cretaceous of eastern England. Subsequently, evidence has emerged of changes in the

fossil pollen record, charophytes and ostracod faunas (Allen and Wimbledon, 1991; Fiest et al., 1995) which places the base of the Cretaceous as defined in Continental Europe in the Cypris Freestones (middle Mupe Member of Westhead and Mather, 1996), near the base of the Purbeck Group. This boundary is adopted here, thus making the greater part of the Purbeck Group Cretaceous in age. Recent studies by Abbink et al. (2001) suggesting that the base of the Cretaceous lies within the Cherty Freshwater Beds (= top Worbarrow Tout Member of Westhead and Mather, 1996) are based on correlations with Russian successions, where the base of the Cretaceous has traditionally been defined at a slightly younger horizon.

PURBECK GROUP

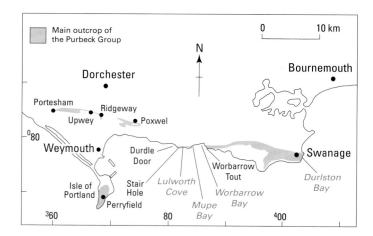

Map 10   Purbeck Group.

Towards the end of the Jurassic, falls in global sea level largely terminated marine sedimentation in the Wessex Basin, where the variable carbonate-dominated succession of the Purbeck Group indicates deposition in lagoons, sabkhas, hypersaline lakes and freshwater lakes (Chadwick, 1985b). Occasional marine incursions produced important faunal 'events' that are valuable for correlation. In Dorset, the group has a fragmented outcrop between Weymouth and Swanage, but includes some superb coastal exposures; the type section of the lower part of the group lies on the west side of Worbarrow Tout [SY 8688 7955] and that for the upper part is along the northern half of Durlston Bay [between SZ 0384 7842 and 0414 7865]. The principal inland outcrops are in the Upwey–Poxwell area, between Durdle Door and Durlston Bay, and on the Isle of Portland. The group occurs in the subsurface beneath

Table 1 Lithostratigraphical classification of the Purbeck Group in Dorset. Numbers for Ensom (1985a) and Clements (1993) refer to beds on their sections (based on a figure by Westhead and Mather, 1996).

		Upwey (beds after Fisher, 1856)	Worbarrow (members after Ensom, 1985a)		Durlston (members after Clements, 1983)		This account (follows Westhead and Mather, 1996)	
UPPER PURBECK		Paludina Clays	Upper Cypris Clays & Shales		Upper Cypris Clays & Shales		DURLSTON FORMATION	Peveril Point Member
		Upper Cypris Clays						
		Unio Bed	Unio		Unio			
		Upper Broken Shell Limestone	Broken Shell Limestone & Chief Beef		Broken Shell Limestone	220		
MIDDLE PURBECK		Chief Beef		187	Chief Beef	219		Stair Hole Member
		Corbula Beds	Corbula	186	Corbula			
			Scallop		Scallop			
		Intermarine Bed	Intermarine		Intermarine			
		Cinder Bed	Cinder	119	Cinder	111		
		Cherty Freshwater	Cherty Freshwater	118	Cherty Freshwater	110	LULWORTH FORMATION	Worbarrow Tout Member
LOWER PURBECK		Marly Freshwater	Marly Freshwater		Marly Freshwater			
		Soft Cockle	Soft Cockle		Soft Cockle			
		Hard Cockle	Hard Cockle & Cypris Freestones	31	Hard Cockle	34		Ridgeway Member
		Lower Insect		30		33		
		Cypris Freestones		18	Cypris Freestones	17		
				17		16		Mupe Member
		Broken Beds	Caps, Broken Beds & Dirt Beds		Caps, Broken Beds & Dirt Beds			
		Hard & Soft Caps						

Plate 27 Fossil Forest (Mupe Member, Lulworth Formation), Lulworth Cove [SY 829 797]. Algal 'burrs', 1 to 2 m in diameter, formed by thick masses of algae that accumulated around the bases of coniferous trees (P673302).

Figure 27   Correlation of the
Purbeck Group across Dorset
(based on a figure by Westhead
and Mather, 1996).

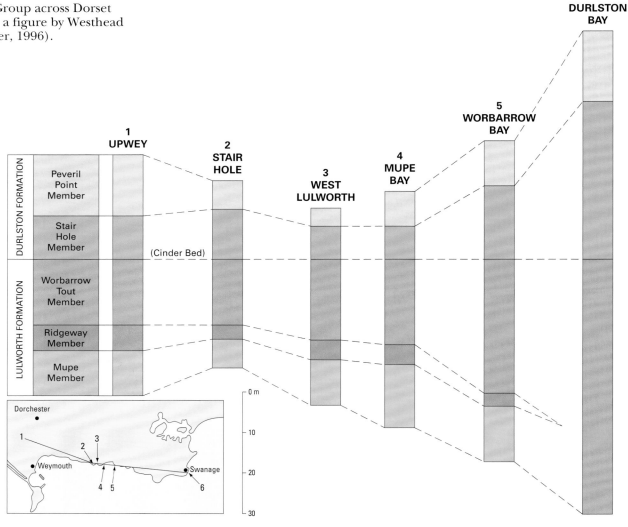

Wealden and younger strata in limited areas west of
Upwey, around Poxwell and north of the larger outcrop
around Swanage. In west Dorset, the group is about
60 m thick, but thinner (50 m or less) in central areas
around Lulworth and Poxwell. It thickens to over 110 m
at Durlston Bay in east Dorset (Figure 27), and offshore
oil wells and seismic data indicate that the group
continues to thicken to the south and east of Durlston
Bay, reaching a maximum of 200 m at depth to the west
of the Isle of Wight (Ainsworth et al., 1998; Underhill,
2002), within an east–west basin adjacent to the southern
side of the Purbeck–Isle of Wight Monocline. North of
the Purbeck Fault, on the South Dorset High, the group
has been removed by pre-Aptian erosion associated with
Alpine tectonism, and it is also absent across the Cranborne–Fordingbridge High in central and north Dorset.
According to Underhill (2002), thickness and lateral
facies variation within the Purbeck Group in south
Dorset can be largely explained by syndepositional extensional movement on the Abbotsbury–Ridgeway Fault

and Purbeck Fault systems, which experienced episodic
downthrow on their southern margins. This movement
may have triggered sudden marine flooding in the near-
shore environment that the Purbeck Group was formed
in, and explain the localised preservation of fossil coniferous trees (e.g. Mupe Member; see below) (Underhill,
2002).

The base of the Purbeck Group in Dorset is taken at the
first occurrence of finely laminated, ostracod-rich limestones above the more massive, shelly marine limestones
of the Portland Group; the top is at the last occurrence of
significant limestone beds beneath the sandy mudstones
of the Wealden Formation. The traditional Lower, Middle
and Upper Purbeck divisions that were defined in the
mid 19th century (Forbes 1851, in Lyell, 1855; Fisher,
1856) have been superseded by the Lulworth and overlying Durlston formations formalised by Townson (1975)
from divisions originally proposed by Casey (1963; see
also Morter, 1984). Five mappable members form subdivisions of the two formations (Westhead and Mather, 1996;

Plate 28 Purbeck Group exposed in the 'Lulworth Crumple' at Stair Hole [SY 8229 7983]. Mupe Member rocks form the bluff to the right (south) of the picture, with several metres of 'Broken Beds' towards the top. Height of cliff is c. 25 m (P005799).

R base of Ridgeway Member; **W** base of Worbarrow Tout Member; **S** base of Stair Hole Member; **P** base of Peveril Point Member

Table 1). There are a further 15 or so finer divisions of the Purbeck Group considered here to have the status of beds (Bristow and Fisher, 1857; Bristow, 1884; Westhead and Mather, 1996 following Fisher, 1856; and references therein), but termed members in some other publications (El-Shahat and West, 1983; Ensom, 1985a; Wimbledon, 1987; Clements, 1993).

In the absence of ammonites, geologists have resorted to a variety of taxa to subdivide and correlate the Purbeck Group. The potential of ostracods for biostratigraphy has been recognised by many geologists, and a variety of different schemes have been proposed for the Purbeck Group (Arkell, 1947; Sylvester-Bradley, 1949; Wilson et al., 1958, Anderson and Bazley, 1971; Anderson, 1985; Clements, 1993; Horne, 1995; Table 1). The most influential of these workers was F W Anderson, who divided the group into 4 zones, within which he recognised six successive ostracod 'assemblages', and 39 'faunicycles', tentatively linked to regular climatic fluctuations (Anderson and Bazley, 1971). However, problems in applying the faunicycle concept have led some authors to propose replacements for Anderson's scheme (Clements, 1993; Horne, 1995, 2002).

Norris (1969, 1970), using palynology, recognised three successive intervals in the Purbeck Group ('A', 'B' and 'C'), characterised by different suites of fossil miospores. Subsequently, Hunt (1985) recognised three palynological biozones equating with part of Norris's threefold succession (Table 1). More recently, charophytes (calcified reproductive structures of fresh and brackish water algae) have been used to subdivide the succession. Feist et al. (1995) recognised five charophyte zones, and these have been related to the ostracod 'Assemblages' of Anderson (1985) (Table 1).

Finally, Morter (1984) showed that the Purbeck Group contained nine distinctive mollusc assemblages, thought to be salinity controlled. These assemblages of bivalves and gastropods show a similar cyclicity to the ostracod faunicycles, and Morter (1984) demonstrated that there was a fairly good correlation with them, and also with lithology. The pattern of mollusc-based salinity changes through the Purbeck Group was summarised by Radley (2002, fig. 1), but correlations based on these could be unrealistic if they are related to localised factors as suggested by Underhill (2002).

Lulworth Formation

The Lulworth Formation ranges in thickness from about 27 to 63 m, with 39 m proved in the Upton 2 Borehole [SY 7395 8339]. The type section lies on the west side of Worbarrow Tout [SY 8688 7955] (Westhead and Mather, 1996).

Mupe Member

The type section of the member is the west side of Mupe Bay (Bacon Hole) [SY 8394 7966]. Its thickness ranges from 11 m at Upwey to 16 m in the Upton 2 Borehole in east Dorset; 7 m occur at Stair Hole [SY 8229 7983] (Plate 28). The basal part of the member is dominated

Figure 28 Reconstruction of early Purbeck Group environment in Dorset (from Sellwood and Wilson, 1990).

by white-weathering calcareous mudstones and micrites containing algal lamination; some evaporitic material (West, 1975), and interbedded carbonaceous mudstones (Caps and Dirt Beds; Table 1) also occur. These strata have been extensively researched (e.g. Brown, 1963; West, 1964, 1975; Pugh, 1968; Francis, 1984; Worssam and Ivimey-Cook, 1984; Anderson, 1985; Perry, 1994), in particular the Caps and Dirt Beds, which contain evidence of fossil trees (Figure 28). In the 'fossil forest' at Lulworth Cove [SY 829 797] (Plate 27) and on the Isle of Portland, the remains comprise mostly hollow moulds of stumps enclosed in algal limestone, but prior to 1880 silicified specimens preserving the exquisite detail of cell structure and growth rings were found (West, 1979).

Higher in the succession, the middle part of the Mupe Member in central and eastern Dorset has common brecciated limestone pockets, traditionally termed Broken Beds. The brecciation is probably caused by the collapse of strata following the dissolution of former evaporite horizons (House, 1989), although West (1975), following Arkell (1938), favoured local tectonic fracturing of the succession. Farther west, brecciation is less typical, as illustrated by sections at Portesham [SY 609 859] and Perryfield [SY 694 712] (House, 1958, 1989; West et al., 1969; Barker et al., 1975; West, 1975), and led Wimbledon (1987) to suggest the alternative name of Kingbarrow Slatt Beds for this interval. In the upper part of the member, ostracod-rich limestones containing abundant parallel laminations and ripples are common (lower part of Cypris Freestones; Table 1).

Ridgeway Member

The base of the Ridgeway Member is taken at the first significant occurrence of dark grey or brown mudstones above the limestone of the Mupe Member. Generally the member varies in thickness from 2.5 to 7 m; it is 2.8 m thick in the Upton 2 Borehole, but locally absent at

Plate 29 Some characteristic fossils from the Lower Cretaceous of Dorset and south-east Devon. Unless otherwise stated, scale bars represent 10 mm (P669424).

1	'Protocardia' major (Purbeck Group)
2	Unio (Purbeck Group)
3	Neomiodon (Purbeck Group)
4	Viviparus (Purbeck Group)
5	Praeexogyra [Liostrea] distorta (Purbeck Group)
6	Corbula (Purbeck Group)
7a–b	Cheloniceras (Lower Greensand)
8a–b	Deshayesites forbesi (Lower Greensand)
9a–b	Hoplites dentatus (Gault)
10	Anahoplites planus (Gault)
11	Costagyra digitata (Upper Greensand)
12	Amphidonte obliquatum (Upper Greensand)
13	Hysteroceras (Gault)
14a–b	Callihoplites vraconensis (Upper Greensand)
15	Actinoceramus concentricus (Upper Greensand)
16	Neithea gibbosa (Upper Greensand)
17	Pleurohoplites renauxianus (Upper Greensand)

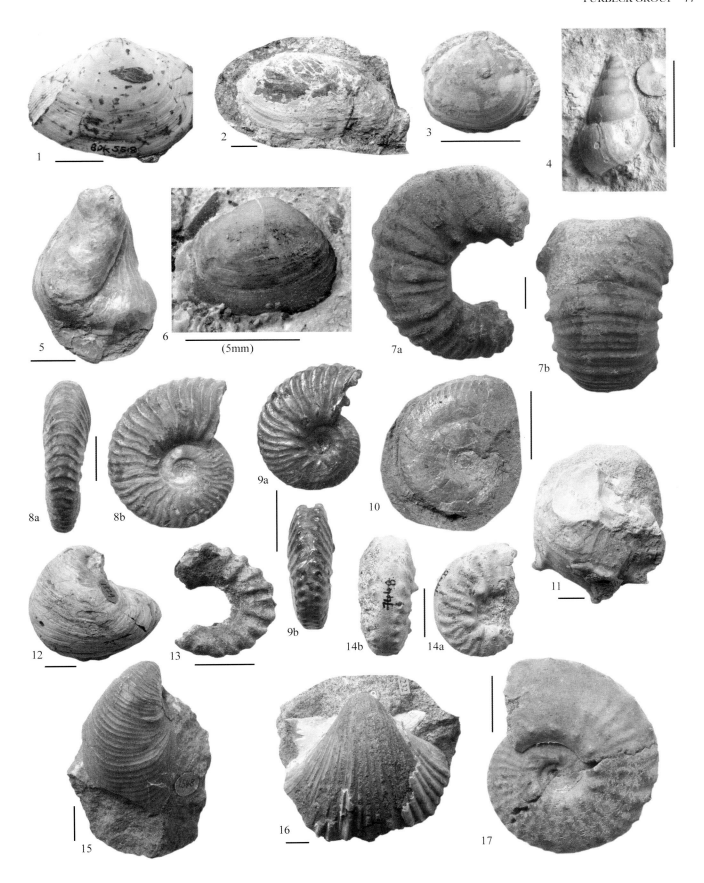

(5mm)

Table 2 Biostratigraphical schemes for the Purbeck Group.

FAUNICYCLES (Anderson, 1985)	Ostracod assemblages and biozones (Anderson, 1985) — Assemblage	Ostracod assemblages and biozones (Anderson, 1985) — Zone	Ostracod zones (Clements, 1993)	Ostracod biozones (Horne, 1995, 2002) — Subzone	Ostracod biozones (Horne, 1995, 2002) — Zone	Charophyte zones (Feist et al., 1995)	Palynology — Dorofer and Norris (1977)	Palynology — Hunt (1985)	Lithostratigraphy (Westhead and Mather, 1996) — Member	Formation	Chrono
40 Battle / 39 Tyneham / 38 Durdle / 37 Tisbury / 36 Brede	6	*Cypridea setina*	*Cypridea setina*	*Cypridea propunctata*	*Theriosynoecum forbesi*	5 (no index species)	C2	?	Peveril Point Member	DURLSTON FORMATION	CRETACEOUS
35 Mupes / 34 Lulworth / 33 Greenwood / 32 Foxwell / 31 Bacon	5	*Cypridea vidrana*	*Cypridea vidrana*			?	?	?			
30 Studland / 29 Scallop / 28 Langton / 27 Worth / 26 Corfe	4	*Cypridea granulosa*	*Cypridea granulosa fasciculata*	*Cypridea granulosa*		4 *Flabellochara grovesi*	C1	*Matonisporites elegans* ?	Stair Hole Member		
25 Royal / 24 Croydon / 23 Nothe / 22 Cinder Beds / 21 Peveril			*Cypridea granulosa granulosa*			?	?	?			
20 Durlston / 19 Netherfield / 18 Swanage / 17 Ashdown / 16 Goldspur / 15 Mountfield / 14 Burwash / 13 Robertsbridge / 12 Ringstead / 11 Penshurst	3	*Cypridea dunkeri*	*Cypridea dunkeri*	*Cypridea dunkeri*		3 *Globator protoincrassatus*	B	*Apiculatisporis verbitskayae*	Worbarrow Tout Member	LULWORTH FORMATION	
10 U. Soft Cockle / 9 L. Soft Cockle / 8 Wardour / 7 Hard Cockle / 6 Upwey	2					?	?	?			
5 Swindon / 4 Stair						2 *Globator praecursor*			Ridgeway Member		
3 Ridgeway / 2 Warren / 1 Quainton	1					1 *Globator rectispirale*	A	*Parvisaccites radiatus*	Mupe Member		? — ? JURASSIC

Plate 30 Wealden Formation (foreground), Upper Greensand Formation and Chalk Group, Durdle Cove [SY 809 803]. The succession is locally inverted, and dips 70° towards the south. The Chalk cliffs in the middle distance reach 95 m in height (P673113).

Durlston Bay. The type section is in an old quarry at Ridgeway [SY 6712 8515], north of Weymouth. The member is equivalent to the upper part of the Cypris Free-stones Beds and to the Lower Insect Beds of traditional usage (Fisher, 1856; Table 1).

The characteristic lithologies are very dark greyish brown, carbonaceous mudstones and pale calcareous mudstones and micrites, commonly containing thin detrital quartz laminations that may form isolated ripples. The dark mudstones make the member easy to distinguish in the coastal sections west of Mupe Bay, but are best developed in the west at Upwey, where they can be mapped by augering. At Worbarrow Tout and Stair Hole (Plate 28), mudstone becomes less impor-tant, but the member can still be discerned between the thicker limestones at the top of the Mupe Member (Cypris Freestones; see below) and the base of the over-lying Worbarrow Tout Member (Hard Cockle Beds). In the east, at Durlston Bay, the member dies out as mudstones are replaced by micritic limestone, which can not be distinguished from the overlying Worbarrow Tout Member.

Worbarrow Tout Member

The base of the Worbarrow Tout Member is taken at the first significant bed of quartz-detrital limestone (Hard Cockle Beds of traditional usage; Table 1) above mudstones of the Ridgeway Member. The member thick-ness is fairly consistent in the west of Dorset, ranging from 17 m at Upwey to 21 m at Worbarrow Bay, although it thickens progressively eastwards, reaching 39 m at

Durlston. The type section is the west side of Worbarrow Tout [SY 8688 7956].

From Upwey to Worbarrow, the lower part of the member contains prominent, brown-weathering lime-stones containing quartz sand (Hard Cockle Beds) and exhibiting abundant ripple cross-lamination. These lime-stones are well exposed in cliff sections at Stair Hole (Plate 28) and Worbarrow Tout. At Durlston, however, they are poorly developed (Clements, 1969, 1993). The rest of the member comprises regularly interbedded alternations of white-weathering micrite and dark grey mudstone (Soft Cockle and Marly Freshwater beds). Salt pseudomorphs, hardgrounds and rare algal laminae are present in the micrites, particularly in the central part of the member. Algal lamination increases in the east and may be associated with zones of multiple hardgrounds. The highest part of the member comprises thicker bedded, chert-rich micrites.

The low diversity fauna in the lower and middle parts of this member has been compared with modern day brackish and hypersaline environments (West, 1979). It contrasts with the fauna found in the higher part of the member, where the gastropods, ostracods and charo-phytes suggest a shallow, carbonate-rich, low-salinity lake environment (West, 1979).

Durlston Formation

The Durlston Formation is thinnest in central areas, with 18 to 19 m in the Upton 2 Borehole and between Stair Hole and Mupe Bay. It thickens westwards to 25 m at Upwey and eastwards to 57 m at Durlston. The type sections for the formation and its two members lie in the northern half of Durlston Bay, between [SZ 0384 7842 and SZ 0414 7865].

Stair Hole Member

The base of the Stair Hole Member is taken at the first occurrence of very shelly limestone (Cinder Bed) above more pure carbonate mudstones of the Worbarrow Tout Member. The member is 8 to 14 m thick westwards from Mupe Bay, and 9 m thick in the Upton 2 Borehole. It thickens eastwards to 19 m at Worbarrow Tout and 40 m at Durlston Bay.

The characteristic lithology is medium- to coarse-grained bioclastic limestone. In the basal part, an oyster-rich calcareous mudstone (Cinder Bed) forms a distinctive and easily correlated marker-bed. The oysters, mostly the species *Praeexogyra* [*Liostrea*] *distorta*, are associated with the serpulid *Serpula coacervata*, the echinoid *Hemicidaris purbeckensis* and less commonly '*Protocardia*' *major* (West, 1979; Kelly, 1988; Plate 29). Echinoid remains towards the middle of the Cinder Bed are indicative of normal marine conditions, and represents a conspicuous increase in salinity (West, 1979) that Casey (1963, 1973) believed to represent a brief basal Cretaceous marine incursion. Morter (1984) suggested that the Cinder Bed represents a threefold package of deposits, comprising a transgressive freshwater unit, a marine unit, and a regressive freshwater unit.

The Cinder Bed passes up into a succession of inter-bedded shell-fragmental limestone and mudstone (Intermarine and Scallop beds). The limestones contain cross-stratification, particularly in the east. Thicker, carbonaceous mudstones, with numerous fibrous calcite veins ('beef') become more common again towards the top of the member (Corbula and Chief Beef beds; Table 1) particularly in the east. In these sedimentary rocks above the Cinder Bed, the mollusc fauna is more varied and includes *Neomiodon* and the gastropods *Viviparus* (Plate 29), *Physa*, *Hydrobia* and some *Liostrea*, and there are records of dinosaur footprints (*Iguanodon* and *Megalosaurus*), crocodiles, fish, turtles and pterosaurs (West, 1979). Gastropods and the small bivalve *Corbula* dominate in the higher part of the member (West, 1979), where fossil insects are again common (Clifford et al., 1993; Jarzembowski, 1993). Local concentrations of the scallop '*Chlamys*' (possibly *Camptonectes* of the 'Marine Association' of Morter, 1984) towards the middle of the member record a short-lived return to normal marine conditions (West, 1979), but most of the fauna from the higher part of the Stair Hole Member is consistent with a shallow, brackish or freshwater environment, with periods of subaerial exposure indicated by dinosaur trackways. The beds with abundant *Corbula* near the top of the Stair Hole Member could have formed in an estuarine environment.

Peveril Point Member

This member, equivalent to the old 'Upper Purbeck', is similar to the Stair Hole Member, comprising medium-to coarse-grained bioclastic limestone, interbedded with carbonaceous mudstone. The base of the Peveril Point Member is taken at the first occurrence of thickly bedded, coarsely shell-detrital limestone (base Broken Shell Limestone Bed; Table 1) above mudstone and finer-grained limestone at the top of the Stair Hole Member. The top of the member (i.e. top of Purbeck Group) is taken at the last occurrence of significant limestone beds beneath the Wealden sandy mudstones. The Peveril Point Member varies from 7 to 17 m thick across Dorset, and is 8.5 m thick in the Upton 2 Borehole.

The Broken Shell Limestone Bed at the base fines upwards into a biomicrite and carbonaceous mud-dominated succession with glauconite-rich beds that, in the west, are commonly rich in detrital quartz (= Unio Bed and Upper Cypris Clays and Shales Beds of traditional usage; Table 1). The fauna is dominated by gastropods, but the remains of fish, turtles and crocodiles also occur, and there are records of phosphatised ammonites derived from the Kimmeridge Clay, including *Pavlovia* sp. (West, 1979; Ensom, 1985b), demonstrating that Upper Jurassic strata were being eroded from adjacent land areas at the beginning of the Cretaceous. Underhill (2002) suggested that this may relate to uplift and erosion of the footwall of the Abbotsbury–Ridgeway Fault. A predominantly freshwater environment is indicated by the abundance of the bivalve *Unio* and gastropod *Viviparus* through much of the Peveril Point Member. This association is the 'least saline' of Morter's (1984) nine mollusc assemblages, and West (1979) envisaged a shallow lake that swarmed with aquatic life.

WEALDEN FORMATION

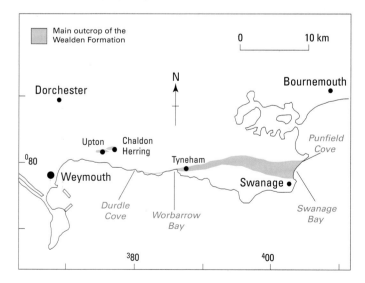

Map 11 Wealden Formation.

The Wealden Formation comprises a thick accumulation of almost entirely nonmarine clastic sedimentary rocks (mudstones and channel sandstones) produced by the erosion of adjacent landmasses, particularly the now emergent Cranborne–Fordingbridge High (Chadwick, 1985b). The coarser beds were deposited by braided streams that traversed a system of lakes and channels; the more argillaceous units accumulated in brackish and freshwater lagoons and bays (Chadwick, 1985b). In south Dorset, the formation is best seen in coastal sections where it thickens eastward from about 65 m at Durdle Cove (the most westerly coastal exposure; Plate 30) to about 425 m at Worbarrow Bay, and perhaps 700 m (Arkell, 1947) or 1000 m (Ruffell and Batten, 1994) in Swanage Bay. Inland, the formation was seen in a trial pit [SY 6742 8520] east of the Bincombe cutting, in the Upton Syncline where 70 m were proved, and in the core of the Chaldon Anticline, where the Chaldon Herring 2 Borehole proved 149.2 m. The formation is absent on the South Dorset High.

The distribution of the Wealden Formation is approximately co-extensive with the Purbeck Group and there is a lithological and palaeontological transition from one formation into the other. Strahan (1898) wrote 'no line can be drawn which does not either include beds of Purbeck type in the Wealden or beds of Wealden type in the Purbeck, the two formations being absolutely inseparable'. In practice, the formation base is taken at the top of the last significant limestone bed of the Durlston Formation (Westhead and Mather, 1996) and is mapped at the foot of its dip slope.

The Wealden succession of Dorset and the Isle of Wight is generally regarded as comprising two main parts (Arkell, 1947): the 'Variegated Marls and Sandstones' below (Wessex Formation of Daley and Stewart, 1979) and the much thinner 'Wealden Shales' above (Vectis Formation of Daley and Stewart, 1979). In Dorset, strata equivalent to the Vectis Formation have been recognised only at Swanage, where the formation consists of 10.5 m of evenly stratified, dark, fissile mudstone with some thin beds of shelly limestone. As this interval does not form a mappable unit inland, published maps of the Dorset succession treat the Wealden as a single unit, the Wealden Formation. This approach is maintained herein for consistency with nomenclature shown on the published maps, but following Hopson et al. (2008), these strata should correctly be redesignated Wealden Group.

The formation consists dominantly of red, purple, green, grey and mottled sandy or calcareous mudstone, and forms the brilliantly coloured cliffs on the east side of Worbarrow Bay, where nearly the whole of the succession (425 m thick) is exposed (Arkell, 1947). Beds of sandstone occur throughout the succession and tend to predominate toward the top; most are between 0.15 to 0.6 m thick, and die out when traced laterally. Some of the sandstones are very coarse-grained or conglomeratic, for example the 'Coarse Quartz Grit' of Arkell (1947), and are commonly cemented by iron. In the Upton area [SY 742 829], Lulworth Cove and from Worbarrow eastwards through Tyneham [SY 882 803] to Blackmanston Farm [SY 916 808], there appears to be only one bed of

'quartz grit', but east of this last locality, feature-forming sandstones are developed at more than one level. The lithology (Kirkaldy, 1947) and heavy mineral assemblages (Groves, 1931; Bathurst, 1951) of the conglomeratic horizons suggest derivation from an uplifted landmass in south-west England.

The Wealden Formation is poorly fossiliferous in Dorset, the principal remains comprising plant debris (conifers, cycads and ferns) and locally the fresh-water bivalves *Unio* and *Viviparus*. Larger gastropods found both at Corfe Castle and Punfield are referable to *Paraglauconia strombiformis*. Hesselbo and Allen (1991) recorded vertical cylindrical trace fossils at Mupe Bay, and bones of the dinosaur *Iguanodon* have been recorded about 0.8 km north of Swanage (Buckland, 1835), and at Ridgeway (Fisher, 1856). An extensive reptile fauna collected from the foreshore (Delair, 1966) probably derives from subtidal outcrops of Wealden strata in Swanage Bay.

In the absence of marine fossils such as ammonites, biostratigraphical and chronostratigraphical subdivision of the Wealden Formation relies on ostracods and palynology (fossil spores). The ostracod scheme (Anderson, 1985) is founded mainly on successions in the stratotype area in the Weald of south-east England, but in Dorset and adjoining areas, the Wealden Formation is generally unfossiliferous, and so few of the subdivisions can be recognised. Hesselbo and Allen (1991) recorded that the basal Wealden Formation at Mupe Bay [SY 844 797] belonged to the top of the *C. setina* Zone or base of the *C. brevirostrata* Zone, and Rawson and Riley (1982) tentatively correlated the basal Wealden Formation of Dorset with the *S. stenomphalus* Zone in the ammonite-bearing succession of eastern England. The top of the Wealden Formation near Swanage contains ostracods that are typical of the upper part of the *C. valdensis* Zone (Anderson, 1967). Recently, Horne (1995) has suggested a revised ostracod scheme for the Wealden Formation based on data published by Anderson (1985).

The Wealden Formation spans the Valanginian, Hauterivian, Barremian, and, locally, basal Aptian stages (Rawson et al., 1978), the recognition of which is mainly based on palynological evidence. Allen and Wimbledon (1991) assigned the basal Wealden Formation to the earliest Valanginian, and suggested that the Berriasian–Valanginian boundary was approximately at the top of the underlying Purbeck Group. Spore and pollen assemblages from near the top of the Wealden Formation at Punfield Cove are comparable with material from the Isle of Wight and the Weald that is considered to be Barremian (Ruffell and Batten, 1994). Hughes and McDougall (1989) detailed the inferred extent of the Valanginian, Hauterivian and Barremian in the Wealden Formation at Worbarrow Bay based on bioevents recognised in the *Cicatricosisporites* group of palynomorphs.

LOWER GREENSAND FORMATION

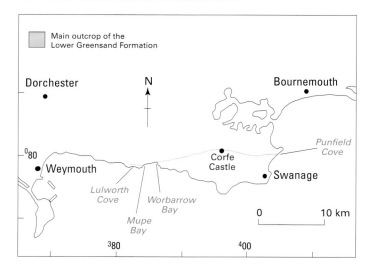

Map 12 Lower Greensand Formation.

Regional subsidence coupled with a global rise in sea level re-established shallow marine conditions across the district in the Early Aptian (Chadwick, 1985c), resulting in the deposition of the Lower Greensand. In Dorset, the formation comprises a succession of mudstones overlain by poorly consolidated sandstones that form a narrow belt in the steep limb of the Purbeck Monocline. The succession has been mapped as a single formation, and is treated as such herein for consistency with nomenclature shown on the published maps, but following Hopson et al. (2008) should correctly be regarded as a group. The formation extends eastwards as a wedge of strata, thickening from about 0.5 m at Lulworth Cove to 20 m at Mupe Bay, 35 m at Worbarrow Bay where the formation is best exposed (Arkell, 1947; Ruffell and Batten, 1994) and 49 m at Corfe Castle [SY 9605 8205]. The thickest Lower Greensand is at Punfield Cove [SZ 0380 8105], where Arkell (1947) and Casey (1961) attributed 59 m of strata to this unit. However, Ruffell and Batten (1994) reported new exposures at this locality that suggested that the formation might be as much as 170 m thick. North of the Purbeck Fault, 3.78 m of Lower Greensand was proved in the Winterborne Kingston Borehole, 3.2 m in the Creech Borehole, 6.1 m in Wareham 3 Borehole, 2.45 m in Stoborough 1 Borehole, 4.94 m in the Arne G1 Borehole, and 10.36 m in the Bushey Farm A1 Borehole; elsewhere north of the structure, the Lower Greensand appears to have been largely removed by inter-Aptian erosion.

Although not shown on the resurveyed Sheet 342/343 Swanage, the Lower Greensand Formation is divisible into three members: a lower mudstone unit, the **Atherfield Clay Member**, a median arenaceous unit, the **Ferruginous Sands Member**, and an upper arenaceous unit, the **Sandrock Member**. The key features of these members are discussed below.

The biozonation of the Lower Greensand (Figure 29) is based on ammonites, and mostly follows Casey (1961),

but with modifications proposed by Ruffell and Owen (1995) and Owen (1996). Rawson et al. (1978) show that the base of the Lower Greensand is diachronous in Dorset and Devon, but the extent to which this can be demonstrated in coastal exposures in Dorset is limited, since the top of the Wealden and base of the Lower Greensand mostly lack biozonally diagnostic macrofossils (Simpson, 1985). With the exception of a highly fossiliferous horizon within the middle part of the formation, the Punfield Marine Band (Arkell, 1947), relatively little has been published on the detailed biostratigraphy, the most recent and detailed account being that of Ruffell and Batten (1994) in which they document the occurrence of zones and subzones in the Aptian and Albian.

By integrating faunal and lithological data, Ruffell and Batten (1994) concluded that the westward thinning of the Lower Greensand Formation reflects in part the original limits of deposition with the marine-influenced environment of the Swanage succession passing westward into marshes, lagoons and swamps.

Atherfield Clay Member

The best section through this member in south Dorset is on the coast at Punfield Cove. About 15 m of strata have usually been attributed to this member (Simpson, 1985), although Ruffell and Batten (1994) suggested that it was over 40 m thick. It comprises a pebbly, phosphatic basal bed (0.9 m thick) with fish teeth, overlain by fossiliferous blue, buff and red mudstone with thin interbeds of sandstone. The topmost part of the member is formed by the Punfield Marine Band, 0.5 to 1.5 m thick and composed of three units: a lower unit of hard, ferruginous, shelly limestone with pebbles and concretions of argillaceous limestone; a middle part composed almost entirely of oyster shells (Judd, 1871); an upper unit of hard, laminated, micaceous, poorly fossiliferous calcareous sandstone with much carbonaceous and lignitic material. The basal pebble bed of the Atherfield Clay, also seen at Corfe Castle, but not at Worbarrow Bay, can be correlated with the Atherfield Bone-Bed, Chale Clay and Lower Lobster Bed members of the Atherfield Clay of the type locality on the Isle of Wight (Simpson, 1985; Figure 29).

Fossils from the Atherfield Clay at Punfield Cove are mostly bivalves, such as *Nuculana scapha*, *Aptolinter aptiensis*, *Pseudoptera subdepressa*, *Freiastarte subcostata*, *Panopea gurgitis* and *Plectomya anglica* (Arkell, 1947), with fish teeth near the base and abundant specimens of the zonal index ammonite *Deshayesites forbesi* (Plate 29) near the top (Casey, 1961). Good biostratigraphical data from the base of the member (and of the Lower Greensand) seems to be lacking, although Rawson et al. (1978) imply that it is diachronous from within the *fissicostatus* Zone to the top of the *forbesi* Zone (Figure 29), and Arkell (1947, p. 165) suggests that the base of the formation becomes younger between Punfield and Corfe. Just above the Marine Band at Punfield, Casey (1961) and Ruffell and Batten (1994) recorded fragments of the ammonite *Deshayesites*, indicating the *callidiscus* Subzone at the top of the *forbesi* Zone.

Figure 29 Bio-zonation of the Dorset Lower Greensand Formation, and correlation of the Atherfield Clay Member with the type succession of the Isle of Wight.

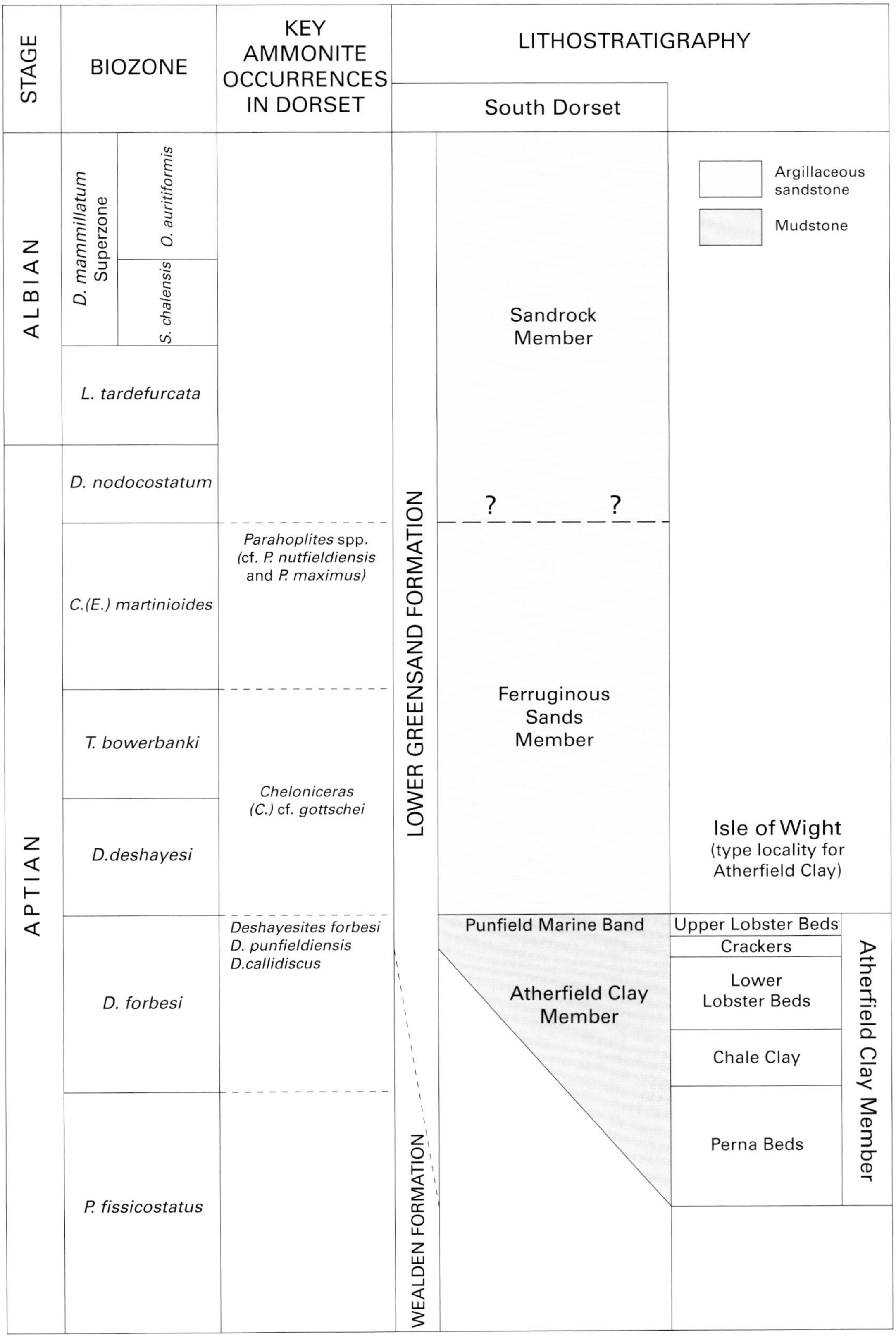

Much debate has centred on the palaeoenvironmental significance of the Marine Band fauna. Based on the occurrence of the bivalve *Eomiodon*, Casey (1961) considered that the Punfield Marine Band at Punfield was formed in brackish water, and that the associated ammonites were drifted specimens. However, Simpson (1983) noted that the diversity of the fauna there, including ammonites and echinoids, indicated a fully marine deposit, although at other Dorset localities it may have formed in an environment of reduced salinity. Cleevely et al. (1983) suggested that at Punfield Cove the Marine Band probably represents an estuary or inshore protected bay.

Ferruginous Sands and Sandrock members

In south Dorset, most of the succession above the Atherfield Clay has been attributed to the Ferruginous Sands Member by previous authors (Arkell, 1947, Casey, 1961). These strata include fine-grained, weakly cemented, yellow, brown and white bioturbated sandstone with some interlaminated and interbedded mudstones. Rounded quartz pebbles occur on top of a sandstone in the upper part of the succession at both Worbarrow Bay and Punfield Cove, although Strahan (1898) implied that they occur throughout the sandstone at Punfield. Arkell (1947) thought that these pebbly beds equated with the base of the Sandgate Beds and Bargate Beds in the Weald. At Punfield Cove, a bed (3.6 m to 4.5 m thick) of dark grey or green sandy mudstone occurs at the top of the Ferruginous Sands, and has been correlated with Bed XV of Fitton (1847) of the Isle of Wight and the Marehill Clay of Sussex (Arkell, 1947).

The only south Dorset locality that appears to preserve the Sandrock Member is the thick succession at Punfield Cove. There, the highest 2.4 to 6.4 m of sandstone (Arkell, 1947; Heap, 1951), comprising white, tabular cross-stratified sandstones (= Bed 15 of Arkell) have been attributed to this unit, although both Arkell and Casey (1961) included this bed with the Ferruginous Sands in their logs of the succession. Ruffell and Batten's (1994) interpretation of a much expanded Punfield Cove succession shows about 55 m of Sandrock overlying about 67 m of Ferruginous Sands.

Arkell (1947) commented that the Lower Greensand above the Punfield Marine Band was unfossiliferous, but Casey (1961) and Ruffell and Batten (1994) added to the faunal records of this part of the succession, including the ammonite *Cheloniceras* (Plate 29) possibly indicative of the *T. bowerbanki* Zone. Higher in the Punfield succession, Ruffell and Batten (1994) recorded *Parahoplites*, associated with a phosphatic nodule bed horizon containing reworked Upper Jurassic ammonites and fossil wood. The fauna is probably indicative of the *P. nutfieldiensis* Zone of Ruffell and Owen (1995), and can possibly be interpreted as belonging to an erosive trangressive unit, seen in correlative strata on the Isle of Wight (Ruffell and Batten, 1994). The *jacobi* Zone (= *nodosocostatum* Zone of Ruffell and Owen, 1995) is also questionably indicated in the higher part of the succession at Punfield Cove, overlain by the *tardefurcata* Zone, the presence of which is supported by palynology indicating an Early Albian age (Ruffell and Batten, 1994).

GAULT FORMATION

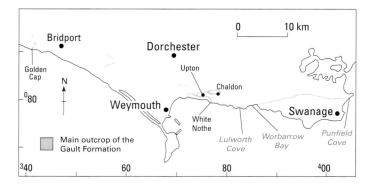

Map 13   Gault Formation.

A second Lower Cretaceous marine transgression, towards the end of the early Albian, carried shallow-water mud of the Gault across the Lower Greensand and farther westwards over exposed Jurassic formations (Chadwick, 1985c). In the west of the district, the formation crops out at the margins of outliers of Upper Greensand, for example at Golden Cap [SY 405 920], and in a more-or-less continuous outcrop from just north of Beaminster [ST 460 040] to Portesham [SY 595 857]. However, it is displaced by several major faults and frequently obscured by landslips. The formation also crops out around the Chaldon Anticline and Upton Syncline, and from just west of Lulworth to the eastern margin of the district forms a narrow, steeply dipping outcrop on the south side of the Purbeck Monocline, although cover of superficial debris limits exposure. In boreholes north of the Purbeck Monocline, the thickness of the formation ranges from 20.7 m at Chaldon Down (boreholes G1 and G2) to 32.6 m at Coombe Keynes. At outcrop south of the Purbeck Monocline, where the formation has been deformed, the thickness ranges from about 15 m in the Broadwey to Osmington area (and possibly only 11.3 m at Lulworth) to about 35 m at Worbarrow (Arkell, 1947). At Punfield Cove farther east, it may be up to 48 m thick (Strahan, 1898). In the west of the district, the Gault is mostly 9 to 12 m thick, but may increase to 17 m near Cattistock [ST 585 005] (Wilson et al., 1958).

The base of the formation is generally marked by a pebbly unit, up to 1.7 m thick, with well-rounded quartz and lydite (chert) pebbles. The pebbles occur in a ferruginously cemented sandstone, or are scattered in a basal bed of dark grey, sandy and micaceous clay as at White Nothe [SY 7715 8068] (Arkell, 1947). Wright (in Arkell, 1947) noted that a metre or so above the basal bed, there is a locally fossiliferous, ferruginous stone or shaly bed. The higher part of the succession consists of poorly fossiliferous, fine-grained sandy, micaceous and weakly glauconitic mudstone, with calcareous cemented sandstone horizons in the upper part.

The biostratigraphy of the Gault Formation, based on ammonites (Owen, 1971, 1975; Figure 30), shows that there is a diachronous facies change from Gault to

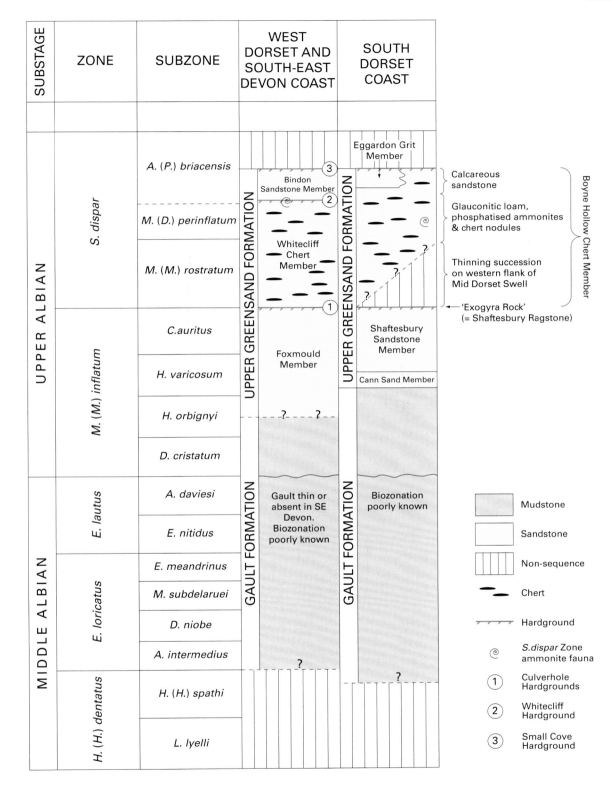

Figure 30 The biozonation of the Gault and Upper Greensand formations.
For consistency with earlier publications, the biozonal scheme follows Owen (1975,
1984, 1999), rather than the recently modified scheme of Owen and Mutterlose (2006).

Upper Greensand across the district. The Gault equates mostly with the Lower Gault, which is of Mid Albian age, but locally in Dorset strata equivalent to the Upper Gault, of Late Albian age, also occur. The distinction between the Mid and Late Albian is based on changes in ammonite and bivalve faunas, but at outcrop is typically marked by an erosion surface between the Lower Gault and Upper Gault. Lithological distinction between darker grey Lower Gault and paler grey Upper Gault is usually seen in south-east England and East Anglia, but is not apparent on the Dorset and south-east Devon coast where the lithological transition to Upper Greensand is close to the base of the Late Albian.

In the lower part of the Gault, the ammonites *Hoplites* and *Anahoplites* are particularly characteristic, as seen between Worbarrow Bay and Lyme Regis. Where the Gault ranges up into the Late Albian, as at Fontmell Magna (Bristow and Owen, 1990), *Hysteroceras* is common (Plate 29). However, the remains of other fossils, especially bivalves, are more numerous in places, and particularly characteristic is *Actinoceramus* (formerly *Birostrina*), which ranges through much of the Gault and shows morphological changes that can be used to infer the horizon within the formation (Owen, 1984). At Punfield Cove, a few metres of Gault pass gradually upwards through sandy mudstone with serpulid-rich horizons, into glauconitic sandstone of the Upper Greensand Formation. There, the oldest visible Gault possibly belongs to the *orbignyi* Subzone.

UPPER GREENSAND FORMATION

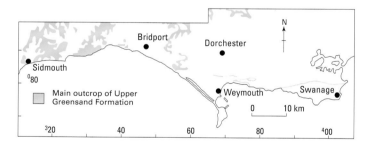

Map 14   Upper Greensand Formation.

The Upper Greensand represents a basinward progradation of near-shore, shallow water, sandy facies derived from land areas farther west. Across southern England, the contact with the underlying Gault is demonstrably diachronous, although this is not especially marked within the confines of the district described herein (Rawson et al., 1978). The formation comprises a succession of variably cemented glauconitic sandstones that form a subsidiary feature at the base of the Chalk scarp. The sandstones are soft to very hard, greenish grey to bright green when fresh, weathering to soft yellow-brown sandstone (Edwards and Gallois, 2004). It is best seen in south-east Dorset, where there are good coastal exposures at White Nothe and Punfield Cove, Swanage. The inland distribution is similar to that of the

Gault with a wide crop in the folded successions around Osmington and Chaldon Herring, and large outliers west of Bridport. The base of the formation is marked nearly everywhere by springs and is often involved in extensive landslips with the underlying Gault. In boreholes north of the Purbeck Monocline, the formation is 26 to 33 m thick. At outcrop, 22 m of Upper Greensand has been recorded at Worbarrow Bay and 23.6 m at White Nothe. The 11.9 m at Punfield stated by Arkell (1947) is possibly a partial, incomplete thickness. Farther north, the formation is 36 m thick at Winterborne Kingston, and in south-east Devon, up to 65 m occur in coastal sections around Seaton and Beer.

The Upper Greensand of south Dorset is mainly late Albian (*M.* (*M.*) *inflatum* and *S. dispar* zones), and shows a similar lithological succession to that recognised in the Shaftesbury district (Bristow et al., 1995). At the base, a unit of fine-grained, glauconitic sandstone (**Cann Sand Member**), is succeeded by shelly, calcareous sandstone (**Shaftesbury Sandstone Member**), overlain by sandstone with nodules of chert (**Boyne Hollow Chert Member)** (Figure 30). Younger subdivisions recognised in the Shaftesbury district, named the Bookham Conglomerate and Melbury Sandstone (and now classified as part of the Chalk Group; Hopson, 2005), are absent in south Dorset and south-east Devon.

In west Dorset and south-east Devon, the Cann Sand and Shaftesbury Sandstone are known collectively as the **Foxmould Member**, which at many localities is overlain by a variably developed thickness of chert-bearing sandstones (**Whitecliff Chert Member**) (Figure 30). Hard, coarse-grained shelly sandstones that occur above the Whitecliff Chert in south-east Devon, and which have traditionally been referred to as the Top Sandstones (e.g. Smith, 1961b, fig. 2), form the **Bindon Sandstone Member**, at the top of the Upper Greensand. Eastwards from the Bridport district, the youngest Upper Greensand is the **Eggardon Grit Member**, the correlation of which with the upper part of the Bindon Sandstone is strongly suggested by field evidence (Figure 31), but is as yet unproven.

South Dorset coast succession

Cann Sand Member

The Cann Sand, 4 to 15 m thick, consists of fine-grained, strongly glauconitic sandstone and weakly cemented sandstone. The outcrop can usually be traced by debris from rabbit burrows and badger setts, and is commonly much disturbed by landslipping. The member probably falls entirely in the *H. varicosum* Subzone, although there is some unpublished ammonite evidence for the presence of the late Mid Albian between Punfield Cove and Holworth House [SY 7637 8165] (information from H G Owen, formerly of the Natural History Museum London, 2004). At Osmington, loose blocks of soft, glauconitic sandstone doggers with *Mortoniceras, Prohysteroceras, Anahoplites picteti* and other ammonites of the *varicosum* Subzone (Arkell, 1947, p. 193) probably come from the top of the Cann Sand or possibly the base of the Shaftesbury Sandstone. Wright (1947) recorded *varicosum* Subzone ammonites from inferred correlative strata at Punfield Cove, and at Black Ven in west Dorset, the Foxmould (see below) has yielded *Mortoniceras (Deiradoceras) cunningtoni*, *M. (D.) albense* and *Hysteroceras varicosum* (Spath 1933, 1934), which collectively indicate the *varicosum* Subzone.

Shaftesbury Sandstone Member

The lower part of the Shaftesbury Sandstone is rarely seen, but consists of weakly cemented sandstone with indurated horizons. At the top of the member, there is hard, nodular sandstone, between 0.6 and 3 m thick, the Exogyra Rock ('Ragstone' or 'Exogyra Sandstone') crowded with oysters that have traditionally been referred to *Exogyra*, although more probably comprising other genera (e.g. *Pycnodonte* and *Amphidonte*; Plate 29). The thickness of the Shaftesbury Sandstone ranges from 4 to 20 m in south Dorset and up to 30 m in the type area near Shaftesbury.

At Punfield Cove, correlative strata contain records of *Mortoniceras (M.) inflatum* and ?*Callihoplites horridus*, suggestive of the *auritus* Subzone. A similar, or slightly older (*varicosum* Subzone), age is indicated by an ex-situ fauna inferred to be from the Shaftesbury Sandstone of the Shaftesbury district (Bristow et al., 1995).

Boyne Hollow Chert Member

The Boyne Hollow Chert Member, up to 4 m thick along the south Dorset coast between Osmington and Steeple, is a glauconitic sandstone with prominent chert beds and concretions; it occurs at or near the top of the Upper Greensand escarpment across much of the district. The cherts are typically yellow-brown, but grey in places, and, occur as isolated nodules or lenticular bands separated by hard sandstone or siliceous glauconitic sandstone. The presence of sedimentary structures and bioturbation within the cherts suggests that they were formed by postdepositional redistribution of silica (Williams, 1986). Where strongly developed, the Boyne Hollow Chert forms the plateau-like hill caps in west Dorset, such as Pilsdon Pen [ST 405 018] and Lambert's Castle [SY 370 987]. Along the south coast, the member locally disappears across the axis of the Mid Dorset Swell (e.g. Punfield Cove; Figure 31; *see* Chapter 7); it is however present near Bincombe [SY 6889 8451], below East Hill, Sutton Poyntz [SY 7097 8432 to 7092 8420], near Osmington [SY 731 825], above White Nothe [SY 7715 8094], and at two points [SY 9070 8152 and 9450 8219], respectively, north of Steeple and north-east of Church Knowle.

At its stratotype locality in the Shaftesbury district, the Boyne Hollow Chert is inferred to belong to the *S. dispar* Zone, although direct faunal evidence for this is scant (Bristow et al., 1995). On the south Dorset coast, the member locally contains a rich phosphatised and reworked ammonite fauna ('Ammonite Bed' of Wright, 1947), which includes *Stoliczkaia*, *Pleurohoplites*, *Callihoplites* (Plate 29), *Ostlingoceras*, *Arrhaphoceras*, *Idiohamites*,

Mariella and *Discohoplites*, indicative of the late *S. dispar* Zone, *M. (D.) perinflatum* Subzone and slightly older than the ammonite fauna from the overlying Bindon Sandstone at Shapwick in south-east Devon (Hamblin and Wood, 1976; see below).

Eggardon Grit Member

In Dorset, the highest and best-exposed part of the Upper Greensand is the Eggardon (or Calcareous) Grit (Wilson et al., 1958). The lower part of the Eggardon Grit is white or grey, poorly cemented sandstone containing subangular to fairly well-rounded granules of milky quartz generally about 6 mm across, with many shell fragments in a groundmass of fine quartz sand and calcite. The upper part of the member is generally much coarser grained with fewer shell fragments, capped by an irregular glauconitised and phosphatised surface. The member is very resistant to weathering, and commonly protrudes as bluffs or forms a steep feature on valley sides. It is particularly well developed in the western crop of the Upper Greensand in Dorset, such as at the stratotype locality on Eggardon Hill [SY 536 952] (Wilson et al., 1958), but it also occurs between Bincombe and Chaldon (Arkell, 1947, p. 194). It was proved in the Winterborne Kingston Borehole, where it is 4.2 m thick (Morter, 1982).

The Eggardon Grit overlies the Boyne Hollow Chert or, where the latter is absent across the Mid Dorset Swell [e.g. Evershott ST 574 044], rests directly on Shaftesbury Sandstone. Kennedy (1970) assigned the Eggardon Grit to the basal Cenomanian, but the fauna upon which this age determination was based is possibly from chalk-filled fissures in the top of the member (Wright and Kennedy, 1984, p. 12), and a Late Albian age for the Eggardon Grit is strongly suggested (Woods et al., 2009).

South-east Devon succession

Foxmould Member

The member is 20 to 25 m thick in the coastal succession around Beer, in south-east Devon, and comprises fine- to medium-grained, grey-green argillaceous glauconitic sands, with clay beds in the lower part, and locally developed hard, tabular, calcareous sandstone beds throughout. Near Lyme Regis, large rounded calcareous concretions in the lower part of the member have traditionally been named 'Cowstones'. In coastal successions, at the top of the Foxmould is a pair of mineralised erosion surfaces, named the Culverhole Hardgrounds. Bivalves and gastropods are locally very abundant, and some of the indurated bands are rich in serpulids, especially *Rotularia*. Sporadic remains of ammonites show that the member belongs to the *M. (M.) inflatum* Zone, and that it is approximately coeval with the Cann Sand and Shaftesbury Sandstone members of Dorset.

Whitecliff Chert Member

The Whitecliff Chert Member in south-east Devon is the lateral equivalent of the Boyne Hollow Chert of

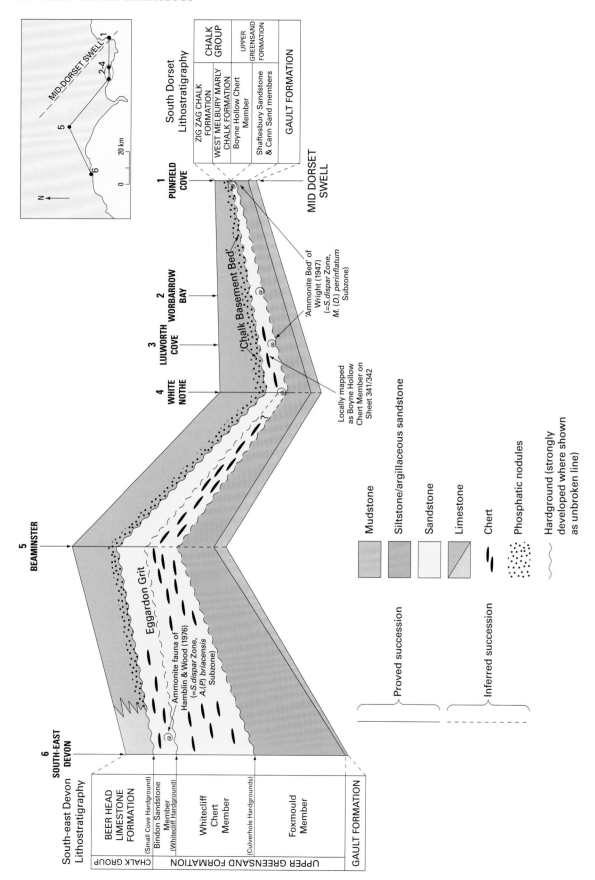

Figure 31   Lithostratigraphical variation across the Mid Dorset Swell.

Bristow et al. (1995) in north Dorset. However, on the south Dorset coast, strata mapped as Boyne Hollow Chert may actually be coeval with the stratigraphically younger Eggardon Grit (see above) and Bindon Sandstone (see below). The Whitecliff Chert is up to 32 m thick, and comprises fine- to medium- grained sandstone and calcarenite, with many horizons of nodular and tabular chert. The fauna is less diverse than the Foxmould, and consists predominantly of bivalves, particularly the oyster *Costagyra digitata*. There are no definite in-situ records of ammonites, but from its stratigraphical position, the member evidently belongs to the *S. dispar* Zone.

Bindon Sandstone Member

This member comprises up to 8 m of fine- to coarse-grained sandstone and calcarenite, typically showing slumped structures in the uppermost part. A thin bed of shell-rich, glauconitic sandstone occurs at the base of a 3.5 m-thick succession at Shapwick Grange Quarry, and there are thin beds of chert in the overlying succession. The highest 1.5 to 2.5 m of the succession at Shapwick is distinctly sandier and chert-free, with glauconite concentrated into thin beds. There is a westward decrease in the overall carbonate content of the member, accompanied by a reduction in chert content, with the result that chert is entirely absent in the Bindon Sandstone west of Beer Head. The most biostratigraphically important fauna is a collection of ammonites detailed by Hamblin and Wood (1976) from Shapwick Quarry, indicative of the Late Albian, *S. dispar* Zone (including the youngest Albian *Arrhaphoceras* (*Praeschloenbachia*) *briacensis* Subzone; information from H G Owen, formerly Natural History Museum London, 2004).

FIVE

Upper Cretaceous: Chalk Group

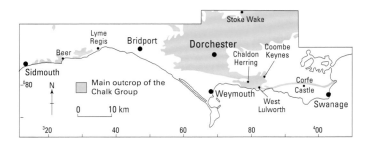

Map 15 Chalk Group.

In the Upper Cretaceous, global sea level rose, perhaps to as much as 300 m above the present level (Gale, 2000b) covering most of the pre-existing land areas in the UK, including the whole of the Dorset region. For the next 30 million years, vast numbers of planktonic algae bloomed in these subtropical waters; their tiny calcite skeletons rained down almost continuously on the sea floor to form the distinctive soft, white limestone of the Chalk Group, which, aided by prolonged regional basin subsidence in the Upper Cretaceous, forms a succession that is more than 400 m thick in Dorset

In Dorset, the outcrop of the Chalk Group is 10 to 15 km wide where it dips gently on the north and west side of the Wareham Basin, and outliers of sub-horizontal Chalk occur as far west as south-east Devon. South of the Wareham Basin, the Chalk was folded during Alpine tectonism and commonly dips steeply northward. Because of the steep dip, the outcrop is less than 1 km wide adjacent to parts of the Abbotsbury–Ridgeway Fault, and less than 0.5 km wide in the near-vertical limb of the Purbeck Monocline east of West Lulworth. The Chalk typically forms the highest ground in the district, rising to over 265 m at Gore Hill [ST 637 038] in the north and to almost 200 m on Povington [SY 880 811] and Godlingston [SZ 007 812] hills in the south.

Chalk is typically a white or off-white, very fine-grained, weakly cemented microporous limestone composed predominantly of the microscopic fragmentary skeletal remains of calcareous planktonic algae, called coccoliths. Coarse-grained carbonate material is also present and includes foraminifera, ostracods, echinoderm, bryozoan, coral, inoceramid and a range of other fossil remains. Other lithological types within the succession include glauconitised chalkstone (hardgrounds), which may indicate periods of local shallowing and erosion, calcarenites and flint. The most conspicuous of these are flints, formed through a complex process of syndepositional chemical replacement of Chalk by biogenic silica derived from the dissolved skeletons of siliceous sponges and microfossils (radiolaria and diatoms) (Clayton,

1986). This process preferentially acted on burrow-fill sediments, accounting for the irregular burrow-like form of many nodular flints. Some flints are replacements of the distinctive spiral-shaped trace fossil *Zoophycos*, and these characterise particular levels within some Chalk Group formations. Noncarbonate mud-grade material may comprise 30 to 40 per cent of the rock mass in the basal part of the Chalk succession, where calcareous mudstone (marl) is interbedded with muddy limestone. Thin seams of marl are more typical higher in the Chalk succession, the lateral persistence of some of these making them valuable for correlation. Some of these thin marls are decomposed volcanic ash layers while others are detrital. Pure white chalk dominates the upper part of the group, where mud declines to less than 5 per cent of the rock mass (Destombes and Shepard-Thorn, 1971).

The Chalk Group has been subdivided into nine formations using geomorphic feature mapping combined with lithology, palaeontology and aerial photography (Bristow et al., 1997; Rawson et al., 2001). In the subsurface, the stratigraphy can be traced using seismic data and borehole geophysics (Evans and Hopson, 2000). The principal subdivision into two subgroups is taken at the base of a prominent mudstone interval, the Plenus Marls, located within the lower part of the succession. Below the Plenus Marls, the **Grey Chalk Subgroup** largely comprises thin argillaceous and marly grey and greyish white chalk, while the overlying **White Chalk Subgroup** comprises thick white chalk and nodular chalk. This classification supersedes the traditional scheme of Lower, Middle and Upper Chalk (Table 3).

Except in the lower part of the Chalk Group, ammonites are rare, and consequently a variety of other taxa have also been used to biostratigraphically subdivide the Chalk, including brachiopods, bivalves, echinoids, crinoids, belemnites and foraminifera (Table 3). Fossil ranges and the occurrence of lithologically distinct marker-bed horizons have been used to achieve refined correlations between successions.

GREY CHALK SUBGROUP

Where fully developed, the Grey Chalk Subgroup is generally divided into two formations, the **West Melbury Marly Chalk Formation** overlain by the **Zig Zag Chalk Formation** (Table 3), ranging from 13 to more than 50 m thick. Both can be traced from Dorset and Wiltshire into Sussex and Kent, although the West Melbury Marly Chalk is missing over the Mid Dorset Swell (Drummond, 1970; Figure 32). In south-east Devon, the West Melbury Marly Chalk and Zig Zag Chalk are replaced by a single formation, named the **Beer Head Limestone**.

Table 3
Stratigraphy of the Chalk Group of Dorset and south-east Devon (not to scale).

STAGE	BIOZONATION			TRADITIONAL SUBDIVISIONS	SUBGROUP	South-east Devon lithostratigraphy	Dorset lithostratigraphy
CAMPANIAN	*B. mucronata*			UPPER CHALK	WHITE CHALK		(Studland Chalk)
							PORTSDOWN CHALK FORMATION
	G. quadrata	Post *Applinocrinus* Beds					Spetisbury Chalk Member *(CULVER CHALK FORMATION)*
		A. cretaceus					Tarrant Chalk Member *(CULVER CHALK FORMATION)*
		Hagenowia Horizon					
	O. pilula	Subzone of abundant *O. pilula*	Upper belt *O. pilula*				NEWHAVEN CHALK FORMATION
			E. cincta belt				
			Lower belt *O. pilula*				
		E. depressula					
	U. anglicus						
SANTO-NIAN	*M. testudinarius*						SEAFORD CHALK FORMATION
	U. socialis					SEAFORD CHALK FM	
CONIA-CIAN	*M. coranguinum*						
	M. cortestudinarium					LEWES NODULAR CHALK FORMATION	LEWES NODULAR CHALK FORMATION
TURONIAN	*S. plana*						(Spurious Chalk Rock)
	T. lata			MIDDLE CHALK		NEW PIT CHALK FORMATION	NEW PIT CHALK FORMATION
	Mytiloides ssp.					HOLYWELL NODULAR CHALK FORMATION (includes Pinnacles Member of Jarvis and Woodroof, 1984)	HOLYWELL NODULAR CHALK FORMATION
	N. juddii						(Plenus Marls Member)
CENOMANIAN	*M. geslinianum*			LOWER CHALK (Grey Chalk)	GREY CHALK	BEER HEAD LIMESTONE FORMATION (excludes Pinnacles Member of Jarvis and Woodroof, 1984) (highly condensed with non-sequences)	ZIG ZAG CHALK FORMATION
	C. guerangeri						
	A. jukesbrownei						
	A. rhotomagense	*T. acutus*					
		T. costatus					
	C. inerme				(Chalk Marl)		WEST MELBURY MARLY CHALK FM *(Chalk Basement Bed)*
	M. dixoni						
	M. mantelli	*M. saxbii*					
		S. schlueteri					
		N. carcitanense					

* Holywell Nodular Chalk Formation includes the *T. lata* zone in the Purbeck Monocline east of Weymouth.

West Melbury Marly Chalk Formation

The West Melbury Marly Chalk, though glauconitic and sandy in the basal part (= Glauconitic Marl Member), generally comprises grey or off-white, soft argillaceous chalk, with a few thin hard beds of off-white chalk. The formation has been proved in boreholes at Spetisbury (19 m) and Shapwick (17 m) at the north-east margin of Sheet 328 Dorchester, and is known from outcrops north of the district, on Sheet 313 Shaftesbury, and in the subcrop in Wytch Farm Borehole 25 (8 m), just east of the district on Sheet 329 Bournemouth. The formation is absent across most of southern Dorset, due probably to the influence of the Mid Dorset Swell (Figure 31; see chapter 7). Kennedy (1970) showed that the Mid Dorset Swell separated a region of coarse clastic deposition in south Dorset and south-east Devon from typical Grey Chalk Subgroup facies farther east; progressive south-westward thinning of the lower part of the Grey Chalk Subgroup occurs against the eastern margin of this

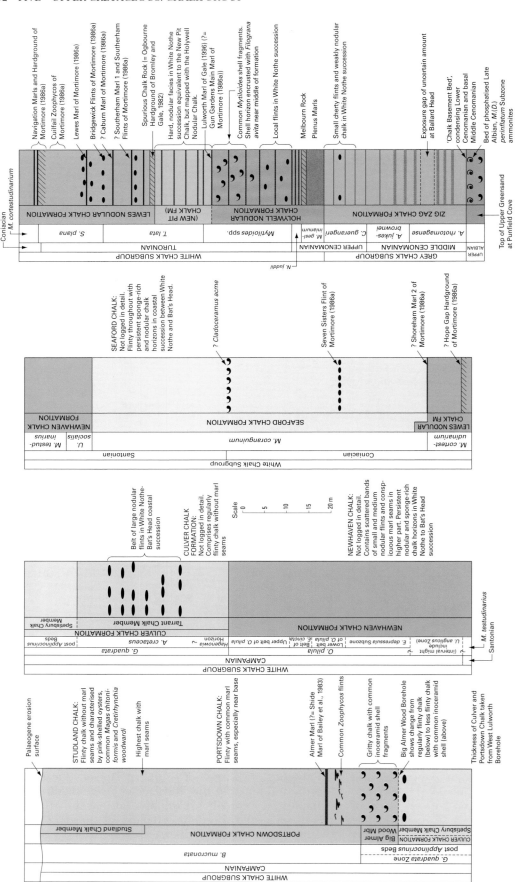

Figure 32 The stratigraphy of the Chalk Group of Dorset. Composite section based on cliff sections and boreholes.

structure in north Dorset with the biozones concomitantly condensed (Drummond, 1970, fig. 6A; Kennedy, 1970, fig. 19; Bristow et al., 1995, fig. 47). Consequently, on the flanks and across the axis of the Mid Dorset Swell, the West Melbury Marly Chalk and part of the overlying Zig Zag Chalk are replaced by an ammonite-rich phosphatic conglomerate, referred to by Kennedy (1970) as the 'Chalk Basement Bed' (Plate 31). This bed is an informal, diachronous unit within the Grey Chalk Subgroup.

Where fully developed in north Dorset, the West Melbury Marly Chalk belongs to the Lower Cenomanian *M. mantelli* and *M. dixoni* zones, and the lowest Middle Cenomanian *C. inerme* and basal *A. rhotomagense* zones. However, in south Dorset the fauna of the West Melbury Marly Chalk is condensed into the Chalk Basement Bed, and in south-east Devon is represented by phosphatised and reworked fossils in the lower part of the Beer Head Limestone Formation (= Cenomanian Limestone of historical accounts).

Zig Zag Chalk Formation

The Zig Zag Chalk, typically 30 to 50 m thick, crops out around Plush [ST 7145 0210] and Hilton [ST 7820 0300] on the northern edge of Sheet 328 Dorchester, and all around the western margin of the Chalk from Portesham [SY 600 859] to north of Beaminster [ST 475 035] and on the coast below White Nothe and Ballard Down. At outcrop, the base of the Zig Zag Chalk Formation is marked by a steepening of the topographical gradient above the more gently sloping ground developed on the West Melbury Marly Chalk. In the subsurface, the formation has been proved in boreholes at Coombe Keynes (38 m), Creech (38 m), Wytch Farm (Borehole F15, 40 to 45 m), Wareham (41 to 49 m) and Arne (G1 Borehole 46 m). The typical lithology is firm, off-white chalk. Over the Mid Dorset Swell, the lower part of the Zig Zag Chalk is represented by the condensed, phosphatised fauna of the Chalk Basement Bed, which in turn rests unconformably on the pitted and phosphatised top of the Upper Greensand. Away from the Mid Dorset Swell, where the Zig Zag Chalk succession is complete, the basal beds contain common marl seams and equates with the upper part of the Chalk Marl of the traditional southern England stratigraphy (Table 3). This is well developed in the Winterborne Kingston Borehole where the more marly succession is 13.7 m thick (Lott, 1982). Towards the top of the marly interval is Jukes-Browne Bed 7, a bed of gritty, silty chalk with lenticular, laminated, calcarenite-filled lenses, that forms a useful marker. The higher part of the Zig Zag Chalk consists of about 6 to 12 m of blocky, greyish white chalk with common marl seams up to 20 cm thick and locally (e.g. Worbarrow Bay, Mupe Bay, White Nothe) scattered black flints.

The Zig Zag Chalk belongs to the greater part of the Middle and Upper Cenomanian, although some of the constituent zones (*A. rhotomagense*, *A. jukesbrownei*, *C. guerangeri* and *M. geslinianum*) are variably condensed in the area affected by the Mid Dorset Swell (see Chapter 7), as at Punfield Cove, where the base of the formation

Zig Zag Chalk Formation

Chalk Basement Bed ?

Upper Greensand Formation

Plate 31 The Chalk Basement Bed (basal Chalk Group), a phosphatised conglomerate 0.2 m thick, overlain by Zig Zag Chalk Formation, Holworth House [SY 7660 8150] (P672350).

contains abundant *Sciponoceras baculoides*, indicative of the middle part of the *T. costatus* Subzone. Some indigenous Cenomanian fossils occur in crevices in the top of the Upper Greensand.

Beer Head Limestone Formation

In west Dorset and east Devon, the Grey Chalk Subgroup is represented by a succession of thin, highly condensed, fossiliferous, sandy limestones. These are well exposed on the coast between Beer [SY 2320 8914] and Hooken Cliff [SY 219 881], where they collectively form the Beer Head Limestone Formation, included in the Cenomanian Limestone of historical accounts. Following Mortimore et al. (2001), the Beer Head Limestone Formation excludes the Pinnacles Member recognised by Jarvis and Woodroof (1984), which is herein classified within the Holywell Nodular Chalk Formation. The stratotype locality is Beer Head [SY 227 879], where it is about 5 m thick; it thickens rapidly westwards to a maximum of about 10 m at Hooken Cliff [SY 219 879]. East of Beer Head, the formation is locally reduced to less than half a metre. Its most easterly occurrence is at Shapwick Grange Quarry [SY 313 919], near Lyme Regis (Wright and Kennedy, 1981).

The rich fauna of the Beer Head Limestone, which includes ammonites, echinoids, brachiopods and bivalves, shows a variety of preservation modes, and represents the greater part of the Cenomanian. Heavily phosphatised, abraded and reworked specimens are commonly associated with hardgrounds; less reworking is suggested by less strongly phosphatised fossils, and unphosphatised examples are likely to be contemporaneous with the matrix sediment. Detailed examination of the faunas shows that the biozonal succession is broken by several non-sequences that are coincident with hardgrounds (Kennedy, 1970; Wright and Kennedy, 1984).

WHITE CHALK SUBGROUP

The White Chalk Subgroup, 350 to 385 m thick, comprises seven formations (Figure 32; Table 3), the Holywell Nodular Chalk, New Pit Chalk, Lewes Nodular Chalk, Seaford Chalk, Newhaven Chalk, Culver Chalk and Portsdown Chalk. The Culver Chalk is divided into the Tarrant and Spetisbury Chalk members, and the higher part of the Portsdown Chalk corresponds with the 'Studland Chalk' of Gale et al. (1987). In the outcrop along the Purbeck Monocline, the whole of the White Chalk Subgroup is generally much harder, making subdivision of the succession in this area more problematic.

Holywell Nodular Chalk Formation

The Holywell Nodular Chalk crops out in the northern part of the Dorchester district (Sheet 328); around the western margin of the Chalk from Portesham to just north of Beaminster; on the coast below White Nothe and Ballard Head, and sporadically in coastal sections in south-east Devon. It also occurs on the southern flanks of the Purbeck Hills, where it is locally exposed in old quarries [e.g. SY 9805 8188; SY 9503 8218; SY 9737 8205]. The formation, comprising a basal marly unit, a median interval of hard nodular chalk, and an upper unit of shell-detrital chalk, maintains a fairly constant thickness across southern Dorset of between 21 and 23 m, but thins in the west of the district, with as little as 8 m in south-east Devon. The development of nodular chalk at this and stratigraphically higher levels reflects enhanced sea-floor cementation of the accumulating chalk sediment, probably in response to increased water currents. During prolonged breaks in sedimentation, progressive cementation converted thin units of nodular chalk into hardgrounds that were subsequently bored into and encrusted by macrofaunas.

The **Plenus Marls Member**, formed of marl and marly chalk, is the basal unit of the Holywell Nodular Chalk Formation following Rawson et al. (2001). Historically, this marker horizon was considered to be the topmost part of the Lower Chalk, and more recently, the top of the Zig Zag Chalk of Bristow et al. (1997). In a detailed study, Jefferies (1963) divided the member into eight 'beds', each with a distinctive fauna. The base of the member is the so-called 'Sub-Plenus erosion surface' that marks the base of the White Chalk Subgroup. It is clearly seen in the coastal section below White Nothe. Recognition of the member at localities along the Purbeck Monocline is more problematic. There it appears to comprise an interval of hard chalk with anastomosing marl seams; the marls appear to have acted as shear planes during folding. The Plenus Marls are 4.5 m thick at Punfield, 2.5 m thick at Sandy Hill Farm [SY 9737 8205] near Corfe Castle and 3.3 m thick at Durdle Cove [SY 805 803] (Jefferies, 1963). Their clay-rich lithology produces a conspicuous high gamma-ray peak in borehole geophysical logs.

Overlying the Plenus Marls is the **Melbourn Rock**, a feature-forming unit originally described from the Chilterns (Hill and Jukes-Browne, 1886). It consists of up to 3 m of hard, nodular, poorly fossiliferous chalk forming a marked lithological contrast to the underlying Plenus Marls. The base of the Melbourn Rock is easily mapped using brash and topography and can be readily detected as a major high peak in borehole resistivity logs. Broken and fragmented shells, mostly of the inoceramid bivalve *Mytiloides*, become increasingly common in the middle and higher parts of the Holywell Nodular Chalk, and are particularly abundant at the top of the formation. Locally, flints occur near the base of the Holywell Nodular Chalk, for example at Ballard Head (Mortimore and Pomerol, 1987, p. 110), and near the top of the formation between White Nothe and Bat's Head [SY 795 803] (e.g. Arkell, 1947, p. 209), although they are rare in the Holywell Nodular Chalk elsewhere in southern England.

Plate 32 Some characteristic fossils from the Upper Cretaceous (Chalk Group) of Dorset and south-east Devon. Unless otherwise stated, scale bars represent 10 mm (P669425).

1	*Micraster coranguinum* (Seaford Chalk)
2	*Terebratulina lata* (New Pit Chalk)
3	*Watinoceras* (Holywell Nodular Chalk)
4	*Echinocorys elevata* (Newhaven Chalk)
5	*Mytiloides mytiloides* (Holywell Nodular Chalk)
6a–b	*Calycoceras (Newboldiceras) hippocastanum* (Beer Head Limestone)
7	*Belemnitella mucronata* (Portsdown Chalk)
8	*Mytiloides hattini* (Holywell Nodular Chalk)
9	*Turrilites acutus* (Zig Zag Chalk)
10	*Mytiloides* ex gr. *hercynicus-subhercynicus* (New Pit Chalk)
11	*Marsupites testudinarius* (Newhaven Chalk)
12	*Sternotaxis plana* (Lewes Nodular Chalk)
13	*Cladoceramus undulatoplicatus* (Seaford Chalk)
14	*Volviceramus involutus* (Seaford Chalk)

1

2

(5mm)

3

4

5

6a

6b

7

8

9

10

11

12

13

14

In south-east Devon, strata equivalent to the Plenus Marls and Melbourn Rock are represented by the **Pinnacles Member**, a unit (2.3 to less than 0.1 m thick) of sandy glauconitic limestone with hardgrounds, formerly included in the top of the Beer Head Limestone Formation (Mortimore et al., 2001). The member is well exposed at Hooken Cliffs, west of Beer Head. Above this, between Beer and Hooken Cliff, the Holywell Nodular Chalk shows pronounced lateral changes in thickness because the sequence is variably condensed at the Branscombe Hardground surface (Jarvis and Woodroof, 1984). The lower part of the succession is locally thicker near Beer, forming a unit several metres thick made up of highly comminuted fragments of echinoderms. This is the 'Beer Stone', which has been used as a building stone since Roman times.

Over much of Dorset, the Holywell Nodular Chalk equates with the Upper Cenomanian *M. geslinianum* (pars) and *N. juddii* zones, and the basal Turonian *Mytiloides* spp Zone. However, east of Weymouth, the steeply dipping Holywell Nodular Chalk of the Purbeck Monocline extends into the *T. lata* Zone. The Plenus Marls (*M. geslinianum* Zone) contain a fauna that includes common large *Pycnodonte vesiculare* in the lower part and *Praeactinocamax plenus*, from which the horizon takes its name, in the middle and higher parts (Jefferies, 1963). Widespread faunal 'events' in the lower Holywell Nodular Chalk (*M. geslinianum* and *N. juddii* zones) include acmes of the straight-shelled ammonite *Sciponoceras* (near Corfe Castle [SY 9737 8205; SY 9503 8218] and Studland [SZ 0165 8092]), the asteroid *Crateraster quinqueloba,* and the oyster *Pycnodonte vesiculare* (Gale, 1996). Higher in the succession (basal *Mytiloides* spp. Zone), there are local rock-forming quantities of the microcrinoid *Roveacrinus communis,* and the inoceramid bivalves *Mytiloides kossmati* and *M. hattini,* replaced upwards (middle and upper *Mytiloides* spp. Zone) by increasingly common *M. mytiloides.* Where the Holywell Nodular Chalk includes the *T. lata* Zone, the bivalves *Inoceramus cuvieri* and *Mytiloides* ex gr. *hercynicus–subhercynicus* occur with the zonal index (Plate 32).

New Pit Chalk Formation

New Pit Chalk crops out in the northern part of the Dorchester district (Sheet 328), and on the coast in south-east Devon. In south Dorset, strata of equivalent age form part of the Holywell Nodular Chalk Formation. North of the Purbeck Monocline, the boundary between the Holywell Nodular Chalk and New Pit Chalk is generally sharp when seen in sections and boreholes. The base of the formation coincides with the first appearance of firm, smooth, white, flaggy chalk and the loss of nodular and shell-detrital chalk. This boundary is thought to be approximately coincident with the Lulworth Marl of Gale (1996), used by that author to define the base of the New Pit Chalk in Dorset and traced across much of southern England. The lithology typically comprises firm, blocky chalk with regularly developed marls and marly chalk horizons, and sporadic occurrences of small to medium-sized nodular flints. Key marker marls, present in the

upper part of the New Pit Chalk in the Sussex stratotype succession, are missing in Dorset; this interval equates with a non-sequence above a hardground complex at the base of the overlying Lewes Nodular Chalk Formation (Gale, 1996). Farther west, at Beer in south-east Devon, the New Pit Chalk is abundantly flinty (**Beer Roads Flinty Chalk Member**), and the upper part of the succession is more complete than in Dorset. In the Wareham Basin, the New Pit Chalk maintains a constant thickness of between 10 and 11 m; it increases westward to about 29 m at Hooken Cliff, in south-east Devon.

The New Pit Chalk encompasses the greater part of the *T. lata* zone, the typical fauna comprising the thin-shelled inoceramid bivalves *Mytiloides* ex gr. *hercynicus–subhercynicus* in the basal part, with occurrences of the small index brachiopod *Terebratulina lata* (Plate 32) and the inoceramids *Inoceramus cuvieri* and *I. lamarcki* in the upper part.

Lewes Nodular Chalk Formation

The Lewes Nodular Chalk Formation crops out across the north-western part of the Dorchester district (Sheet 328) between Portesham and Toller Down Gate [ST 520 030], in the Purbeck Monocline, on the coast below White Nothe and Ballard Down, and in cliff sections in south-east Devon between Chapel Rock [SY 312 906] and Hooken Cliff.

The base of the formation is defined by the appearance of hard, nodular chalks, producing a gritty, coarser grained field brash compared with the New Pit Chalk below and the Seaford Chalk above. In Dorset, this is coincident with the base of a strongly indurated chalk horizon, traditionally named the Spurious Chalk Rock (Figure 32), and equating with the Ogbourne and Pewsey hardgrounds of Bromley and Gale (1982). The surface of this hardground complex is a non-sequence, equating with the upper part of the New Pit Chalk Formation in Sussex (Gale, 1996). Farther west, in south-east Devon, the hardgrounds are absent, and the underlying New Pit Chalk succession is more complete. Stratigraphically younger hardgrounds, equivalent to the Chalk Rock of the Shaftesbury district in north Dorset (Bristow et al., 1995), are not developed in south Dorset or south-east Devon, although a feature-forming band of hard, nodular chalk with green-coated nodules, recorded 9 to 14 m above the Spurious Chalk Rock by Wilson et al. (1958), may represent the 'Top Rock'. The latter is a succession of hardgrounds above the horizon of the Chalk Rock, that probably includes the equivalent of the Navigation Hardground of Sussex (Bromley and Gale, 1982; Mortimore, 1983).

In the steeply dipping succession of the Purbeck Monocline, there is no clear-cut lithological distinction between the Lewes Nodular Chalk and the underlying Holywell Nodular Chalk (that there includes strata coeval with the New Pit Chalk Formation). However, the boundary can be inferred from local occurrences of the Spurious Chalk Rock or extrapolated between the highest records of *Mytiloides* ex gr. *hercynicus–subhercynicus* (see above) and the lowest occurrences of regularly flinty chalk. The thickness of the Lewes Nodular Chalk is mostly in the range 30 to 45 m across southern Dorset and south-east Devon, but in boreholes at Wytch Farm the thickness varies from 20 to 32 m.

Much of the Lewes Nodular Chalk consists of extremely hard, locally porcellanous, nodular and flinty chalk with marl seams. The onset of significant and conspicuous nodularity occurs at approximately the same level as the first appearance of consistently developed flint horizons, and marks the base of markedly flinty chalk in the Chalk Group. The south Dorset succession includes marker beds defined in the stratotype Chalk of Sussex. The Southerham Flints and Marls, Caburn Marl, Lewes Marl, Cuilfail Zoophycos, Navigation Hardground and Marls and Hope Gap Hardground all occur in the coastal succession between White Nothe and Bat's Head. In south-east Devon, coastal sections of Lewes Nodular Chalk between Beer and Chapel Rock contain a laterally persistent nodular flint, named the Annis' Knob Flint (Jarvis and Woodroof, 1984), which is probably equivalent to the Breaky Bottom Flint in Sussex (Mortimore et al., 2001). North of the Purbeck Monocline, the nodularity and hardness decrease upwards in the Lewes Nodular Chalk and there is a transition over a metre or two into the succeeding Seaford Chalk.

The Lewes Nodular Chalk has a diverse fauna of brachiopods, inoceramid bivalves and echinoids, and belongs to the upper *T. lata* Zone, the *S. plana* and *M. cortestudinarium* zones, and locally, in central Dorset, the basal *M. coranguinum* Zone. There are acmes of fossils associated with particular horizons, which are valuable for correlation, such as the abundance of the giant foraminifer *Labyrinthidoma* (= *Coskinophragma* of Mortimore, 1986a) in Southerham Marl 1, and the acme of *Eomicraster leskei magna* (= large form of *Micraster leskei*) in the Lewes Marl. Species of inoceramid bivalves, particularly *Mytiloides* and *Cremnoceramus*, and of the echinoid *Micraster* are biostratigraphically useful through much of the Lewes Nodular Chalk.

Seaford Chalk Formation

The Seaford Chalk Formation crops out widely in the eastern part of the Bridport district (Sheet 327) and the north-western part of the Dorchester district (Sheet 328), and is well exposed in the coastal succession between White Nothe and Bat's Head. It occurs as tectonically hardened chalk in the Purbeck Monocline and is the youngest part of the Chalk Group represented in south-east Devon, where it occurs in coastal landslips between Pinhay and Whitlands. The formation comprises firm, white, flinty chalk, with marl seams common in the basal part only; abundant shell detritus characterises the lower beds. In mapping, it is distinguished by its fine-grained slabby brash. Unlike most other chalk units, there is rarely a consistently developed topographical expression at the base.

Conspicuous, semicontinuous bands of large nodular flints are a feature of this formation. One of these, seen in the cliffs between White Nothe and Bat's Head, represents the Seven Sisters Flint of Sussex, a widespread marker across southern England and northern France (Mortimore and Pomerol, 1987, fig. 24). In the White Nothe–Bat's Head section, the Seaford Chalk is about 76 m thick, but slightly thinner in boreholes north of the Purbeck Monocline, with 52 m at Creech, 64 m at Wareham 3, 70 m at Arne (G1 Borehole), and 57 to 61 m at Wytch Farm.

The Seaford Chalk Formation belongs to the *M. coranguinum* Zone, and is characterised by a locally rich fauna of inoceramid bivalves and echinoids. In south-east Devon, the fauna seen at Chapel Rock is dominated by shell fragments of the inoceramid bivalve *Platyceramus*, suggesting that the succession lies below the horizon of the Seven Sisters Flint. However, the much thicker Chalk succession preserved in Dorset spans the whole of the zone. The distinctively thick-shelled *Volviceramus involutus* occurs abundantly around the Seven Sisters Flint in the lower part of the Seaford Chalk. (Plate 32). Above this, the *M. coranguinum* Zone is typically rather barren of macrofossils until the Coniacian–Santonian boundary, indicated by flood abundances of the inoceramid bivalve *Cladoceramus undulatoplicatus* (Plate 32), seen south of Chaldon Herring [SY 7940 8228] and at Stratton [SY 657 943] near Dorchester. The higher part of the *M. coranguinum* Zone is characterised by locally very thick-shelled *Platyceramus*, large specimens of the echinoid *Echinocorys*, and the echinoid *Conulus albogalerus*.

Newhaven Chalk Formation

Newhaven Chalk crops out in the south-eastern part of the Bridport district (Sheet 327) and the northern part of the Dorchester district (Sheet 328). In some areas it has not been possible to map this formation; it is combined with the Seaford Chalk Formation in south Dorset, and with the Seaford and Culver Chalk formations in the Purbeck Monocline. The best coastal exposure is between White Nothe and Bat's Head [SY 772 806 to 795 803]. The formation is about 71 m thick between White Nothe and Lulworth, and about 62 m at Arish Mell. In boreholes and at outcrop north of the Purbeck Monocline across south Dorset, the thickness of the Newhaven Chalk varies from 33 to 44 m.

The Newhaven Chalk is a unit of firm, white, chalk with horizons of widely spaced nodular flints and common marl seams. On the Dorset coast, marl seams are well developed at Arish Mell [SY 856 802], but thin rapidly westwards (Brydone, 1914). South of the Purbeck Monocline, the chalk is extremely hard, commonly nodular and has only weakly developed marl seams. In the subsurface north of Bournemouth, seismic reflection data suggest the presence of erosional channels in the Newhaven Chalk Formation that locally remove large parts of the underlying Seaford Chalk Formation (Evans and Hopson, 2000; Evans et al., 2003; Figure 33); possibly analagous features occur in northern France (Mortimore et al., 1998, fig. 10).

The Newhaven Chalk belongs to the *U. socialis*, *M. testudinarius*, and *U. anglicus* zones and the greater part of the *O. pilula* Zone. The lower part of the formation, below the *O. pilula* Zone, is mostly characterised by isolated calyx plates and brachials of the index crinoid

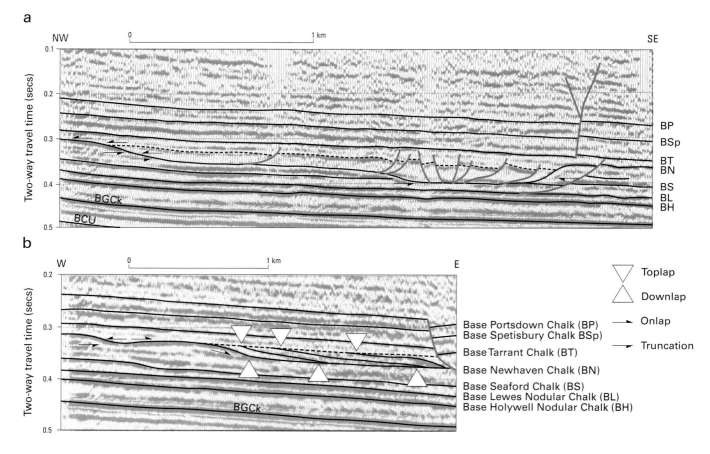

Figure 33   Seismic reflection lines, acquired to the north of Bournemouth, illustrating important intra-formational concave-up and concave-down features, within the Chalk. In both cases, the base Tarrant Chalk reflector is largely unaffected, indicating depositional topography had been infilled by that time.

species. In the case of *Uintacrinus* in the *socialis* and *anglicus* zones, these are very small and inconspicuous. In contrast, *Marsupites testudinarius* is usually represented by highly distinctive polygonal calyx plates (Plate 32).

The higher part of the Newhaven Chalk encompasses the greater part of the *O. pilula* Zone. A rich oyster fauna that occurs in the basal part of the Newhaven Chalk continues up into the lower part of the *pilula* Zone (*E. depressula* Subzone), where echinoids are the most characteristic fossils, notably *Echinocorys tectiformis* and *E. depressula*, with rare *Offaster pilula*. In the upper part of the *pilula* Zone (Subzone of abundant *O. pilula*), the echinoid *Offaster pilula* has two abundance peaks, at the base and top of the subzone, and other distinctively shaped forms of *Echinocorys* occur (e.g. *Echinocorys truncata* and *E. cincta*). At the top of the *pilula* Zone, large *Offaster* provide an easily identifiable biomarker.

Culver Chalk Formation

In contrast to the underlying Newhaven Chalk, marls are rare in the Culver Chalk Formation and flints are more conspicuously developed, particularly in the lower part. Two subdivisions are recognised on the basis of

feature-mapping, namely the **Tarrant Chalk** and **Spetisbury Chalk** members.

Tarrant Chalk Member

The Tarrant Chalk takes its name from the Tarrant valley, near Blandford Forum (Bristow, 1991), where it comprises firm white chalk with large, relatively widely spaced flint bands. It crops out widely in the northern and central parts of the Dorchester district (Sheet 328) and occurs in the Purbeck Monocline. The best exposure in south Dorset is the coastal section between White Nothe and Bat's Head. The base, mapped at the top of a scarp feature of the underlying Newhaven Chalk, is slightly diachronous. In the White Nothe–Bat's Head section, the lowest 10 m of the member contains common, regularly spaced, nodular flint beds, that may equate with the Castle Hill Flints of Sussex and it is probable that they are responsible for the prominent feature used to map the base of the member inland. In the coast section, the base of the inferred Castle Hill Flints lies some 10 m above the top of the *pilula* Zone. In central Dorset, the base of the Tarrant Chalk is inferred from palaeontological evidence (Wilkinson in Bristow,

Plate 33 Portsdown Chalk Formation, Old Harry Rocks [SZ 0554 8255]. The upper part of the formation (Studland Chalk Member) comprises relatively marl-free chalk. Height of cliffs c. 20 m (P615359).

1991) to be slightly older, within the higher part of the *pilula* Zone, and close to the equivalent of the Meeching Marls in Sussex. Regularly spaced flint beds appear to be absent from the lower part of the Tarrant Chalk at Arish Mell, but are possibly faulted out. South of the Purbeck Monocline, the Tarrant Chalk is extremely hard and cannot be distinguished lithologically from the Seaford and Newhaven Chalk below, or the Spetisbury Chalk above, and are mapped as one unit.

The thickness of the Tarrant Chalk in south Dorset is probably between 30 and 35 m, but may be only 20 m locally. At Arish Mell, the combined thickness of the Tarrant and Spetisbury Chalk is only about 65 m, although part of the succession may be faulted out. At depth, north of the Purbeck Monocline, the member appears to thicken to between 50 and 60 m.

The Tarrant Chalk Formation belongs mainly to the lower and middle parts of the *G. quadrata* Zone ('*Hagenowia* Horizon' and *A. cretaceus* Subzone), although, because of diachronism of the basal strata (see above), it locally includes the upper part of the *O. pilula* Zone (Bristow et al., 1995). The *G. quadrata* Zone is typically rather poorly fossiliferous, and the subzonal index species are small and fragmentary. Distinctive morphotypes of the echinoid *Echinocorys*, named the 'large form' and 'small form' by Gaster (1924), more readily distinguish the '*Hagenowia* Horizon' and a rich mesofauna (bryozoa, small brachiopods, echinoid spines, and a small variant of the echinoid *Offaster*) distinguishes the *A. cretaceus* Subzone.

Spetisbury Chalk Member

The Spetisbury Chalk is named after the village of Spetisbury, south-east of Blandford Forum (Barton, 1992). It crops out extensively in the north-east of the Dorchester district (Sheet 328), and more sporadically south-west-wards of this. In south Dorset, Spetisbury Chalk occurs inland from White Nothe, and is mapped with the Seaford, Newhaven and Tarrant Chalk in the Purbeck Monocline. Elsewhere, the base of the member is mapped at the top of the Tarrant Chalk scarp. The characteristic lithology is firm, white chalk with large flints, including tabular forms in the lower part, and *Zoophycos* flints in the higher part. The exact stratigraphical level of the feature-forming beds has not been established in the type area, but, in Sussex, is inferred to occur at about the level of the Whitecliff Flint (Mortimore, 1986a; 1986b). In south Dorset, the member is probably between 28 and 55 m thick, although slightly greater than this in boreholes at Wytch Farm (about 60 m), north of the Purbeck Monocline.

The Spetisbury Chalk belongs to an interval in the higher part of the *G. quadrata* Zone ('Post Applinocrinus Beds' of Christensen, 1991). The fauna is sparse and more readily identified by the occurrence of more fossiliferous adjacent intervals in the *A. cretaceus* Subzone below and topmost *G. quadrata* Zone above. The locally abundant bryozoa found in the *A. cretaceus* Subzone give way to increasingly common inoceramid shell fragments, and there are records of the belemnite *Gonioteuthis*, the brachiopod *Cretirhynchia* and the echinoid *Galeola* (Bristow et al., 1997).

Portsdown Chalk Formation

The Portsdown Chalk is the youngest formation of the White Chalk Subgroup and comprises soft to firm, white, flinty chalk with common marl seams. It occurs extensively in central and southern parts of the Dorchester district (Sheet 328), around the outcrop of Cenozoic (Tertiary) strata; in south Dorset, north of West Lulworth, and along the northern margin of the Purbeck Monocline. The cliff sections south and east of Handfast Point [SZ 055 825] provide the best exposures of the formation (Plate 33). The formation is typically 80 to 90 m thick in south Dorset, but thinner to the north and east in boreholes at Hurn (61 m), Bransgore (60 m) and Woodlands (45 m).

The base of the Portsdown Chalk is mapped at the base of a conspicuous 15 m-high scarp feature. In the Big Almer Wood Borehole (Bristow et al., 1997; 2002b) the base is marked by the downward change (at 11 m depth) from soft to firm, white, gritty (inoceramid shell-rich), virtually flint-free chalk (= Big Almer Wood Member of Bristow et al., 2002b) to chalk with common large flints that forms the top of the underlying Culver Chalk Formation. The Big Almer Wood Member, which was also recognised in the West Lulworth Borehole, is further distinguished by its lack of well-developed marl seams, in contrast with the marly basal part of the Portsdown Chalk in Hampshire (e.g. Isle of Wight). The top of the formation is the top of the Chalk Group in south Dorset, marked by a palaeokarstic surface with solution hollows at Studland Bay.

Several localities in the Dorchester district, for example Maddox Barn [SY 8436 9675], Stinsford Farm [SY 7178 9168] and Herringston Barrow [SY 6860 8834], expose the lower part of the formation, in which orangey brown Zoophycos flints are common and are associated with the Almer Marl, which is about 50 mm thick (Bristow et al., 2002b). The Zoophycos probably correlate with the 'Précy–Warren Farm Zoophycos Event' of Mortimore and Pomerol (1991), and the Almer Marl probably equates with the Shide Marl of Bailey et al. (1983).

On the Dorset coast at Studland and in the Isle of Wight, the upper part of the Portsdown Chalk is largely marl-free, and locally contains large, irregular flints (Plate 33). This part of the succession, termed the 'Studland Chalk' by Gale et al. (1987), can be recognised by the common occurrence of purple-pink-coloured oysters and the brachiopods *Magas chitoniformis* and *Cretirhynchia woodwardi*. The most westerly recorded occurrence of Studland Chalk is just west of Broadmayne [SY 7057 8669]; eastwards it occurs at Coombe Keynes [SY 8424 8475] between East and West Lulworth [SY 8767 8129; 8775 8131; 8781 8134; 8514 8035; 8513 8035; 8512 8035], and in Studland Bay, for which the member is named.

The Portsdown Chalk belongs to the highest *G. quadrata* Zone and the *B. mucronata* Zone. The lower part of formation records a significant increase in macrofauna compared with underlying strata with the belemnites *Gonioteuthis* and *Belemnitella* (Plate 32), and the echinoid *Echinocorys brydonei* occurring in the top of the *G. quadrata* Zone. Above the Farlington Marls, in the lower *B. mucronata* Zone, *Belemnitella* occurs with the echinoid *Echinocorys subconicula*, and inoceramid shell fragments are common in the succession (Bristow et al., 1997).

SIX

Palaeogene

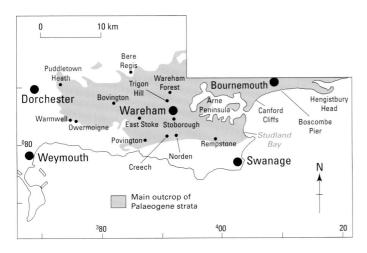

0   10 km

Map 16   Palaeogene.

In the earliest Paleocene (Danian), a combination of earth movements and a major global fall in sea level transformed most of the British Isles into land, gently folding the Chalk and exposing it to erosion. A major time gap (about 15 million years) separates the Chalk Group from the overlying Palaeogene deposits, during which up to 100 m of Late Campanian and Maastrichtian chalk was removed across most of southern England (Gale, 2000b). Regional uplift of the British Isles was concentrated particularly in the north-west (Murray, 1992), with sea extending across most of the current area of the North Sea and shallow marine embayments across south-east England (Figure 34).

Within the Dorset and south-east Devon district, Palaeogene strata, comprising siliciclastic sands and clays, occur within a west–east-trending syncline that lies north of the Purbeck Monocline. This area is generally termed the 'Wareham Basin' and is the westward continuation of the 'Hampshire Basin' to the east (Figure 36). The Palaeogene succession in south Dorset includes representatives of the **Lambeth**, **Thames**, **Bracklesham** and **Barton** groups and is summarised in Figure 35. The Palaeogene strata rest unconformably on the eroded top of the Chalk Group, but without marked angular discordance. The stratigraphy is only partially exposed in the cliffs between Studland Bay [SZ 044 825] and Hengistbury Head [SZ 178 904], but boreholes and mapping (Bristow et al., 1991; Bristow, 1999a; b) have added much to our knowledge of the succession. The biostratigraphy of the Palaeogene succession is based on palynology (Costa and Downie, 1976; Eaton, 1976; Riding *in* Bristow, 1999a; b), which additionally provides important information about palaeoclimate and the depositional environment.

Deposition of Palaeogene strata took place in a mangrove-fringed coastal plain and shallow-marine environments in a warm to subtropical climate (Hubbard and Boulter, 1983) under a regime of fluctuating marine transgressions and regressions. Rivers from the south and west, and southward-directed longshore drift are the most likely supply routes for sediment, which was derived from the erosion of Scottish, Armorican and Cornubian massifs (Morton, 1982). The subtropical weathering and erosion of older mudrock successions contributed kaolinite-rich clays (= 'Ball Clays' — see below) to the succession.

LAMBETH GROUP

Strata of the Lambeth Group are represented by the **Reading Formation**. The formation does not crop out at the surface in the district, but occurs at depth in boreholes at Wytch Farm and Christchurch; westwards it is overlapped by younger (Thames Group) strata. The formation comprises a relatively uniform succession of red-mottled clay that is devoid of primary structure and macrofauna, but contains rare rootlets, burrows and glauconite grains (Buurman 1980). The burrows and glauconite are evidence of marine-influenced deposition, and red mottling and rootlet horizons suggest extended periods of soil formation in a warm climate. A brown clayey sand with glauconite, flint pebbles and oyster shells (Reading Formation Basement Bed) is locally present at the base, infilling cavities in the eroded top of the Chalk Group. Boreholes in the Wytch Farm area show that the formation is between 6 and 23 m thick (Bristow et al., 1991), while farther east, it is 20 m thick in the Christchurch Borehole, and up to 50 m thick on the Isle of Wight.

THAMES GROUP

The Thames Group is represented by the **London Clay Formation**, typically 65 m thick in the Wareham Basin. It was deposited following an Early Eocene marine transgression that originated in the North Sea and advanced westwards, inundating the river flat and nearshore environments in which the underlying Reading Formation was deposited (Knox and Harland, 1979). The contact with the Reading Formation is a sharp erosion surface overlain by a transgressive, glauconitic sand with flint pebbles and shell lenses containing abundant *Ditrupa* and a diverse assemblage of molluscs. The London Clay has a fairly wide outcrop on the northern and western margins of the basin, around East Lulworth [SY 861 821], and from Warmwell [SY 753 858] north-eastwards to East Morden [SY 915 955], but is narrow or absent in the

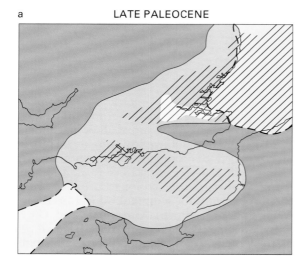

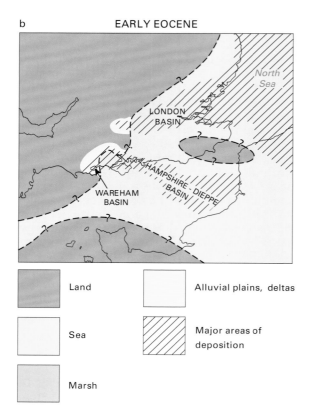

Land

Sea

Marsh

Alluvial plains, deltas

Major areas of
deposition

Figure 34 Early Palaeogene palaeogeography of southern England (based on figures by Murray, 1992).

south due to steep dip or faulting. In the Wareham Basin, the typical olive grey, bioturbated sandy mudstone facies of the London Clay contains three lithologically distinct intervals, in ascending stratigraphical order: the **West Park Farm Member**, **Warmwell Farm Sand Member** and **Lytchett Matravers Sand Member**.

The palynofloras recovered from the forma-tion include terrestrially derived miospores and

relatively diverse indigenous microplankton. The dinoflagellate cyst associations are typically dominated by chorate (spine bearing) forms and include *Homotryblium tenuispinosum, Achomosphaera* spp., *Adnatosphaeridium multi-spinosum, Apectodinium* spp., *Areoligera* spp., *Cleistospha-eridium diversispinosum, Cordosphaeridium* spp., *Deflandrea* spp., *Dracodinium simile, Eatonicysta ursulae, Glaphyrocysta* spp., *Hystrichokolpoma cinctum, Hystrichosphaeridium* spp., *Muratodinium fimbriatum, Thalassiphora delicata,* and *Wetzeliella* spp.; all suggest a nearshore depositional setting and indicate an Early Eocene (Ypresian) age.

West Park Farm Member

This member comprises red-mottled clay and sand, up to 40 m thick, which overlie the Chalk Group in parts of the Wareham Basin. Previously they had been mapped as Reading Formation (Bristow et al., 1991), which is litho-logically rather similar, but gamma-ray logs show that the member contains coarsening-upward cycles characteristic of the London Clay. The member has an irregular crop along the northern and western margin of the basin, with extensive tracts of grey-red clay between Warmwell [SY 753 858] and Owermoigne [SY 770 852], from Marl Pits Wood [SY 802 920] to the old Briantspuddle works [SY 810 923], around Blackhill brick works at Bere Regis [SY 843 938], and around Knoll Manor clay pit [SY 973 977] where it is worked for the manufacture of tiles.

At the base of the member there is 1 m of glauconitic sand or sandy clay, commonly shelly with glauconite-coated flint pebbles and cobbles. Near Kingston Farm [ST 97 04] it forms a gravel-like pavement on the field surfaces. The succeeding strata, 8 to 30 m thick, consist principally of mottled orange and grey silty clay, though locally, as at Knoll Manor clay pit [SY 973 977], the clay is strongly red or purplish red. There are also subordinate sands within the succession, as seen north-west of Combe Almer [SY 948 980], where a sand and pebble bed is thick enough to map over a 1 km-long tract.

Warmwell Farm Sand Member

The Warmwell Farm Sand, named for exposures in the lanes and banks near Warmwell Farm [SY 949 964], is generally up to 6 m thick, but locally reaches 15 m. It has an extensive crop between Warmwell [SY 753 719] and Lulworth Park [SY 850 920], at Puddledown Heath [SY 745 925], on Morden Heath [SY 910 950], and in the area south-west of Henbury Plantation [SY 966 980]. The constituent sands are well sorted, very fine- to fine-grained and locally clayey. There are at least two pebble beds, composed of well-rounded black flints. Locally, the basal bed is richly fossiliferous with common bivalves and gastropods (Bristow et al., 1991). Fossils support assign-ment to the *meckelfeldensis* Zone (Bristow and Freshney, 1986; Bristow et al., 1991).

Lytchett Matravers Sand Member

The sand of this member forms extensive flat areas around Lytchett Matravers [SY 945 955], where it is fine-grained,

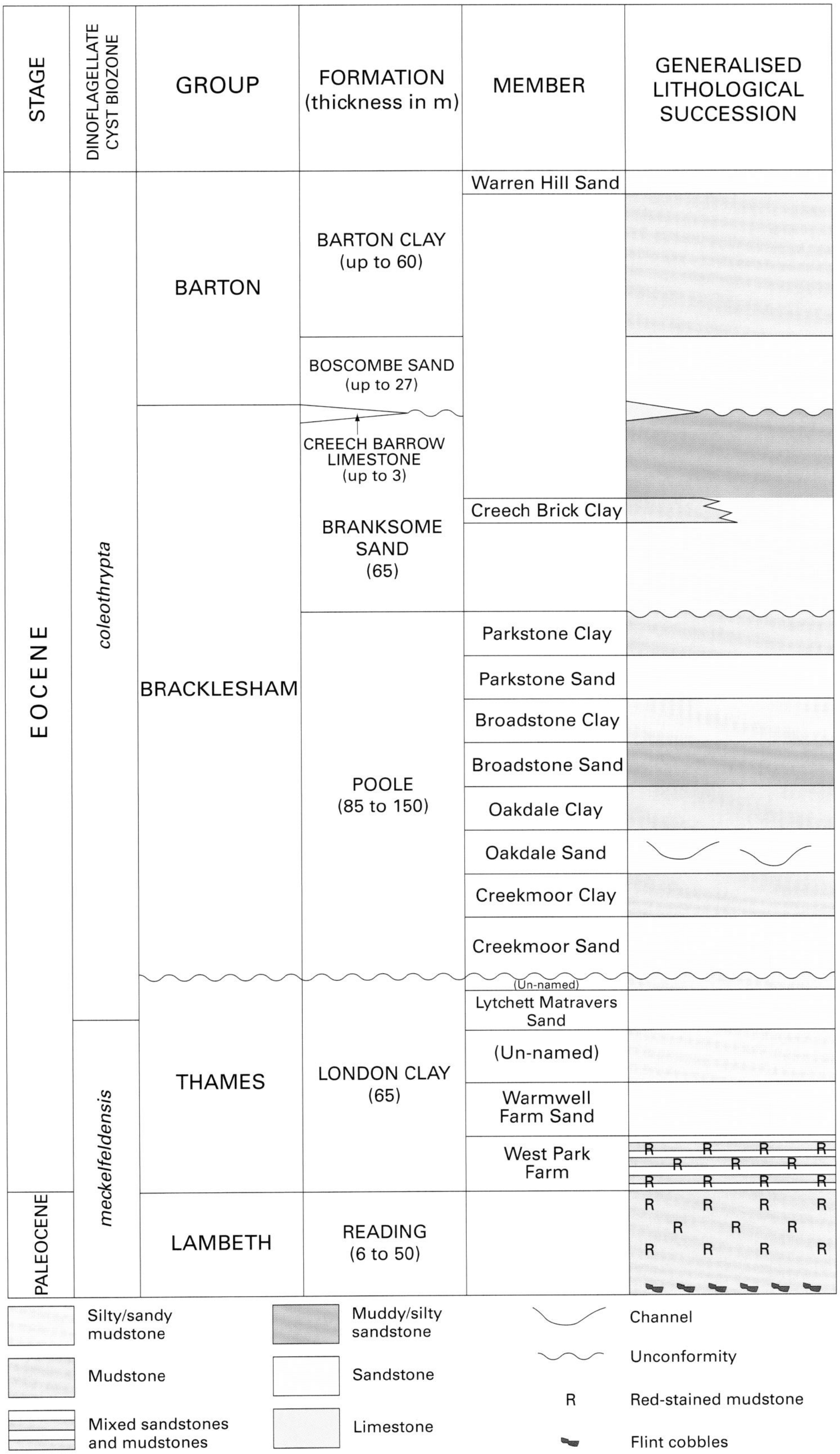

Figure 35 The stratigraphy of the Palaeogene strata of south Dorset.

STAGE	DINOFLAGELLATE CYST BIOZONE	GROUP	FORMATION (thickness in m)	MEMBER	GENERALISED LITHOLOGICAL SUCCESSION
EOCENE	coleothrypta	BARTON	BARTON CLAY (up to 60)	Warren Hill Sand	
			BOSCOMBE SAND (up to 27)		
		BRACKLESHAM	CREECH BARROW LIMESTONE (up to 3)		
			BRANKSOME SAND (65)	Creech Brick Clay	
			POOLE (85 to 150)	Parkstone Clay	
				Parkstone Sand	
				Broadstone Clay	
				Broadstone Sand	
				Oakdale Clay	
				Oakdale Sand	
				Creekmoor Clay	
				Creekmoor Sand	
	meckelfeldensis	THAMES	LONDON CLAY (65)	Lytchett Matravers Sand	
				(Un-named)	
				Warmwell Farm Sand	
				West Park Farm	R R R R / R R R / R R R R
PALEOCENE		LAMBETH	READING (6 to 50)		R R R R / R R R / R R R R

Legend:

- Silty/sandy mudstone
- Mudstone
- Mixed sandstones and mudstones
- Muddy/silty sandstone
- Sandstone
- Limestone
- Channel
- Unconformity
- R   Red-stained mudstone
- Flint cobbles

commonly ferruginously cemented and hard enough to have been worked as a building stone. Glauconite has been noted in the basal beds near Wimborne (White, 1917). A sharp break in slope and spring-lines commonly mark the lower boundary of the member, which reaches its maximum thickness of 8 m north of the River Stour. It ceases to be a mappable unit in the area extending from just north of Corfe Mullen to Wimborne, but reappears between Wimborne and the northern margin of the Bournemouth district. Along the southern margin of the basin, the member crops out over two small areas at Highwood [SY 857 861 and 865 859] and north-east of Combe Beacon [SY 855 846].

BRACKLESHAM GROUP

Strata of this group comprise a lower unit of fine- to medium-grained sand, clayey sand and sandy clay, designated the **Poole Formation**, overlain by generally coarser grained sand deposits that constitutes the **Branksome Sand Formation**. The group is locally capped by the sandy limestone of the **Creech Barrow Limestone Formation**. Dinoflagellate cysts indicate that the whole succession belongs to the Early Eocene *Charlesdownia coleothrypta* Interval Biozone (Ccl) of Powell (1992).

Poole Formation

The Poole Formation crops out over a large area in the western part of the Wareham Basin. On the coast, it occurs from Studland [SZ 034 825] northwards to Poole Head [SZ 051 883], and inland it extends westwards via Wareham to within a few kilometres of Dorchester. The formation comprises sand and clay that sharply overlie the London Clay, and is most completely developed in the south near Creech, where a borehole showed it to be about 150 m thick; northwards it thins to about 85 m under Trigon Hill. Over much of the rest of the district the higher parts of the succession have been removed by erosion. The sands vary from fine- to coarse-grained, and range from very well to poorly sorted. The laminated and patchily red-stained clays that occur in the succession are up to 50 m thick with rapid lateral thickness changes, and are locally silty, carbonaceous and lignitic (Plate 34). The alternation of clay and sand units represents a series of marine transgressions during which lagoonal clays, and locally beach-barrier sands, were deposited, interrupting a mostly fluvial sedimentary environment (Bristow et al., 1991). The sands and clays usually have erosive tops and bases and deep channelling, producing rapid lateral variation in thickness and a complex geographical distribution. Palynology provides supporting evidence for the palaeoenvironmental interpretation; marine flooding events are indicated by dinoflagellate cysts and floodplain deposition is indicated by freshwater and freshwater–brackish microplankton (Plate 35). The miospore assemblages suggest proximity to a mangrove-fringed shoreline.

In the central and eastern part of the outcrop, east of Bovington [SY 834 897], north of the River Frome, and from East Stoke [SY 867 862] eastwards to the south of the Frome, there are four mappable clay units, named, in ascending stratigraphical order: the **Creekmoor Clay**, the **Oakdale Clay**, the **Broadstone Clay** and **Parkstone Clay** members. These members host commercially important ball-clay deposits (Bristow et al., 2002a), comprising laterally impersistent beds of plastic kaolinitic clay. Most of the kaolinite in the ball clays of Dorset originated from the erosion of tropical to subtropical soils developed on land surfaces of various ages. This weathering produced a fine-grained disordered kaolinite that leads to high plasticity and high strength (Bristow, 1968). In the Dorset ball clays, kaolinite occurs mixed with material from other sources, and evidence suggests that the most likely depositional environment was an estuary, via which an eastward-flowing river carried sand and clay to the sea. Intermittent exposure to subaerial weathering and erosion (Bristow et al., 2002a) produced mottled red and lilac staining that reduces the commercial value of the clay.

Creekmoor Sand Member

The member is known mostly from subsurface records, and crops out only in the south-west of the basin, around East Lulworth and Coombe Keynes. Farther north, both the Creekmoor Sand and Creekmoor Clay are overstepped by the Oakdale Sand. The Creekmoor Sand ranges from less than 3 m to 35 m thick, and is fine to coarse grained. Borehole gamma-ray logs suggest an upward reduction in the clay content of the sand, and there is a gradational fining-upward contact with the overlying Creekmoor Clay.

Creekmoor Clay Member

This crops out in a structurally complex zone adjacent to the Purbeck Monocline: there is a limited crop [SY 900 820 to 9110 8195] south of Creech Grange, near East Creech [SY 933 825 to 9390 8256], at Norden [SY 9425 8260 to 9550 8255], and near Rollington Farm [SY 9625 8265 to 9695 8264]. There is a wide, partially drift-covered crop south-west of Stoborough [around SY 904 855], in which area the clay has been extensively worked in the Squirrel Cottage Pit [SY 906 854] (now backfilled and restored) and is currently being exploited in Doreys Pit [SY 914 850]. The member is about 30 m thick in the middle of the basin, increasing to about 40 m near Norden, but is only 3 m thick in the East Holme Farm area [around SY 911 850].

At outcrop, the clay is generally off-white to pale grey, red stained and mottled, with subordinate dark grey, carbonaceous clay, laminated pale grey and brown silty clay. Fine-grained sand laminae in the clays are usually discontinuous and lenticular. Polygonal networks of pink staining noted in places on bedding surfaces are thought to be related to desiccation cracks formed during periods of subaerial exposure. Red-staining of the clay is more common in the north of the basin, as is an increase in sand content and decrease in kaolinite.

Plate 34 Creekmoor Clay Member (excavations in quarry floor), sharply overlain by sands containing the dark grey, carbonaceous Oakdale and Broadstone Clay members (Poole Formation); Povington Pit [SY 888 826] (quarry face is 7 m high) (P615355).

Broadstone Clay

Large-scale accretion surfaces in medium–coarse-grained fluvial sands

Oakdale Clay

Oakdale Sand Member

The member comprises fine- to very coarse-grained, very well to moderately sorted, strongly cross-bedded sand, varying from 2 to 33 m thick, but more typically 13 m thick. It has a limited crop, restricted largely to the northern margin of the basin, around Oak Hill, and south of the River Frome in the East Stoke, Stoborough and Norden areas. Northwards, the Oakdale Sand is overstepped by the Broadstone Sand, and is absent north of Hamworthy. East of Upton [National grid line SY 98] where the overlying Oakdale Clay Member is thin or absent, Oakdale Sand is overlain by the Broadstone Sand Member (see below), and the two units form a single body.

The member is locally pebbly, and gamma-ray logs from boreholes in the Wytch Farm Oilfield indicate the presence of both coarsening- and fining-upwards sequences. Ferruginous cementation of the basal bed of the member gives rise to an indurated horizon ('stone bed(s)') up to 0.2 m thick, and the basal part of the member is locally a sandy gravel, with rounded quartz and flint pebbles and mudstone and siltstone clasts derived from the underlying Creekmoor Clay. Channels are common in the main part of the member, usually infilled with laminated sandy silt, some with silt and clay clasts, and abundant lignite. These lithologies record a change in the depositional environment, when river channels cut across the marine shelf during a temporary fall in sea level.

Oakdale Clay Member

This member is present only locally, being best developed in the north and east of the basin where an extensive outcrop occurs in Wareham Forest [around SY 897 928]. It varies greatly in thickness, averaging 5.6 m, but on the Arne peninsula [around SY 97 88], reaches an exceptional 35 m thick. The member consists mainly of stiff clay, typically fissured, grey, silty and commonly carbonaceous and laminated. Locally, carbonaceous laminated clay passes laterally into red-stained grey clay.

The Oakdale Clay correlates with the Whitecliff Bay Bed, a major palaeosol in the Isle of Wight and Southampton areas (Edwards and Freshney, 1987). The presence of abundant dinoflagellate cysts in the Oakdale Clay, including a predominance of *Apectodinium*, denotes a marine flooding event, and a tropical depositional environment is indicated by floras obtained by Chandler (1962, 1963) from the Oakdale Clay at Arne.

Broadstone Sand Member

North of the River Frome, most of the sand at outcrop, including the extensive deposits worked on Stokeford Heath [SY 874 885], belong to this member. There are extensive outcrops around Wareham Forest and in the north-east around Beacon Heath [SY 975 943]. South of the Frome, the Broadstone Sand crops out around Holme and Stoborough heaths [SY 904 846 and 925 850], and (together with the Oakdale Sand) around Studland. Averaging 10 m thick, but locally exceeding 40 m, the Broadstone Sand is predominantly silty, medium-grained, cross-bedded sand, although very fine- to very coarse-grained sand also occurs. Typically, it has an erosional contact with underlying strata, and palaeocurrent directions deduced from cross-bedding at Tatchell's Pit [around SY 906 885], in the north-west of the area, show a sediment transport direction dominantly from the south-west (Bristow, 1999b, fig. 12); in the east of the basin the higher parts of the Poole Formation and Branksome Sand show that sediment transport was predominantly from the north-west. A local marker bed near the base of the Broadstone Sand in the Arne–Rempstone–Norden area is known as the Green Bed, and comprises bioturbated silty clays and sands, locally with well-rounded black flint pebbles, and invariably associated with a 0.45 m-thick bed of lignite (Bristow, 1999b).

Broadstone Clay Member

This member is named after the area where the clay was worked for brickmaking [SZ 0085 9575] in the 1890s (White, 1917), and crops out extensively in the south of the district on South Heath [SY 812 897] and east of Hurst Mill [around SY 895 840] towards Ridge and Rempstone. In the extreme south, an inlier is preserved along the axis of a syncline [SY 818 813 to 900 822] south of Povington Pit [SY 893 826]; it occurs in a limited area around Trigon, was formerly mined at Grange [SY 9052 8260], and has a sub-Drift occurrence east of Wareham. Generally 10 to 15 m thick, but locally over 35 m in the east of the district, the member varies from pale to medium grey, homogeneous or silty clay, to laminated, lignitic and carbonaceous, silty and fine-grained, sandy clay. Locally the clays are stained brick-red or lilac.

Parkstone Sand Member

Most of the sand at outcrop south of the River Frome belongs to this member, and forms many of the heaths in that area. North of the River Frome, near Trigon Hill,

Plate 35   Selected palynomorphs from the Poole Formation of the Wareham area, Dorset (P615360). Magnification, all figures ×500. All specimens photographed in plain transmitted light except xxi, which was taken using phase contrast. All specimens are curated in the BGS type and figured microfossil/palynomorph collection and may be located by the unique 'MPK' number. Specimens i–ix and xii–xiv are pollen grains and specimen xv is a spore. Specimen xvi is a reworked Jurassic pollen grain. Specimens xvii–xix and xxii are dinoflagellate cysts. Specimens xi, xx and xxi are freshwater algae.

Key:
i, ii   *Porocolpopollenites* spp. **i** MPK 12370, Arne Clay Pit, Oakdale Clay Member: **ii** MPK 12371, Dorey's Clay Pit, Creekmoor Clay Member
iii   *Plicapollis pseudoexcelsus* (Krutzsch, 1958) Krutzsch, 1961. MPK 12372, Arne Clay Pit, Oakdale Clay Member
iv   *Pompeckjoideapollenites subhercynicus* (Krutzsch, 1954) Krutzsch in Góczán et al. 1967. MPK 12373, Dorey's Clay Pit, Creekmoor Clay Member
v, x   *Tiliaepollenites* spp. **v** MPK 12374, Dorey's Clay Pit, Creekmoor Clay Member; **x** MPK 12375, Trigon Clay Pit, Parkstone Clay Member
vi, vii   *Corsinipollenites oculusnoctis* (Thiergart, 1940) Nakoman, 1965. **vi** MPK 12375; **vii** MPK 12376; both specimens from the Oakdale Clay Member at Arne Clay Pit
viii   *Caryapollenites simplex* (Potonie, 1931) Raatz, 1937. MPK 12377, Arne Clay Pit, Oakdale Clay Member
ix   *Milfordia hungarica* (Kedves, 1965) Krutzsch and Van Hoorne, 1970. MPK 12378, Arne Clay Pit, Broadstone Sand Member
xi   *Tetraporina* sp. MPK 12380, Arne Clay Pit, Oakdale Clay Member. This species represent the zygospores or aplanospores of the freshwater zygnemataceous alga *Spirogyra* (Division Chlorophyta)
xii   *Diporites* sp. MPK 12381, Trigon Clay Pit, Parkstone Clay Member
xiii   *Taxodiaceaepollenites hiatus* Potonié, 1932 ex Potonié, 1958. MPK 12382, Dorey's Clay Pit, Creekmoor Clay Member
xiv   *Spinizonocolpites baculatus* Muller, 1968. MPK 12383, Dorey's Clay Pit, Creekmoor Clay Member
xv   *Laevigatosporites* sp. MPK 12384, Dorey's Clay Pit, Creekmoor Clay Member
xvi   *Callialasportites dampieri* (Balme, 1957) Sukh Dev, 1961. MPK 12385, Arne Clay Pit, Broadstone Sand Member. A reworked Jurassic pollen grain
xvii   *Apectodinium quinquelatum* (Williams and Downie, 1966) Costa and Downie, 1979. MPK 12386, Arne Clay Pit, Oakdale Clay Member
xviii   *Apectodinium homomorphum* (Deflandre and Cookson, 1955) Lentin and Williams, 1977. MPK 12387, Arne Clay Pit, Broadstone Sand Member
xix   *Lejeunecysta hyalina* (Gerlach, 1961) Artzner and Dörhöfer, 1978. MPK 12388, Arne Clay Pit, Broadstone Sand Member
xx   *Brazilea parva* (Cookson and Dettmann, 1959) Backhouse, 1988. MPK 12389, Arne Clay Pit, Oakdale Clay Member. This species represent the zygospores or aplanospores of the freshwater zygnemataceous alga *Spirogyra*.
xxi   *Pediastum* sp. MPK 12390, Arne Clay Pit, Broadstone Sand Member. *Pediastrum* is a colonial freshwater cholorococcalean algal genus (Division Chlorophyta)
xxii   *Wetzeliella articulata* Eisenack, 1938. MPK 12391, Arne Clay Pit, Broadstone Sand Member

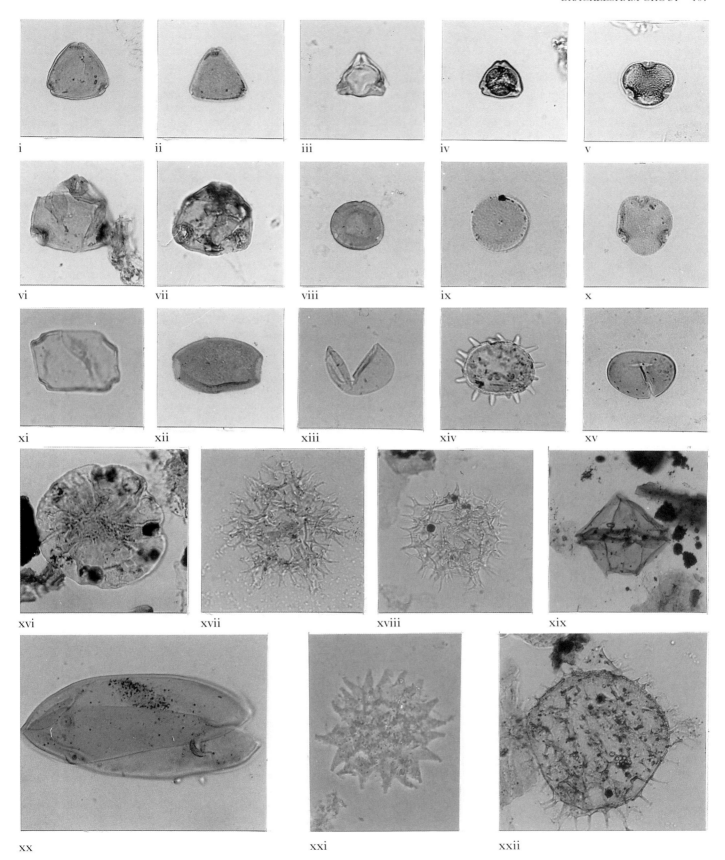

i

ii

iii

iv

v

vi

vii

viii

ix

x

xi

xii

xiii

xiv

xv

xvi

xvii

xviii

xix

xx

xxi

xxii

the Parkstone Sand is either absent or very thin, such that the Parkstone Clay rests on the Broadstone Clay. The Parkstone Sand is up to 28 m thick; 16 to 20 m is typical around Creech Barrow, but the average is about 10 m elsewhere. The lithology varies from silty and fine-grained, to very coarse-grained and pebbly sand; medium- to coarse-grained sand is the most common. Most of the sand is moderately sorted, and there are several graded beds with bases composed of fine-grained gravel. Impersistent breccias with clay clasts up to 10 cm across occur locally. On Canford Heath [SZ 030 968] and Beacon Hill [SY 982 951], in the Bournemouth district, cross-bedding indicates that the principal current directions are from the south-west and west. Convolute bedding is locally common, and can be seen in a conspicuous perched boulder known as the 'Agglestone' [SZ 0235 8284] near the member top on Godlingston Heath, and probably formed by a rapid dewatering of saturated, poorly compacted sediment.

Parkstone Clay Member

The Parkstone Clay typically comprises medium grey to greyish brown and brown, plastic, locally laminated, clay. The principal outcrop of the member is around Trigon Hill [SY 893 898], where it is up to 15 m thick, and around Creech [SY 917 835] in the south where it is up to 25 m thick; there is also a small outlier at Lower Bushey Farm [SY 970 835]. Lenticular deposits occur around Beacon Heath in the north-east, and there is a more-or-less continuous crop at sea level around Brownsea Island. On Trigon Hill, however, where the underlying Parkstone Sand is mostly thin or absent, surface evidence alone is insufficient for separating the Parkstone Clay from the underlying Broadstone Clay.

Branksome Sand Formation

The Branksome Sand, typically about 65 m thick, is well exposed in cliff sections from Canford Cliffs [SZ 065 897] eastwards to Bournemouth Pier [SZ 089 906]. The formation also occurs as scattered outliers in the Wareham Basin: around Trigon Hill and Beacon Heath in the north-east, on Brownsea Island in the east, and on Godlingston Heath and Creech Hill [SY 9204 8236] in the south.

The base of the formation, a transgressive erosion surface at the top of the Parkstone Clay, is nearly everywhere marked by springs. The lower half of the formation (formerly termed the 'Bournemouth Freshwater Beds') is dominated by fine- to coarse-grained, locally pebbly, trough cross-bedded, yellow and orange sands arranged in a number of fining-upward sequences. These facies have been interpreted as representing meandering or braided river deposits, with sparse remains of dinoflagellate cysts in some clay units indicating a local marine influence (Daley, 1999). The top of the formation (formerly termed the 'Bournemouth Marine Beds') is muddier and displays a very distinctive bedding style of inclined sand-mud couplets. The couplets form part of small-scale (1 to 4 m thick) coarsening-upwards cycles, which are separated by erosion surfaces (Bristow et al., 1991). Clay plugs at the top of cycles are rich in plant debris, including the fern *Gleichenia* (Ord, 1914), and can also yield marine dinoflagellates. These facies are thought to represent estuarine channel deposits (Daley, 1999).

On Creech Hill, where the Branksome Sand is up to 74 m thick, the succession, was formerly known as the 'Creechbarrow Beds' (Hudleston, 1902) and divided into lower, middle and upper units, capped by the Creechbarrow Limestone Formation (Arkell, 1947) (see below). Sands form the lower and upper parts of the formation hereabouts, with the locally developed **Creech Brick Clay Member** sandwiched between them. This member can be traced most of the way around Creech Barrow Hill, where boreholes prove a maximum thickness of 5.5 m [SY 9204 8236] (considerably less than the 18 m stated by Arkell, 1947). The lithology is a buff, silty clay with large flints at the base. Similar large flints occur in the sands overlying the Creech Brick Clay.

Creech Barrow Limestone Formation

The Creech Barrow Limestone, up to 3 m thick, has a very limited outcrop only a few metres square on the top of Creech Barrow [SY 9214 8240]. The principal lithology is a white to yellow, micritic and pisoidal sandy limestone having an insoluble residue of about 13 per cent consisting of angular quartz grains, kaolinitic clay and vertebrate fossils (Plint, 1982). Concentrically laminated pisoids, up to 4 cm in diameter, and geopetally filled cavities are common. The limestone yields a diverse vertebrate fauna including mammals and reptiles. Invertebrates include terrestrial and freshwater gastropods, but none are of significant chronostratigraphical value. The limestone probably formed in a shallow freshwater lake (Plint, 1982), perhaps in a fault-controlled setting along the compressional edge of the Purbeck Monocline.

Until the work of Hooker (1977), most workers (Keeping, 1910; Bury, 1934; Cox, 1947, pp. 240–241) correlated the Creech Barrow Limestone with the Oligocene Bembridge Limestone of the Isle of Wight. Hooker (1977, 1986) identified many mammalia from the Creech Barrow Limestone and concluded that it was of Mid to Late Eocene in age and possibly equivalent to the Boscombe Sands of the Bournemouth area. In this account, because of its nonmarine fauna, the Creech Barrow Limestone is regarded as the uppermost formation of the Bracklesham Group, rather than part of the overlying, marine, Barton Group.

BARTON GROUP

The group comprises a lower sand-rich interval, named the Boscombe Sand Formation, overlain by the argillaceous strata of the Barton Clay Formation, both Mid to Late Eocene in age (King, 1988).

The **Boscombe Sand Formation** is 20 to 27 m thick, underlies much of Bournemouth, and is well exposed along the nearby cliffs, and in an outlier at Hengistbury Head [SZ 178 904]. The characteristic lithology is fine- to medium-grained, well-sorted, yellow, grey or brownish grey sands (Plate 36), commonly showing either planar lamination, bidirectional cross-bedding or convolute lamination. Locally at Hengistbury Head, a mud-filled channel in the Boscombe Sand contains up to 2.5 m of bituminous sands that show evidence of synsedimentary reworking (Daley, 1999). The bitumen is probably derived from plant leaf material. At the top of the formation on Hengistbury Head there are two well-developed pebble beds. The base and top of the formation are sharp erosional contacts with the muddier lithologies of the Branksome Sand (below) and Barton Clay Formation (above). The Boscombe Sand is thought to represent an estuarine tidal channel facies; the Hengistbury Head strata formed in 'lower' estuarine conditions, and the succession slightly farther west at Bournemouth represents an estuarine environment that was farther up river (Plint, 1983).

The **Barton Clay Formation** comprises an argillaceous succession up to 60 m thick, exposed in an outlier at Hengistbury Head [SZ 178 904] where it sharply overlies the Boscombe Sand (Plate 36). At Hengistbury Head, the Barton Clay consists mainly of yellow-weathering, greenish grey, glauconitic clay with a variable proportion of both disseminated and bedded very fine-grained sand. A layer of well-rounded flint pebbles occurs at the base of the formation and ironstone nodules are common at four levels, and were once worked as iron ore. The formation is sparsely fossiliferous at Hengistbury, but plants, foraminifera, molluscs, crustaceans, echinoids and fish have been recorded (Bristow et al. 1991). The highest 10 m of the formation seen at Hengistbury Head, comprising very fine-grained, cross-bedded sand, was termed 'Warren Hill Sand' by Bristow et al., (1991). Farther east, at Barton-on-Sea [SZ 235 929], just outside the district, the abundant marine fauna (including corals) of the Barton Clay indicates deposition in open-water, shallow marine conditions (Bristow et al., 1991); the Hengistbury succession may in part represent slightly nearer-shore conditions (Daley, 1999), as evidenced by the less common and less diverse fauna.

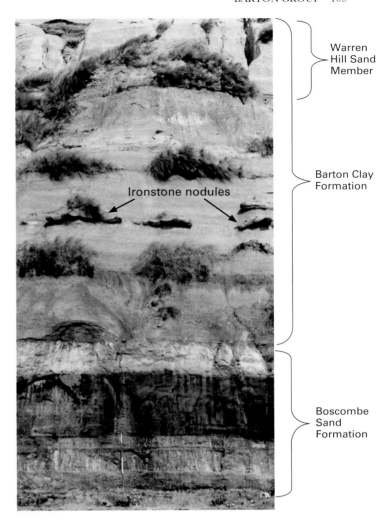

Plate 36 Boscombe Sand Formation (base of photograph) overlain by the Barton Clay Formation and Warren Hill Sand Member (subdivisions on scale pole are 50 cm). The ironstone nodules in the Barton Clay were once worked for iron ore; Hengistbury Head [SZ 170 906] (P669479).

SEVEN

Structure

In southern England, a series of major faults and closely associated folds are developed in strata of Permian to Palaeogene age. The deposits accumulated in major sedimentary basins initially formed in response to tension created by the opening of the Atlantic Ocean, but later modified by compression associated with the creation of the Alpine mountain chain across central and southern Europe (Alpine Orogeny). The locations of these sedimentary basins appear to have been controlled by pre-existing thrust structures, formed in a mountain-building episode at the end of the Carboniferous (Variscan Orogeny). It is in the context of these large-scale tectonic patterns that the complex structural geology of South Dorset and the World Heritage Coast can best be understood.

The Dorset and south-east Devon area forms part of the wider Wessex–Channel Basin that incorporates the onshore Permian–Mesozoic and Cenozoic (Tertiary) sedimentary basins of southern England, and the offshore basins in the central and eastern parts of the English Channel (e.g Penn et al., 1987; Hamblin et al., 1992). The term Wessex Basin is often used to describe the more geographically restricted, onshore area of thick Permian–Mesozoic strata in Wiltshire, Devon and Dorset (Figure 36, inset map). The surface geological structure in this area was described in detail by Arkell (1947), Wilson et al. (1958) and Cope et al. (1969). Many of the east–west faults show reverse throws near surface and are associated with anticlinal or periclinal folds, the majority of which have been the focus of study since the early 19th century (e.g. Buckland and De La Beche, 1835; Strahan, 1898, Arkell, 1936b, 1947). However, only since the acquisition of good quality seismic reflection data, obtained during hydrocarbon exploration in the region, has the nature of these structures and the relationships to the subsurface geology been fully appreciated. These data have revealed how the Wessex–Channel Basin comprises a series of extensional fault blocks bounded by east–west-trending major, subplanar, *en échelon*, and generally southward-dipping normal and reverse fault zones. These structures are responsible for marked thickness variations in the Sherwood Sandstone Group, Jurassic and Lower Cretaceous strata (Figures 37; 38; 39), and they have controlled the location and development of later Cenozoic structures.

STRUCTURAL HISTORY

In Late Carboniferous times, the collision of two major continental masses ('Laurasia' and 'Gondwana') created a supercontinent called 'Pangaea' and generated the Variscan orogenic belt in the collision zone. Deep (4 to 20 km) beneath the Dorset and East Devon region, this episode is recorded by major thrust zones some of which are imaged on seismic reflection profiles (e.g. Chadwick et al., 1983; Whittaker and Chadwick, 1984). These thrusts trend roughly east–west and dip southwards at between 20° and 30°, and exerted a strong influence on the subsequent location and development of Mesozoic extensional and Cenozoic compressional structures.

From Permian to mid-Cretaceous times, horizontal tensional and vertical isostatic forces controlled the tectonic evolution of the north-west European region. East–west extension related to the opening of the Atlantic led to widespread basin subsidence, and the opening and formation of the Bay of Biscay in Late Jurassic to Early Cretaceous times produced a lesser component of north–south extension. These processes strongly influenced subsidence patterns in the Wessex–Channel Basin. East–west-trending Variscan thrusts in the basement were reactivated, and above these, major southward downthrowing normal faults developed, showing predominantly oblique (transtensional) overall displacements. These faults subsequently controlled the extent and location of Mesozoic sedimentation across southern Dorset and south-east Devon.

The structural history of the rocks exposed on the World Heritage Coast begins with fault-controlled crustal extension in both early Permian and Triassic times. This led to the formation of fault-bounded basins in which the thick, pebbly and coarse-grained arkosic facies of the Permian Exeter Group and Triassic Sherwood Sandstone Group were deposited. Late Permian and Triassic times were dominated by postextensional regional subsidence during which the predominantly finer-grained successions of the Permian Aylesbeare Group and Triassic Mercia Mudstone Group were deposited.

Further fault-controlled extension followed by regional flexural subsidence occurred in Early Jurassic, Late Jurassic and Early Cretaceous times, the last accompanied by a marked fall in relative sea level and period of erosion producing the Late Cimmerian Unconformity. During this period the basins of the Wessex–Channel Basin evolved both onshore and offshore. From mid Cretaceous (Aptian) times, active sea-floor spreading in the North Atlantic region marked a transition from fault-controlled subsidence to regional flexural subsidence across southern England. This tectonic regime continued into Late Cretaceous times, when minor episodes of uplift affected the Wessex–Channel Basin. These were precursors to the main Alpine Orogeny, caused by the convergence of the African and European plates in early Neogene (Miocene) times. Compressive tectonic stresses that accompanied this distant continental collision caused the inversion of Mesozoic sedimentary basins in southern England. Consequently, Mesozoic basin-fills now occur beneath regional upwarps (e.g. the Portland–Wight High overlies the Portland–Wight Basin) and the former structural highs

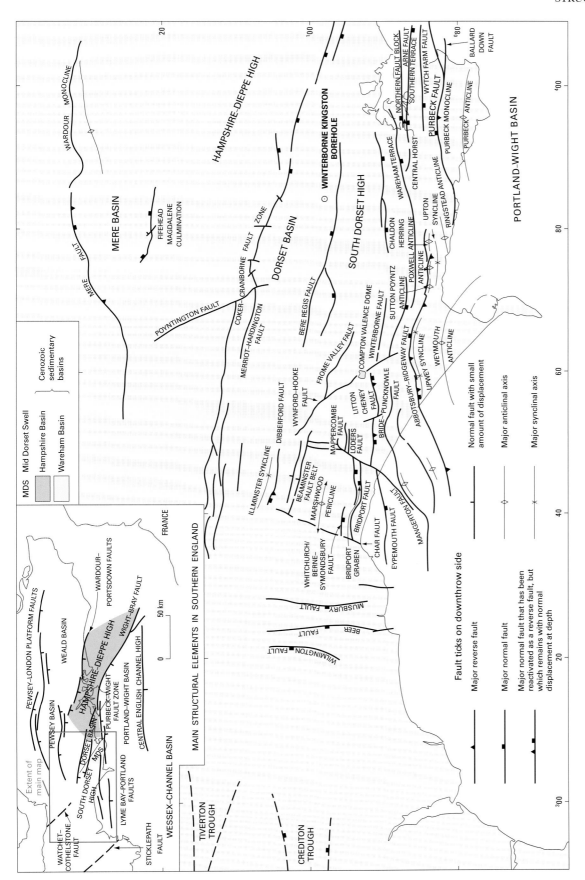

Figure 36 Major structural features of Dorset and south-east Devon. Fault ticks mark direction of downthrow for normal faults and upthrow for reverse faults.

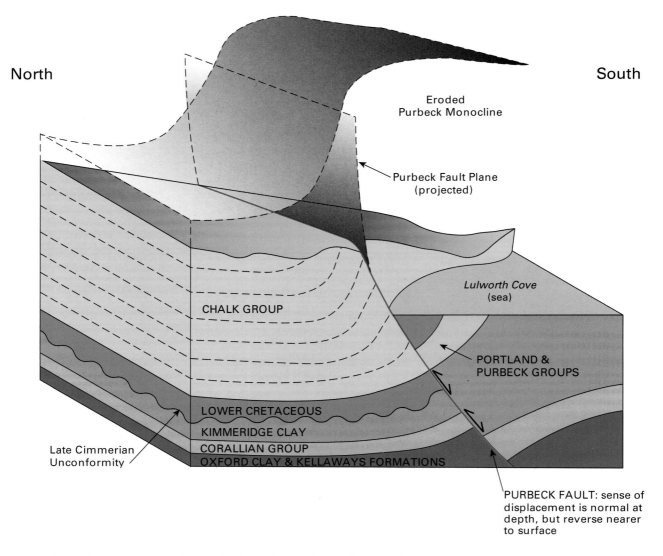

North

South

Eroded
Purbeck Monocline

Purbeck Fault Plane
(projected)

CHALK GROUP

Lulworth Cove
(sea)

PORTLAND &
PURBECK GROUPS

LOWER CRETACEOUS

KIMMERIDGE CLAY

CORALLIAN GROUP

OXFORD CLAY & KELLAWAYS FORMATIONS

Late Cimmerian
Unconformity

PURBECK FAULT: sense of
displacement is normal at
depth, but reverse nearer
to surface

Figure 37 The structure of the Purbeck Fault and Purbeck Monocline at Lulworth Cove. Note greatly thickened Kimmeridge Clay on seaward (south/hanging-wall) side of fault.

now underlie the Cenozoic basins (e.g. the Hampshire–Dieppe basin overlies the Hampshire–Dieppe High). Superimposed upon and delimiting these general regional upwarps are more or less linear *en échelon* inversion structures (typically periclinal or monoclinal flexures), formed above the main basin-controlling normal faults that experienced reactivation and reversal of movement during Cenozoic compression (Stoneley, 1982; Chadwick, 1986, 1993; Lake and Karner, 1987) (Figure 36).

MAJOR STRUCTURES

Hampshire–Dieppe High

The Hampshire–Dieppe High (Cranborne–Fordingbridge High of Chadwick, 1986) is up to 20 km across, and extends westwards from the Solent and Isle of Wight region across mid Dorset. It is a major fault-bounded

intrabasinal horst (Figure 36), the southern margin of which is marked by the southward downthrowing Coker–Cranborne Fault Zone. This fault zone continues south-east, to merge with the Portland–Wight–Bray fault system in the area north of the Isle of Wight. The fault zone shows dextral offset along the Poyntington Fault and has vertical displacements of between 25 and 150 m (Wilson et al., 1958; Bristow et al., 1995). The Poyntington Fault is one of a number of important north-west-trending 'wrench' faults recognised in southern Britain that include the Watchet–Cothelstone–Hatch Fault Zone, and Sticklepath Fault (e.g. Holloway and Chadwick, 1986; Miliorizos and Ruffell, 1998). They are regarded as transfer faults that played important roles in the evolution of the sub-basins, facilitating the extensional development of the Wessex–Channel Basin.

The top of the Variscan basement is proved at relatively shallow depths in a number of boreholes across

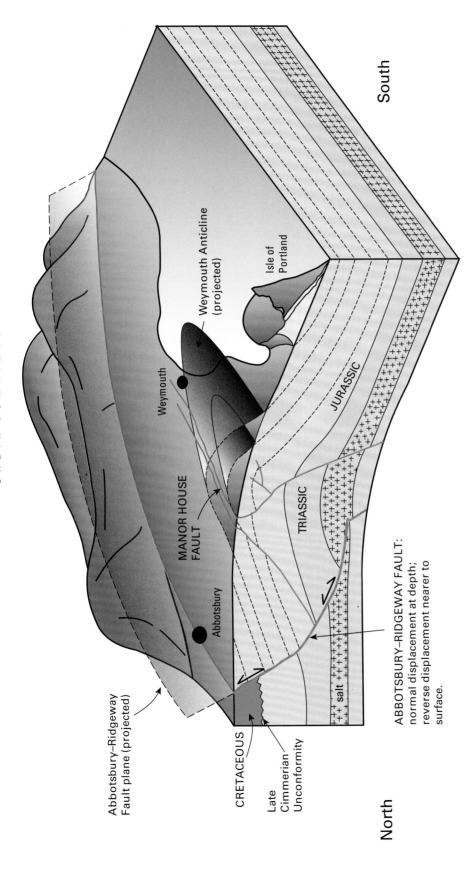

Chalk downland

Abbotsbury–Ridgeway
Fault plane (projected)

CRETACEOUS

Late
Cimmerian
Unconformity

North

South

Weymouth Anticline
(projected)

Isle of
Portland

Weymouth

MANOR HOUSE
FAULT

Abbotsbury

JURASSIC

TRIASSIC

salt

ABBOTSBURY–RIDGEWAY FAULT:
normal displacement at depth;
reverse displacement nearer to
surface.

Figure 38   Simplified three-dimensional view of the structure of the Weymouth Anticline and the Abbotsbury–Ridgeway Fault.

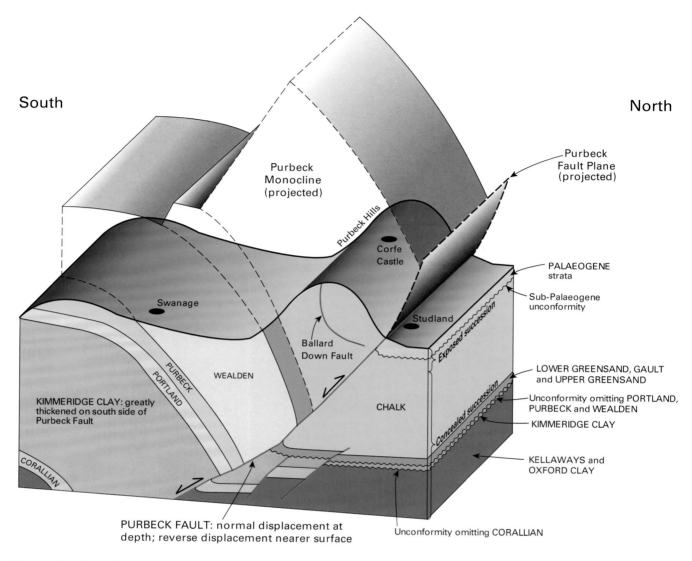

Figure 39 Simplified three-dimensional view of the geological structure between Durlston Bay and Studland. Note major changes in stratigraphy and preserved thicknesses of strata across the Purbeck Fault.

the Hampshire–Dieppe High, for example Spetisbury (1912 m below OD) and Fifehead Magdalen (992 m below OD). The Fifehead Magdalen Culmination is an important feature (Bristow et al., 1995) within a region where the basement generally dips northward into the southerly dipping southward downthrowing Mere Fault.

The Hampshire–Dieppe High remained a positive feature until Late Triassic times, as shown by the thickness changes and onlap of the Sherwood Sandstone Group on the southern flanks of this structure, and its eventual overstep by a thin Mercia Mudstone Group succession (Bristow et al., 1995).

Dorset Basin

The Dorset Basin, formerly known as the Winterborne Kingston Trough or Cerne Basin (Figure 36), formed in the hanging-wall block to the Coker–Cranborne Fault

Zone. The basin is a narrow west-north-west-trending fault-bounded graben. The Winterborne Kingston Borehole within the basin shows a greater thickness of the Permian to Jurassic strata relative to that on neighbouring highs, and shows that faulting commenced in Permian times with syndepositional movement continuing into the Early Cretaceous.

South Dorset High and the Mid Dorset Swell

The South Dorset High is a composite horst-like structure extending over 50 km east–west from the area north of Bridport to the Isle of Wight (Figure 36). The Bere Regis Fault marks the northern boundary with the Dorset Basin and the southern margin is defined by part of the Abbotsbury–Ridgeway and Purbeck–Isle of Wight fault zones. The southern flank and western area of the high is, however, complicated by a series of generally east–west-trending, southward downthrowing normal faults that produced a number of fault blocks or 'terraces'. Some of these faults were active during Mesozoic sedimentation and affected stratal thicknesses.

The Mid Dorset Swell (Figure 36 inset map) has been interpreted as a north-west-trending line of periclinal structures associated with a thinning of Albian–Cenomanian sequences, that extends from central Dorset to the Isle of Purbeck (Drummond, 1970). The trend of this enigmatic line is oblique to that of the underlying Jurassic basins and highs, perhaps indicating a cessation of the east–west faulting by Early Cretaceous times and a period of more general regional uplift of the area.

Abbotsbury–Ridgeway and Purbeck–Isle of Wight fault zones

The Abbotsbury–Ridgeway and Purbeck–Isle of Wight fault zones comprise perhaps the most important structures in the Wessex–Channel Basin. Interpreted as two *en échelon* fault segments offset by about 4 km in the vicinity of the Sutton Poynz, Poxwell and Chaldon Herring anticlines, together they form the boundary between the thinner Jurassic rocks deposited over the South Dorset High and the thicker succession deposited offshore in the Portland–Wight Basin (Figure 36). Both fault zones have suffered repeated episodes of reactivation, both in extension and compression.

The Abbotsbury–Ridgeway Fault Zone is a major curvilinear fault (Darton et al., 1981; Harvey and Stewart, 1998) that has experienced a complicated extensional and compressional history. Faulting of the cover and basement successions has at times been independent of each other due to the presence of evaporites in the Mercia Mudstone Group (Triassic) that have acted as a *décollement* horizon (Harvey and Stewart, 1998). During Cenozoic compression, the Abbotsbury–Ridgeway Fault Zone was reactivated and suffered reversal of movement, as illustrated by the preservation of Cretaceous rocks in the downthrown footwall block in eastern areas. However, because Mesozoic synsedimentary extension produced substantial thickening south of the Abbotsbury–Ridgeway Fault Zone, the effect of Cenozoic inversion on the overall sense of fault displacement lessens at older stratigraphical levels (Figure 37); in western areas the direction of throw at crop becomes southwards.

Subsidiary folds and faults are developed in association with the Abbotsbury–Ridgeway Fault Zone and include the Upwey and Upton synclines and the Weymouth, Sutton Poyntz, Poxwell, Ringstead and Chaldon Herring anticlines. The anticlinal structures have attracted the interest of oil companies. To date, unlike the oilfields at Wytch Farm and Wareham to the east, all wells drilled on the anticlines have proved dry with only limited hydrocarbon shows. The Sutton Poyntz, Poxwell and Chaldon Herring folds represent relatively small, tight periclinal inversion structures developed adjacent to the Ridgeway section of the fault zone. They are developed within the hanging-wall succession and probably relate in the main to Cenozoic compression. The Weymouth Anticline is a larger eastwardly plunging structure, with a thickening

of Triassic evaporites in its core at depth; it formed in the hanging-wall block succession adjacent to the Abbotsbury Ridgeway Fault (a rollover structure) that subsequently may have suffered some tightening during Cenozoic compression (Figure 38).

The Purbeck–Isle of Wight Fault Zone extends over 60 km eastwards from Poole Harbour to just south-east of the 'Needles' on the Isle of Wight, whereupon it is *en échelon* with the major Wight–Bray Fault that swings south-east towards the north coast of France. Seismic reflection data indicate that it comprises a series of subplanar, *en échelon*, southward downthrowing normal faults that cut Variscan basement at depth. Triassic to Early Cretaceous stratal thickening southwards across the Purbeck Fault, demonstrates a long history of syndepositional displacement. In particular, the Lias Group increases from 70 m in the vicinity of Wytch Farm, north of the fault, to 741 m in the Southard Quarry Borehole south of the fault. Unlike the Abbotsbury–Ridgeway Fault, evaporites in the Mercia Mudstone Group, where present, do not appear to have affected development of the fault. At the end of Early Cretaceous times, the total southward downthrow across the Purbeck–Isle of Wight Fault Zone may have been up to 1300 m. Subsequent sea-level falls and uplift of the footwall blocks led to erosion and truncation of successions, creating the Late Cimmerian Unconformity (Figures 37; 38). Cessation of rifting was followed by Late Cretaceous regional subsidence and deposition of the Chalk Group.

Miocene compression led to a substantial reversal of movement along the Purbeck Fault, reducing the normal displacements of Permian to lower Cretaceous strata and causing reverse displacements at higher stratigraphical levels. The Chalk and Cenozoic successions were folded and suffered local reverse faulting, producing a major eastwards-plunging and northwards-verging asymmetrical inversion structure, the northern limb of which comprises a zone of steep northward dipping to vertical (and locally overturned) strata. This structure, the Purbeck Monocline, has also been referred to as the Purbeck Disturbance or Purbeck–Isle of Wight Disturbance (Figures 36; 37; 39), and between Lulworth and Worbarrow Bay has also been referred to as the Lulworth Monocline. Seismic reflection data reveal the overall structure to be a broad asymmetric open anticline with a steeper northern limb and an axis located parallel to, and about 3 km south of the monocline. The onshore part is known as the Purbeck Anticline, the axis and core of which is well exposed from Kimmeridge Bay to just south of Encombe. Structural complications developed in the Jurassic and lower Cretaceous strata adjacent to the Purbeck Fault are well exposed in the 'Lulworth Crumple Zone', at the eastern end of Stair Hole, immediately west of the entrance to Lulworth Cove (Plate 28). There, the Purbeck Group exhibits two asymmetric northward-verging anticlinal folds within a succession dipping northwards at approximately 40° (Underhill and Paterson, 1998).

Along much of the length of the Purbeck Monocline, the Chalk–Palaeogene junction, previously interpreted as an unconformable or normally faulted boundary, more probably represents a high-angle reverse fault. To the north, borehole provings in clay pits demonstrate that there are several reverse faults that cut through the Palaeogene succession; seismic reflection and borehole data suggest that these are most probably splays off the reactivated Purbeck Fault, as depicted on the map and cross-section of Sheet 343 Swanage.

Ballard Down Fault

The Ballard Down Fault is a north-dipping concave-upwards fault, the formation of which was coeval with the Purbeck Monocline (Figure 39). It extends west for 3.5 km from the coastal exposure to the north of Ballard Point [SZ 0493 8148]. South of the fault, the Chalk dips north typically at about 50° but the beds are locally sheared and the strata progressively steepen toward the north such that the upper part of the succession adjacent to the fault (Portsdown Chalk Formation) is vertical (Strahan, 1895; Rowe, 1901). Despite the small stratigraphical displacement (Rowe, 1901), the fault has long been the subject of discussion, with various models proposed for its origin (see Underhill and Paterson, 1998). These range from a northward-dipping extensional fault (Arkell, 1936b, 1938, 1947) to a north- or southward-dipping reverse fault (Strahan, 1895; House, 1989; Ameen and Cosgrove, 1990; 1991) and most recently an 'out-of-the-syncline' bedding plane backthrust (Underhill and Paterson, 1998).

Hampshire Basin and Portland–Wight High

Miocene compressional events caused inversion of Mesozoic basins and their controlling faults. As stated previously, Cenozoic highs lie above former extensional basins and Cenozoic basins lie above former structural highs. Thus the Hampshire Basin, in which over 600 m of Palaeogene strata are locally preserved, developed to the north of the emerging Portland–Wight High, over which Palaeogene sedimentation was minimal as the Portland–Wight Basin was inverted with the formation of the Purbeck Monocline.

Eypemouth–Litton Cheney–Winterborne Fault Zone

A series of east–west-trending faults, offset by north-west- and north-east-trending faults, form a major curvilinear fault zone extending over 20 km across the Bridport district (Figure 36) and continue offshore from Eypemouth a farther 12.5 km into Lyme Bay (Darton et al., 1981). The fault zone is exposed in the cliffs south-east of Eypemouth, and extends eastward to intersect the Mangerton Fault at West Bay, where it is offset 1 km sinistrally to Bothenhampton. It continues eastwards towards Litton Cheney where it is offset 1 km dextrally, and intensely shattered Cretaceous rocks in the footwall are juxtaposed against Upper Jurassic (Corallian to Kimmeridge Clay). The fault zone then disappears beneath Cretaceous strata around Martin's Down, from where it is traced eastward, perhaps offset dextrally around the southern extension of the Wynford–Hooke

Fault near Winterborne Abbas. Thereabouts, the strike swings markedly to the south-east and the fault zone passes near Martinstown. Seismic reflection data illustrate that, as with the Abbotsbury–Ridgeway Fault to the south, the Eypemouth–Litton Cheney–Winterborne Fault is a southward downthrowing Jurassic syndepositional normal fault, the development of which has been influenced by halite in the Mercia Mudstone Group. During Miocene compression, the fault was reactivated with reverse movement; at surface the Eypemouth–Litton Cheney–Winterborne Fault Zone is a high-angle reverse fault structure with Cretaceous strata preserved in the footwall block.

Mangerton Fault

The north-east-trending Mangerton Fault has been mapped onshore from near Eypemouth to south-east of Beaminster, a distance of approximately 11 km (Figure 36). Where imaged by seismic reflection data offshore, it is an intensely deformed, near-vertical fault zone developed in the post-Triassic salt succession and probably not connected to subhalite faults (Harvey and Stewart, 1998). Onshore, it is poorly imaged by the majority of seismic reflection data, yet appears to offset major east–west-trending normal faults across the Bridport district, including the Eypemouth–Litton–Cheney–Winterborne Fault and the Bridport Fault. The Mangerton Fault is thought to be Miocene or younger in age, postdating extensional faulting, and has the same orientation as the smaller eastward downthrowing Char Fault some 8 km to the west. Together, the Char and Mangerton faults may form part of a conjugate strike-slip set that includes the Poyntington Fault and faults that cut the Chalk to the north-west of the Compton Valence Dome (see below), and which are related to the Watchett–Cothelstone–Hatch Fault Zone. These structures are thought to have facilitated east–west lateral movements of fault blocks during the compression associated with Cretaceous–Cenozoic north–south shortening and uplift (Harvey and Stewart, 1998).

Bride–Puncknowle Fault

The Bride–Puncknowle Fault, lying between the Eypemouth–Litton Cheney–Winterborne and Abbotsbury–Ridgeway faults, is a markedly curvilinear, southward downthrowing fault with approximately 50 m throw at surface. It crops out at the coast to the south of Burton Bradstock and may extend offshore up to 10 km into Lyme Bay (Darton et al., 1981; Figure 36).

Marshwood Pericline and associated faults

To the west of the Mangerton Fault several structures are associated with the east–west-trending Marshwood Pericline, an elongate shallow dome exposing Early Jurassic Lias Group strata in the core (Figure 36). It appears to represent a broad Cenozoic inversion structure controlled by roughly parallel east–west fault zones to the north and south. The main faults to the north are the

Figure 40
Seismic profile
through the
Compton
Valence Dome,
with simplified
geological
interpretation.

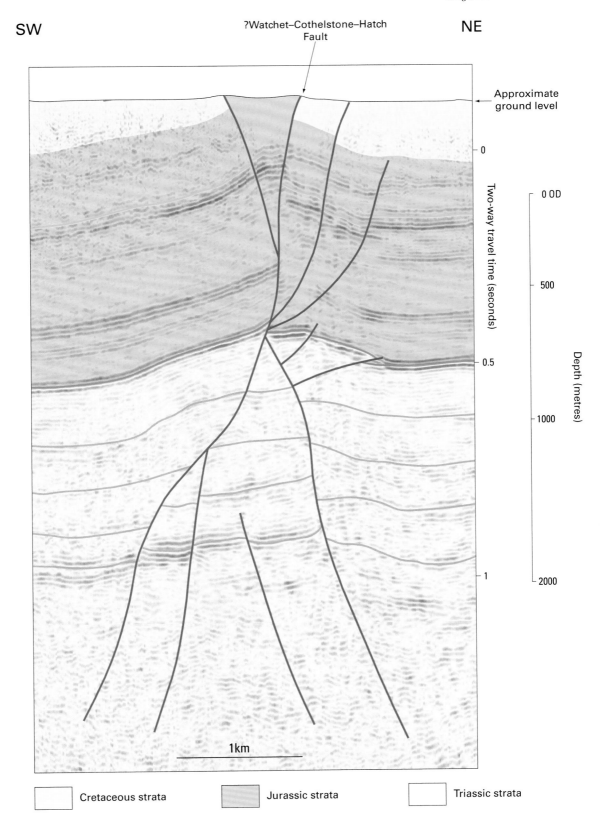

SW

?Watchet–Cothelstone–Hatch
Fault

NE

Approximate
ground level

Two-way travel time (seconds)

0

500

0.5

1000

1

Depth (metres)

0 OD

500

1000

2000

1km

Cretaceous strata   Jurassic strata   Triassic strata

Dibberford Fault and **Beaminster Fault**, both partially concealed by Cretaceous rocks. To the south, the southward dipping **Whitchurch–Berne Fault** and **Symondsbury Fault** are antithetic faults to the main, northward dipping and northward downthrowing **Bridport Fault** in the south. These latter faults define the Bridport Graben, along the southern margin of the Marshwood Pericline. The graben preserves a thin succession of Inferior Oolite that forms an upstanding ridge.

Wynford–Hooke Fault and Compton Valence Dome

The Wynford–Hooke Fault is a north-west-trending fault zone of some complexity. At crop, the Hooke segment appears as a normal fault with downthrow between 35 and 40 m to the north-east (Wilson et al., 1958). Southeastwards it passes into the generally eastward downthrowing **Wynford Fault** around Toller Porcorum, from where the southward downthrowing **Frome Valley Fault** branches off eastwards and then turns south-east towards Stratton.

The **Compton Valence Dome** is apparent as a bulls-eye outcrop pattern on the geological map of the Bridport district (Sheet 327). It is an eroded dome that is manifest as a saucer shaped hollow in the heart of the Chalk downlands at the southern end of the Wynford Fault segment. Middle Jurassic mudstone is exposed in the core, surrounded by low outward-dipping concentric rings of Cretaceous strata (Wilson et al., 1958). Long considered a geological curiosity, the dome has formerly been attributed to salt intrusion. However, its location along the line of the Wynford Fault, together with evidence from seismic reflection data, suggests that it is part of a 'flower structure' (Figure 40) associated with that fault, perhaps near the intersection of a concealed east–west-trending north-dipping and northward downthrowing syndepositional fault.

Wytch Farm and Wareham

Discovered in 1973, the Wytch Farm Oilfield is Britain's largest onshore oilfield. It is developed to the north of the Purbeck–Isle of Wight Fault Zone and Purbeck Monocline, in a series of periclinal closures related to inversion and buried east–west-trending extensional tilted fault blocks (Figure 36). The fault blocks are the foundered southern margin of the South Dorset High, and formed during Mesozoic extension. The most important faults recognised are the southward downthrowing Wytch Farm and Arne faults and the northward downthrowing Northern Fault (Hogg et al., 1999). Thickening of Jurassic successions across the faults illustrates some synsedimentary movement, but the majority of the faulting is Early Cretaceous, postdating the Wealden but predating the Gault.

Discovered by BP in 1964, the Wareham Oilfield lies some 5 km west-north-west of the Wytch Farm Oilfield, on the southern margin of the South Dorset High. The oilfield is located on the northward dipping Wareham Terrace formed by east–west-trending southward downthrowing normal faults, similar to structures of the same age that control the Wytch Farm Oilfield.

Beer, Musbury and Wilmington faults

At variance with the dominantly east–west faulting seen elsewhere in the Wessex Basin and the Crediton and Tiverton troughs to the west, a series of north–south, predominantly west-dipping and westward downthrowing normal faults form a belt of faulting in the Sidmouth district (Figure 36). They have, in part, led to suggestions that such structures represent the presence of an ancient north–south basement lineament often referred to as the 'Bath Axis'. The main faults are the Wilmington, Musbury and Beer faults. The last named is the largest of these faults, mapped up to 20 km inland from the coast at Beer in Seaton Bay where it juxtaposes Upper Greensand and Chalk against Triassic strata. Seismic reflection data indicate that the Triassic Otter Sandstone Formation and lower part of the Mercia Mudstone Group thicken into some north–south faults, which must therefore have moved in Triassic times. However, the exact ages of later movements are difficult to ascertain. They clearly displace, and thus postdate the Lias, but, as the Beer Fault shows, movement also postdates the Upper Greensand and much of the Chalk.

EIGHT

Quaternary

The Quaternary deposits of the district reflect the many oscillations of climate, ranging from cold periglacial to warm temperate, which have occurred in the last two million years or so. During the more extreme cold periods the region lay well to the south of the maximum ice advances but it is likely that there were semipermanent ice caps on the higher chalk hills (Bristow et al, 1995) and the ground would have been frozen. Outwash debris from the ice sheets well to the north was not transported into the district but instead was carried in major rivers roughly along the Severn valley to the west and an early Thames river system to the north. Climatic amelioration, and periodic melting of the permafrost resulted in solifluction, the downslope movement of material under periglacial conditions. Mass slope wasting of this type has probably been the most potent agent of erosion in the district in Quaternary time and has left a legacy of widespread head deposits, not all of which have been possible to map.

The principal river system in the region, the Frome–Piddle, is thought to be a remnant of the Solent River system whose valley extended from the vicinity of Dorchester eastwards to Poole and Bournemouth (Allen and Gibbard, 1993). The development of its drainage system was controlled by the synclinal axis at the eastern end of the Hampshire Basin, probably originating in late Palaeogene time. In the Frome–Piddle, and other principal river valleys such as the Axe and Stour, gravelly deposits occur beneath terrace features and the modern river alluvium. These river terrace deposits, laid down during periglacial episodes, occur at successively lower elevations as the river eroded down through the bedrock. The downcutting was caused by the complex interplay of changing base level, a consequence of sea-level fluctuations, and slow uplift of the land. On the coast, raised beaches, preserved at Portland, were probably formed during interglacial episodes when sea level was relatively high. Following the last cold period about 10 000 years ago, the modern rivers have laid down silt and clay alluvial deposits. More recently, rising sea levels have resulted in the flooding of Poole Harbour, shaped Chesil Beach, and accelerated the ongoing erosion that has produced coastal cliffs and some of the most spectacular landslides in Europe.

CLAY-WITH-FLINTS

Clay-with-flints overlies much of the higher chalk ground of the district. It typically comprises heterogeneous and unbedded, dark brown, silty clay with angular flints arranged randomly throughout. In addition, well-rounded flint, quartzite, subangular chert, sandstone and chalk constitute less than 10 per cent of the clasts. Clast-supported flint gravel with little or no clay matrix occurs locally, and a higher gravel content is observed generally in the west compared to the east of the district (Wilson et al., 1958; Bristow et al, 1995). This is probably a reflection of relatively thick gravelly beds in the Palaeogene sediments formerly present in the area. At the base, unstratified broken flints occur in dissolution pipes within extremely fractured chalk. Deposits of sandy silt with angular flints and rounded pebbles of quartz, quartzite and chert mixed with the more typical clay-with-flints lithology occur locally in the area around Compton Valence [SY 59 93]. These were formerly mapped as 'pebbly clay and sand' (Wilson et al., 1958).

The thickness of clay-with-flints, generally in the order of 2 m, is locally highly variable over short distances due to dissolution of the underlying chalk. The base of the deposit as a whole is gently folded, approximately concordant with the dip of the chalk. Downslope wash masks the boundary between clay-with-flints and flinty head in valley bottoms.

Clay-with-flints oversteps most subdivisions of the White Chalk Subgroup indicating that it was deposited after tilting and erosion of the chalk. Large outcrops dipping at about 2° or less south to south-east overlie dip slopes of Tarrant, Spetisbury and Portsdown chalk that fall from 120 m to 50 m OD on the north side of the Wareham Basin. In contrast, on the south side of the Wareham Basin the deposits overstep folded chalk adjacent to the Abbotsbury–Ridgeway Fault and along the Purbeck Hills, and the base is inclined to the north. This evidence suggests either that the clay-with-flints was laid down on a broadly inclined chalk surface or that the deposit itself has been gently folded. Further constraint on the age of the deposits is the evidence of the oldest terrace gravels of the Frome–Piddle valley, about 100 m above OD, overlying the clay-with-flints. There is poor chronological control on the age of these terrace deposits (see for example, Allen and Gibbard, 1993) but they certainly date from middle to early Pleistocene time.

From the available evidence it is most likely that the clay-with-flints is a residual deposit derived from the dissolution, decalcification and cryoturbation of the Chalk Group and Palaeogene formations and, in the extreme west of its outcrop, the Upper Greensand Formation. The evolution of this residual deposit into the heterogeneous deposit seen today has taken place over more than 30 million years and probably involves multiple phases of reworking, culminating in cryoturbation during the Quaternary.

HEAD

Head results from the downhill movement (solifluction) and accumulation of weathered and unconsolidated rock debris under periglacial freeze-thaw conditions. Some of the deposits mapped as head, particularly those associated with spring lines and in the floor of small valleys, are of colluvial origin and are probably still forming at the present day.

The deposits are heterogeneous and vary in composition, but broadly reflect the upslope parent material. In general, the minimum thickness of mapped head is 1 m; the maximum thickness, proved in boreholes at Ringstead [around SY 7525 8139] is 3.5 m, but greater thicknesses may be present elsewhere.

Head occurs in the district mainly in valley bottoms, particularly in dry valleys on the Chalk, for example at Poxwell, Watercombe [SY 757 849] and Brimstone Bottom [SY 770 825]. It occurs to a lesser extent on valley slopes and as aprons upslope from river terrace gravels. Broad outcrops are present adjacent to alluvial deposits, particularly on the Kimmeridge Clay around Sutton Poyntz, and behind the low cliffs at Ringstead, where the head is locally developed on degraded landslipped material. Extensive head deposits overlie the Palaeogene strata of the Wareham Basin, particularly in valleys cut into the clay members of the Poole Formation, for example on Wareham Common, where deposits occur downslope of spring lines developed at the base of sand beds in the Poole Formation.

RIVER TERRACE DEPOSITS

River terrace deposits are mapped mainly in the valleys of the Axe, Frome, Piddle and Stour. They occur beneath a sequence of former river terrace surfaces that have been differentiated on the basis of altitude. Older terraces occur at greater elevations above the current flood plain than younger terraces, a situation now considered to be a response to continuing neotectonic uplift (Maddy, 1997). In the Frome–Piddle river system individual deposits are identified at 15 elevations, ranging from 1 to 50 m above the alluvial flood plain. Many outcrops of river terrace deposits cannot be assigned to any of these 15 terraces because of difficulty correlating between fragmented outcrops along individual river valleys. The bulk of the gravels was probably deposited during periods when periglacial activity made available a large volume of sediment, and river flow was sufficient to transport a gravel bed load. The terraces numbered 1 to 6 were formerly called 'valley gravel', and those numbered 7 to 15 were 'plateau gravel'.

Outcrops of the third, seventh and eighth river terrace deposits are the most extensive. Large areas of Terrace 8 deposits have been worked, for example at Stokeford Heath [SY 871 884], where up to 4.5 m of reddish brown clay with pebbles (head) overlying up to 4.5 m of gravel and gravelly sand are recorded. Terrace 7, named the Warmwell Terrace (Barton and Bristow, 1996), forms flats around Crossways [SY 774 886] and is up to 3.1 m thick. Terrace 3 deposits occur beneath large outcrops north-east of Owermoigne [SY 784 860], as well as in the area around Moreton, between Winfrith and East Burton, and on the left bank of the Frome.

The deposits consist mostly of subangular flint gravel with small proportions of quartz, quartzite, rounded flint and chert. The uppermost beds of the deposits are generally clayey, due to pedogenic enrichment and a component of solifluction head that is too thin to map. Detailed clast analysis (Gibbard, 1993) indicates in certain terrace deposits a local relatively high proportion of quartz and quartzite clast, derived from Palaeogene gravels in the Dorchester area.

Suballuvial gravels represent the most recent river terrace deposits. They do not crop out but are widespread beneath the alluvial tracts of the main river valleys and occur buried beneath the estuarine deposits of Poole Harbour (Mathers, 1982). Their thickness ranges from about 0.6 to 6 m, and generally increases downstream; more than 10 m of gravel have been proved locally around the confluence of the Frome and Piddle. Allen and Gibbard (1993) described in detail these gravels and their relationship to the other river terrace deposits.

ALLUVIUM

Alluvium is the floodplain deposit of the modern river systems. Typically it consists of up to 2.5 m of poorly stratified brown silt and clay, commonly organic or peaty. Alluvium was laid down following the last major cold period (Devensian) that ended about 10 000 years ago. As the climate ameliorated, vegetation flourished, river flows declined and fine-grained fluvial sedimentation predominated, the sediment being derived from colluvial deposits washed from terrace gravels and bedrock. Alluvium is most extensive, typically forming a tract 200 to 500 m wide, along the rivers Piddle and Frome. It occurs also in the Stour valley, at Empool Bottom [SY 780 869], along the Sherford River near Poole and in tributary streams that drain the clay ground in south-east Dorset and the Chalk on the north side of the Wareham Basin. Palynological work on alluvial deposits at Hyde Farm [SY 866 908] show that they were laid down in the Flandrian stage (Allen and Gibbard, 1993).

ESTUARINE ALLUVIUM

These deposits occur around Poole Harbour below the mean high water mark and in river valleys downstream of the tidal limit. Above the tidal limit, estuarine alluvium passes laterally into fluvially deposited alluvium. Estuarine alluvium is an intertidal deposit aggraded as a result of rising sea level in the last 10 000 years or so, during the Flandrian stage. At the surface it occurs in association with tidal mudflats, saltmarsh and reed beds, and consists of silt and clay up to 5 m thick.

LITTORAL AND BEACH DEPOSITS

Undoubtedly, one of the most famous coastal landmarks in Dorset is Chesil Beach. This 28 km-long feature, containing perhaps 100 million tonnes of material, extends east from Burton Bradstock to the Isle of Portland; in the north-west it forms a beach 12 km long and then becomes a bar for the next 13 km, separated from the land by a shallow brackish lagoon, known as the Fleet. The bar re-attaches to land for a 3 km-long section north of the Isle of Portland. The beach is well known for the size-grading; the material progressively increases in size south-eastwards from sand and fine gravel at Bridport, to 50 to 75 mm size cobbles at Chesilton. Pebble composition is 98.5 per cent flint and chert, the remainder being limestone, vein quartz, porphyry and quartzite derived from the Budleigh Salterton Pebble Beds. The origin of Chesil Beach is uncertain. Arkell (1947) thought the bank originated as a bay bar which the advancing seas pushed northwards into its current position, and subsequent studies (Carr and Blackley 1973; 1974) have largely agreed with this interpretation. Rising sea levels from about 14 000 years B.P. are thought to have driven gravel deposits across Lyme Bay and Chesil Beach reached its current form and position 4000 to 5000 years ago.

On the southern tip of Portland, raised beach deposits provide evidence of higher sea levels at some periods during the Quaternary (Davies and Keen, 1985). First described by De la Beche (1829) and Baden-Powell (1930), these deposits have more recently been shown to comprise two separate beaches of different age (Davies and Keen, 1985). The 'Portland West Beach' lies west of Portland Bill lighthouse [SY 6750 6860], with a base at 14.1 m above OD. The 'Portland East Beach', at 6.95 to 10.75 m above OD, is well exposed in a 200 m section to the immediate east of Portland Bill Lighthouse. The West Beach deposits, up to 2.5 m thick, comprise alternating inclined beds of well-sorted, medium pebble-size gravel and sandy gravel. A 'fossil' sea cliff behind the beach is overlain by about 2 to 2.7 m of crudely stratified calcrete and cemented limestone head, known as 'Portland Loam and Head'. The East Beach deposits are typically 0.45 m thick, and comprise subangular to rounded clasts of Portland and Purbeck limestones, with a few pebbles of flint and chert. Amino-acid analysis of mollusc shells from the Portland West Beach suggests assignment to the temperate oxygen-isotope stage 7 (about 210 000 BP), while the Portland East Beach is slightly younger, belonging to temperate oxygen-isotope stage 5e (Ipswichian, about 125 000 BP) (Keen, 1995).

Farther east, between Studland Bay [SZ 0380 8288] and Shell Bay [SZ 0365 8667], the coastline is distinguished by belts of sand dunes up to 6 m high and about 4 km long, representing the largest accumulation of blown sand in Dorset. The dunes are arranged into three parallel ridges, separated by strips of marsh and peat, of which the innermost widens southward into a 1.5 km freshwater lake called Little Sea. On the west shore of Little Sea is an old sea cliff, up to 15 m high, which marks the former coastline (Diver, 1933). The progressive seaward accretion of the 1 km-wide sand ridges of the South Haven peninsula is documented by old maps, which show that it has occurred largely since the 16th century (Diver, 1933; Arkell, 1947; Goudie and Brunsden, 1997; Figure 41) with an average rate of advance of about 2.5 m per year. The sand is thought to be derived from the destruction of Palaeogene deposits along the Bournemouth and Christchurch cliffs. Sand deposition may now have given way to erosion, as

shown by the relatively recent stabilisation of these cliffs together with rapid rates of erosion in Shell Bay.

LANDSLIDES

The World Heritage Coast displays active and dormant landslides of a variety unrivalled in the UK, providing unparalleled opportunities for study at all levels (Conway, 1977a; Allison, 1992; Culshaw, 1997; Goudie and Brunsden, 1997; Allison and Kimber, 1998; Forster, 1998). Landslides involve the downslope movement of rock and soil by slide, flow or fall. In coastal settings, erosion, constantly changing drainage processes and steep topography combine to increase the likelihood of landslides.

Budleigh Salterton   Between Littleham Cove [SY 040 802] and Budleigh Salterton. [SY 072 820], gently dipping calcareous mudstone of the Littleham Mudstone Formation is overlain successively towards the west by up to 20 m of Budleigh Salterton Pebble Beds Formation and Otter Sandstone Formation. In the eastern part of the bay, where the cliffs are formed entirely in mudstone, failures tend to form small mudslides and falls that accumulate on the foreshore. In the western part of the bay, where relatively strong, impermeable conglomerates and sandstones cap the mudstones, failures tend to be much larger (Figure 42). Channels at the base of the Budleigh Salterton Pebble Beds can concentrate groundwater flow, which in the cliffs produces gulleys, weakening underlying mudstones and allowing the propagation of substantial mudslides and mudflows. In places, the brittle caprock may also break off in rockfalls and reactivate movement in the landslide debris below (Grainger et al., 1985; Grainger and Kalaugher, 1987a, b, 1995; Kalaugher et al., 1987, 2000).

Farther east, the Otter Sandstone dips below sea level and is succeeded on the coast by the Mercia Mudstone Group overlain by the Upper Greensand Formation. Although large-scale failures do not occur in this area, small landslides, associated with local weathering, marine erosion or poor drainage conditions are present [e.g. at SY 113 868]

Hooken Cliff   Between Branscombe [SY 186 881] and Beer Head [SY 226 879], the Mercia Mudstone Group dips below sea level, and strata of the overlying Upper Greensand Formation and Chalk Group form steep cliffs. It was from this near-vertical face, in March 1790, that nearly four hectares of land slid forward, with a shear zone probably within or just above the Upper Greensand, and came to rest nearly 200 m seaward, forming the Hooken Cliff landslide (Rowe, 1903; Arber, 1940; Plate 37).

Haven Cliff   At Haven Cliff [SY 259 898], east of Seaton, the Mercia Mudstone Group reappears at the foreshore overlain by the Upper Greensand Formation. This provides a well-known association for landsliding, where a permeable lithology overlies a relatively impermeable

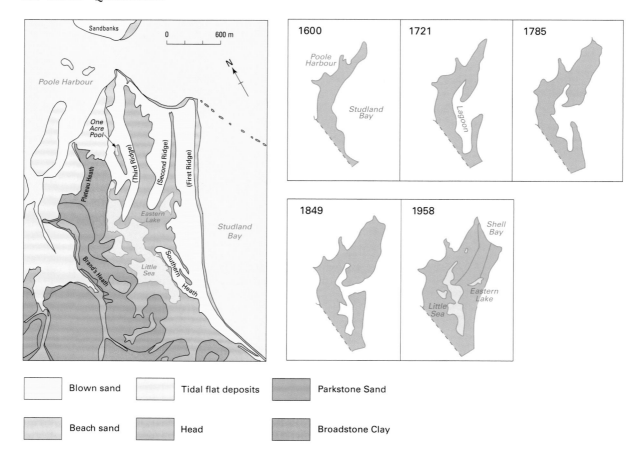

☐ Blown sand	☐ Tidal flat deposits	▨ Parkstone Sand
▨ Beach sand	▨ Head	■ Broadstone Clay

Figure 41 Principal dune ridges and evolution of the South Haven peninsula since the 17th century (with data from Goudie and Brunsden, 1997).

mudstone. Groundwater percolates through the Upper Greensand until the underlying mudstone is encountered. The copious flow of water softens the mudrocks and, if water cannot drain freely (or if there is a particularly heavy flow) hydrostatic pressure may build up, reducing the strength of the rock near the boundary. In this state, overlying material is liable to move along a surface of weakness at the boundary. This situation is more likely to occur in winter when groundwater levels are high, for example when higher than average rainfall has maintained a high water table (Brunsden, 1996). In some materials the response of water pressure to rainfall is slow, and failure may lag behind high seasonal rainfall by two years or more (Forster, 1998).

Axmouth–Bindon Major landslides occur within the Axmouth Undercliff [SY 270 895 to 329 916], between Seaton and Lyme Regis (Pitts, 1981a, b, 1983; Grainger et al., 1996). There, the cliffs are dominated by the Chalk Group, which overlies the Upper Greensand Formation and Penarth Group. This succession produces large-scale, multiple retrogressive landslides in the Chalk, the most famous of which is the Bindon landslide.

Activity of the Bindon landslide was first noticed in the early winter of 1840. However, early in the morning

of Christmas Day more dramatic activity began: 'some labourers.... hurried to the farm, with the information that fissures were opening in the ground around, and the walls of their tenements rending and sinking', Roberts (1840). Over the next days and weeks a chasm 92 m wide, 46 m deep and over 1200 m in length was formed as huge blocks of chalk slipped downwards and away from the mainland (Plate 38). The movement also pushed the foreshore into a ridge, up to 14 m in height. Evidence from contemporary accounts and modern geological and geomorphological investigations (Pitts and Brunsden, 1987, and references therein) have indicated that the failure was some form of block slide, triggered by high water pressures and marine erosion (Figure 43).

Ware Cliff–Black Ven–Golden Cap The coast between Ware Cliff and Golden Cap is one of the most studied areas of coastal landslides in the world (for example Denness, 1972; Brunsden, 1974; Conway, 1974a, 1976a; Allison, 1982; Chandler and Brunsden, 1995). This stretch of coastline includes the well-documented slides at Ware Cliff [SY 326 915], Black Ven [SY 351 933], Fairy Dell [SY 378 930] and Golden Cap [SY 407 921]. The geological succession comprises either the Blue

Figure 42 Cross-section of the cliffs between Littleham Cove and Budleigh Salterton showing development of landslide features (from Pitts, 1983).

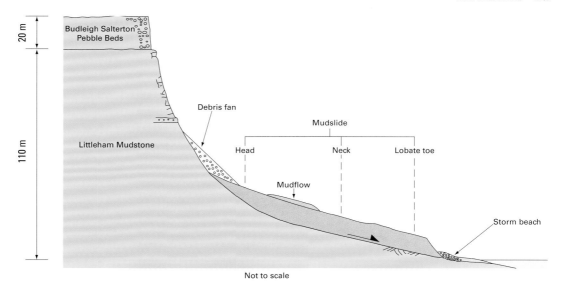

Lias or Charmouth Mudstone formations on the foreshore, overlain by younger formations of the Lias Group, capped by the Gault and Upper Greensand formations.

The succession is best exposed at Black Ven, a complex landslide stretching nearly 1500 m along the coast and extending inland over 400 m from the shore. The distinctive stepped profile of Black Ven (Figure 44) is produced by beds of relatively strong limestones and mudstones that protect the underlying strata and influence the flow of groundwater. Each of the benches at Black Ven is covered by a layer of debris, up to 6 m in thickness (Figure 45). This debris is the result of falls, slides and flows that frequently occur at free faces across the landslide complex. The almost constant addition of material to this debris accumulation slowly pushes the material over each of the benches until it reaches the shore. Occasionally this pattern is interrupted by massive sandflows. These sandflows, which emanate from degraded landslide blocks of Upper Greensand, may cascade down the entire landslide complex, depositing fine sand and silt on each of the benches.

Plate 37 The Hooken Cliff landslide (P226937).

Plate 38 A contemporary sketch of the Bindon landslide entitled 'View of the landslip near Lyme Regis, looking east' (Roberts, 1840) (P666957).

Activity within the Black Ven landslide complex and adjacent cliffs is strongly controlled by fault planes (trending north-west–south-east) and the flow of groundwater concentrated along them. The effect of faulting is more obvious at the Higher Sea Lane landslide [SY 361 932] where a rotational failure in superficial deposits and the Shales-with-Beef Member has propagated along the downthrown side of a high-angle fault striking towards the north-west (Denness et al., 1975).

Downcliff The cliffs between Seaton and West Bay [SY 458 904] were described as part of a regional landslide study by the British Geological Survey (Conway, 1977b). East of Seaton, the cliffs comprise Eype Clay overlain by Downcliff Sand, Thorncombe Sand (Dyrham Formation) and Bridport Sand Formation. Degradation of the cliffs is by a combination of rotational slides, mudflows and shallow mudslides, with steeper sections of cliff affected by rockfalls. Large-scale block slides

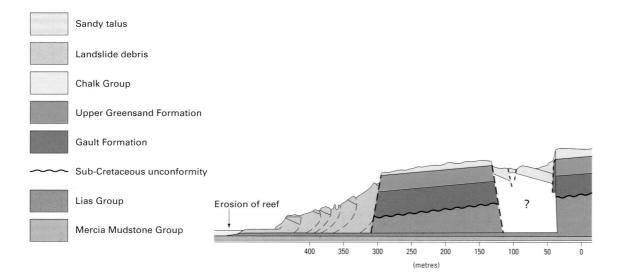

Sandy talus

Landslide debris

Chalk Group

Upper Greensand Formation

Gault Formation

Sub-Cretaceous unconformity

Lias Group

Mercia Mudstone Group

Erosion of reef

Figure 43   Profile of the Bindon landslide (from Pitts and Brunsden, 1987).

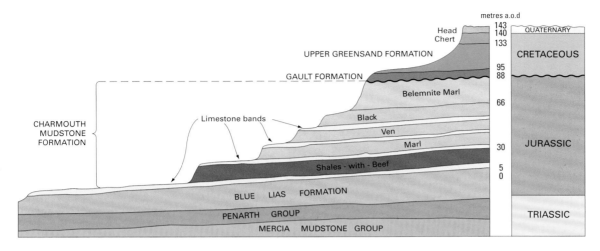

Figure 44   Profile and geological succession of the cliff at Black Ven (from Arber, 1973; Conway, 1974b).

within the Downcliff Sand are present on a terrace formed in the undercliff at Thorncombe Beacon, where blocks up to 1000 m³ in volume have moved across the Eype Clay. This succession and its associated landslides continues eastwards to Eype Mouth. East of Eype Mouth, where the succession is entirely within the Dyrham Formation (Downcliff Sand and Thorncombe Sand members), the cliffs tend to fail in shallow rotations, flows and rockfalls.

Abbotsbury   The cliffs south-east of Abbotsbury comprise Oxford Clay Formation overlain by mudstones, sandstones and limestones of the Corallian Group. Between Linton Hill [SY 579 847] and Merry Hill [SY 603 843] the slope formed by this succession is affected by the arcuate scarp of a dormant rotational landslide, below which is the disturbed landslide deposit which has developed into mudslides and debris flows. Dip measurements of the Nothe Formation at the scarp provide some evidence for

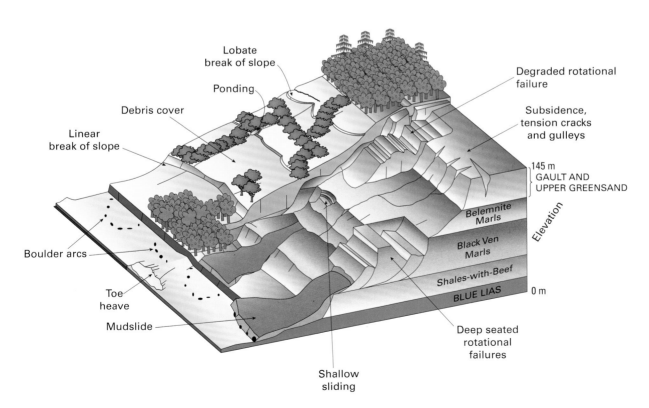

Figure 45   Landslide processes at Black Ven (modified from Jones and Lee, 1994).

Figure 46
Cross-section
through the
Isle of Portland
(from Brunsden
et al., 1996).

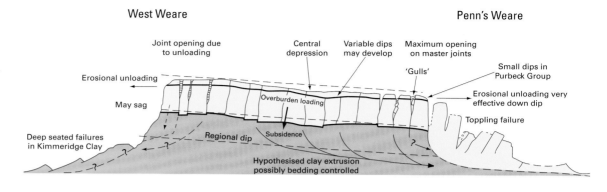

cambering of the slope above, which possibly occurred after the landslide (Culshaw, 1997). The geological succession is repeated closer to sea level at Furzy Cliff, 3 km north-east of Weymouth [around SY 699 818], where a series of rotational failures have developed downslope into mudslides and small mudflows. Similar landslides have been observed towards Redcliff Point [SY 711 816].

Isle of Portland   On the Isle of Portland, Kimmeridge Clay is overlain successively by Portland Group (Portland Sand and Portland Stone formations) and the lower part of the Purbeck Group. Landslides occur along almost the entire perimeter of the island. Water percolates readily through the well-jointed Portland Stone to the underlying sands and clays, and can lead to increased pore water pressure and the weakening of underlying strata (Brunsden et al., 1996). On the western (down-dip) side of the island, softening of the underlying strata has caused the Portland Stone to slide downslope, with joints progressively widening towards the cliff, where large blocks have toppled to form a debris apron (Figure 46). On the eastern (updip and upslope) side of the island, the blocks tilt into the cliff face and so produce less dramatic collapses. The broad pattern of movement on the Isle of Portland is locally modified by exposure to marine erosion and the extensive effects of quarrying and spoil disposal. The local pattern of landsliding is also strongly influenced by local variation (e.g. unit thickness, discontinuities) of individual lithologies.

Osmington   At Osmington Mills [SY 734 816], the Kimmeridge Clay forms much of the lower cliff and is overlain by the Gault and Upper Greensand formations. This succession of permeable sandstone overlying relatively impermeable clay has resulted in series of rotational slides and mudflows that extend up to a kilometre inland in a similar manner to those at Black Ven.

Ringstead   The entire perimeter of Ringsted Bay to White Nothe [SY 757 814 to 772 806] is affected by landslides. The lithological succession in the east of the bay is broadly similar to that described at Osmington Mills and displays a similar pattern of landsliding. However, east of a fault that cuts the bay at Holworth House [SY 763 816], the succession is modified by the presence of Portland

and Purbeck Group strata between the Kimmeridge and Gault formations. There, the landslides consist of mudflows and translational slides, but they are generally less active and are older than those to the west, possibly 1000 to 10 000 years old. The scale of landsliding tends to increase in magnitude towards the south-east, culminating in the White Nothe landslide [SY 772 807].

Lulworth   The coast eastwards of Durdle Door, especially between St Oswalds Bay and Worbarrow Bay, is affected by the western end of the Purbeck Monocline. The strata are steeply dipping, and variations in landsliding can be seen in different rock types (Jones et al., 1983; Goudie and Brunsden , 1997).

The embayments formed by Stair Hole, Lulworth Cove and Worbarrow Bay are continually being enlarged by mudslides and rockfalls. At Stair Hole, failures are mainly mudslides within the Wealden Formation. The steeply dipping, well-jointed Portland Stone has a tendency towards wedge failures, where joint-bounded blocks slide out of position, sometimes interlocking with other blocks and sometimes falling from the slope. At Lulworth Cove, the largest failures are in the Holywell Nodular Chalk Formation, which tends to fail in large rockfalls, as translational slides or in shallow rotational failures. In contrast, the clay and sand of the Gault and Upper Greensand are extensively affected by shallow mudslides and flows. At Mupe Bay and Worbarrow Bay, failures become larger and increasingly rotational with the increasing coastal exposure of the Wealden Formation (Allison and Kimber, 1998).

St Albans Head   At St Albans Head [SY 951 773] gently dipping Portland Stone overlies Portland Sand and Kimmeridge Clay. Falls and topples occur in the cliff when the Portland Sand is eroded by the sea, undercutting the slopes above. Large blocks of Portland Stone fall onto the foreshore, forming a protective apron until they are worn away by the sea.

SWALLOW HOLES

Swallow holes have been known in Dorset for almost two centuries (Stevenson, 1812) and have been described by Fisher (1858; 1859), Reid (1899), Sperling et al. (1977) and Bristow et al. (1991, fig. 27). Most are located within a belt 3 to 5 km wide along the northern edge of the Wareham Basin between Puddletown Heath in the west, through Affpuddle Heath and Wareham Forest to Corfe Mullen–Lytchett Matravers in the east. They range from shallow depressions 2 to 3 m across, to structures up to 15 m deep and 80 m in diameter, and occur mostly where the basal Palaeogene strata or river terrace deposits overlie the Portsdown Chalk, and where the solid strata are gently inclined southwards. Evidence for continuous and recent collapse of swallow holes is provided by Sperling et al. (1977, p. 217), who concluded that they formed by intense and localised chemical weathering promoted by highly acidic conditions under heathland vegetation.

NINE

Economic geology

BUILDING STONE

The varied geological succession of the district is reflected not only in its magnificent coastal scenery, but also in the great diversity of building stone that characterise its rich, vernacular, architectural heritage. Practically any hard limestone or sandstone bed was a potential source of building material, quarried as roughly shaped rubblestone, hand-dressed block stone, sawn ashlar blocks or thick stone roofing tilestones ('slates').

Until the early 19th century, most villages and towns of the south Dorset and east Devon area were characterised by buildings constructed principally of locally quarried stone. Almost every hamlet and farm had a pit that provided stone or lime mortar for building and roof construction. As the rail network extended across the area, new stones were gradually introduced from elsewhere, such as granite and limestone from Devon and Cornwall, or roofing slates from the quarries of north Wales. Hard, pinkish grey Devonian limestones were used extensively for church building, and can be seen, for example, in the fabric of Otterton church. The lack of good freestone in the west of the area encouraged the import of other stones like the distinctive ferruginous yellow Lower Jurassic limestones from the Ham Hill quarries in Somerset. They are a common feature in the carved window and door mouldings of many churches, for example at Uplyme and Otterton (Plate 39c, d). Surprisingly, the Upper Jurassic Portland freestones, perhaps the best known building stone from Dorset, were not generally used in buildings in western parts of the district until the later part of the 19th century.

Permian and Triassic In the western part of the district, the red and brown conglomerates and sandstones of the Permo-Triassic that characterise the coastal cliffline are also a common feature in walls and buildings. Close to Exeter, large blocks of dark red Permian sandstone breccia, termed the Heavitree Stone, were used in the parish church of Clyst St George (Plate 39a). Softer Triassic sandstones and conglomerates were widely used for walling and farm buildings. In Otterton, they are particularly evident in the chimney stacks of its many thatched cottages, and at Woodbury, rounded quartzite pebbles and cobbles from the Budleigh Salterton Pebble Beds (known locally as 'Budleigh Buns'), are a common feature in buildings and garden walls (Gale, 1992).

A more exotic stone, often found as sporadic blocks in the fabric of buildings, is the hard purple-red, volcanic basalt or trap. This is readily distinguished by its 'swiss cheese' appearance, with numerous, large, open vesicles, originally formed as gas-bubbles in the lava flow. It is present in the walls of Woodbury Church (Plate 39b).

Jurassic The hard, grey, limestone beds of the Langport Member and Blue Lias Formation, which crop out in the cliffs between Lyme Regis and Charmouth and extensively inland, were a common building and paving stone in many villages, as well as an important source of hydraulic lime for mortar. Their value was recognised by the early quarrymen who gave each limestone bed a unique name, identifying the different uses to which they could be put. Some examples include:

Anvils — blue building stone
Burrs — rough building stone
Cockles — shelly building stone
Fire Stone — used in arch work
Foot Stone — blue paving and building stone
Gaze Burrs — good building stone
Half-foot Bed — flagstone
Red Size — White Lias used for building stone
Under Bed — blue building stone for paving and steps
White Lias (= Lilstock Formation, Langport Member) — slaty and fissile for flooring.

The quarry at Uplyme supplied much of the limestone used in the buildings of Lyme Regis (Thomas 1998). Today, parts of the newly constructed sea-defence walls utilise blocks of grey, Lias Group limestone, capped by large blocks of white, Portland 'Roach' Stone, replicating the materials used in the original sea walls.

The Thorncombe Sand Member and Beacon Limestone Formation have provided, respectively, sandstone and ferruginous limestone for building close to their outcrop. Similarly, large blocks of the fine-grained, variably calcareous sandstone of the Bridport Sand Formation were used in the construction of many of the old dockside buildings that still survive at West Bay, Bridport (Plate 39e).

From Burton Bradstock eastwards, the ooidal and shelly limestones in the Inferior Oolite Formation provide rubble and ashlar stone for numerous farm buildings and village houses. The picturesque villages of Chideock, Symondsbury and Burton Bradstock are some examples constructed almost entirely from local yellow-brown, ferruginous and bioclastic limestone (Plate 39g).

In contrast to the well-known ooidal limestones of the Great Oolite Group around Bath, the equivalent succession in Dorset is dominated by mudstones. Consequently, only the thinly bedded, shelly limestones of the Forest Marble Formation at the top of the Great Oolite Group have any importance for building. These limestones were extensively quarried in the 18th and 19th century for block stone, paving and for roofing tilestones, most notably around Burton Bradstock, Bothenhampton, Swyre, Puncknowle and Langton Herring, where buildings are commonly constructed

Plate 39   Examples of Devonian, Permo-Triassic, Jurassic and Cretaceous building stones used in Dorset and south-east Devon.

(a) Clyst St George   St George's Church. Blocks of coarse red Permian Breccia with paler grey Devonian limestone mouldings (P669437); **(b) Woodbury**   St Swithin's Church. Mixed rubblestone fabric, including purple-red, vesicular basalt (Heavitree Stone), pale red and pale grey Permo-Triassic (Otterton) sandstones. The window and door mouldings are of pale grey bioclastic limestone (Upper Cretaceous, Beer Stone) (P551985); **(c) Otterton**   Houses and distinctive stone chimney stacks constructed of brown-red Otterton Sandstone (Triassic) (P551991); **(d) Uplyme**   St Peter and St Paul's Church. Grey Limestone blockstone with ferruginous yellow-brown, limestone (Ham Hill Stone) mouldings (all Lower Jurassic Lias Group) (P669459); **(e) Bridport, West Bay Harbour**   Large Blocks of grey to yellow, fine-grained sandstone from the Bridport Sand Formation (Lower Jurassic) (P552018); **(f) Bothenhampton**   Holy Trinity Church. Large stone slates, typically graded in size from the eaves to the ridge, quarried locally from the Forest Marble Formation (Middle Jurassic) (P669431); **(g) Burton Bradstock**   Pale grey to the more typical yellow-brown oolitic and bioclastic ferruginous limestone wallstones from the Inferior Oolite Group (P669436).

entirely of the local Forest Marble limestone. The Bothenhampton roofing tilestones are characteristically large, grading down in size from eave to ridge (Plate 39f).

In the area around Fleet and Chickerell, limestones of the Cornbrash Formation were used as rubblestone (Thomas, 1998). The overlying Oxford Clay was worked for brickmaking, and the hard septarian concretions in the clay quarried near Radipole were cut and polished for decorative tabletops.

Ooidal limestones of the Corallian Group, used in farms, hamlets and villages across their outcrop, have been quarried at Linton Hill, Rodden and Langton Herring (Thomas, 1998), and continue to be worked at Marnhull and Silton. Abbotsbury village displays extensive use of distinctive yellow-brown, ferruginous sandy limestones (Plate 40a), including the Osmington Oolite, but the local Abbotsbury Ironstone was generally too weak to provide a good building stone.

Perhaps the most well known building stone of the region is Portland Stone. Quarried and mined as freestone since Roman times, Portland Stone can be considered to be our pre-eminent building limestone. A number of different beds in the succession have been worked:

Basebed — a fine, well-sorted oolite
Roach — coarsely fossiliferous oolite, with characteristic screw-like, gastropod whorls
Whitbed — well-sorted, shelly and ooidal

Each of the principal towns on the Isle of Portland — Fortuneswell, Easton, Weston and Southwell — have Portland Stone buildings in a variety of styles, unmatched anywhere else in the country. Some are constructed of massive coursed, ashlar stone blocks (Plate 40b), others of smaller rubblestone. Many of the buildings are still roofed with large Purbeck stone 'slates'.

From the early 17th century Portland Stone was championed by eminent architects including Inigo Jones (Banqueting House, London), Christopher Wren (St Paul's Cathedral) and Edward Lutyens (for use in New Delhi). It has become London's most distinctive building stone and its durability and resistance to urban pollution has earned it an enviable reputation among Britain's building limestones. Many city churches and civic buildings, constructed in the 18th, 19th and early 20th centuries were built of Portland Stone, both in London, and in other cities in Britain and abroad.

The quarrying of Portland Stone has extended eastwards along the outcrop into the coastal cliffs of the Isle of Purbeck, where it is often described as Purbeck–Portland Stone. Quarrying there has produced an extensive series of interconnected galleries high in the sea cliffs at St Adhelm's Head, Seacombe, Dancing Ledge and Tilly Whim (Woodward, 1895). Inland, outcrops of Portland Stone at Portesham, Waddon and Windsbatch have been exploited over many centuries for local building needs.

The large-scale quarrying of Portland Stone dates from the early 19th century, and underwent major expansion alongside the development of the railway network. Today six quarries are still producing Portland Stone on the Isle of Portland.

Cretaceous The largely Cretaceous Purbeck Limestone Group has provided prodigious amounts of block, paving and roofing stone, well displayed in villages like Corfe Castle, Langton Mattravers and Worth Mattravers. The limestone beds, locally termed veins, were given specific names by the quarrymen — Laning, Grub, Roach, Thornback, Tombstone, Freestone etc. — and each bed was used for a particular purpose. In the Swanage–Langton Mattravers area, these limestones were extensively worked from shallow adits, underground mines and surface quarrys. The more fissile limestone beds were selectively worked for roofing tilestone; some of the 'slates' are unusually large in size (Plate 40c; Hughes, 2003). Although the quarrying of limestone for building stone in the Isle of Purbeck area has declined, it remains an important local industry with thirteen quarries currently in operation.

The Isle of Purbeck area is perhaps best known for the thin, hard, fossiliferous limestone beds known as Purbeck Marble (Woodward, 1895; Vellacott, 1908). The thinly bedded and steeply dipping nature of the succession required that the stone be worked from inclined shafts driven down to the main 'marble' beds. Once quarried the large, stone slabs were loaded on trolleys and winched to the surface by a horse-driven capstan (Stanier, 1995). The landscape is still pockmarked with shaft sites.

Despite its widespread use in medieval ecclesiastical buildings throughout the Midlands and south of England, the Purbeck Marble occurs in only two beds, each less than 1.5 m in thickness. Typically, large columns seen in many cathedral buildings are made either by stacking together small 'drums' of the 'marble' or, for the more slender types, by shaping limestone slabs on a lathe. The dark, mottled 'marbled' appearance is a result of the presence of myriads of shells of the small freshwater gastropod *Viviparus* sp. The 'marble' beds were most extensively worked up until the beginning of the 16th century and only intermittently since then. In the 19th century the industry saw a brief local revival for use in St James's Church, Kingston. Today the supply of Purbeck Marble is limited, and is quarried only at a single site near Langton Mattravers.

Chert nodules from the Cretaceous Upper Greensand and flint from the Chalk have widespread use as a building material in towns and villages along the coast between Sidmouth and Thorncombe. Chert-free bioclastic sandstones of the Upper Greensand were extensively quarried at Salcombe Regis, Dunscombe and Branscombe, and used in the fabric of Exeter Cathedral and in many local churches (Woolbrook, Sidmouth and Sidbury) and houses (Plate 40d).

'Beer Stone', occurring near the base of the White Chalk Subgroup, has been exploited near the small town of Beer in east Devon since Roman times. Block stone is used extensively in local houses, but its value as a freestone for more intricate carved stone work is evident most notably in Exeter Cathedral and in many local

Plate 40 Examples of Upper Jurassic, Cretaceous and Tertiary building stones used in Dorset and south-east Devon.

(a) Abbotsbury Yellow-brown, ferruginous, sandy, bioclastic limestone from the Corallian Group (Upper Jurassic) (P669427); **(b) Isle of Portland** The walls of this house consist of large blocks of white oolitic Portland limestone (P552031); **(c) Swanage** Cottage built of Purbeck–Portland limestone with a roof of large Purbeck stone slates (Upper Jurassic–Lower Cretaceous) (P669458); **(d) Branscombe** Rubblestone farmhouse built of local Branscombe sandstone (Lower Cretaceous) (P551996); **(e) Beer** This row of quarry workers cottages was constructed in 1883 of chalky limestone from the nearby Beer quarries (Upper Cretaceous) (P669429); **(f) Corfe Mullen** St Hubert's Church. Dark yellow-brown to reddish brown, ferruginous sandstone (Heathstone–Tertiary, Lambeth Group (P669442).

Figure 47 Distribution of superficial sand and gravel deposits in the Wareham Basin (from Bristow et al., 2002a).

churches (e.g. Colyton, Beer, Ottery St Mary, Axminster, Lyme Regis and Charmouth; Plate 40e). Farther afield, it was used in Winchester Cathedral, Norwich RC Cathedral and was exported overseas for Christ Church Cathedral in St Louis, USA.

Palaeogene   In general, the weakly consolidated rocks of this succession provide few stones suitable for building. However, in the basal part of the succession there are locally cemented beds of ferruginous sandstone, with rich red, orange or brown colours. These were once quarried from shallow pits at Combe Almer, Lytchett Matravers and Studland. They have been used sporadically in buildings around Poole Harbour (Thomas, 1998) and more extensively farther inland, notably in Wimborne Minster. Known locally as 'heathstones' they are seen sporadically in the fabric of many buildings and may form a significant proportion of the stonework in certain churches and older houses, as at Lytchett Matravers, Lytchett Minster or Corfe Mullen (Plate 40f).

Quaternary   Beach cobbles, including flint, chert and limestone, derived principally from the erosion of the collapsing cliffline outcrops, were once used extensively for walling in villages and hamlets in coastal regions of the district.

BRICKS AND TILES

Organic-rich clay and sandy clay of the Kellaways and Oxford Clay (Peterborough Member) formations were formerly the principal sources of bricks and tiles in south Dorset, with pits at Bothenhampton [SY 484 914], Rampisham [ST 5518 0338], Chickerell [SY 344 797] and Putton Lane [SY 650 799]. Clay is currently worked from the Wealden Formation at the Swanage brickworks [midpoint [SZ 0205 8040]], and the formation was formerly dug for bricks on the south side of Corfe Common [SY 9618 8052].

In the Wareham Basin, the London Clay is worked at Knoll Manor Clay Pit [SY 973 977], near Corfe Mullen, for the manufacture of red-bodied unglazed floor tiles. The raw material is blended with other material, principally Dorset ball clay, china clay and feldspar. The Lytchett Matravers Sand from the London Clay is worked in conjunction with Poole Formation sand, at Henbury [SY 965 975] for calcium silicate bricks, concrete roofing tiles and as a sand body for clay bricks.

Many of the ball clays of the Poole Formation have been extensively worked for brick and tile manufacture, in places by underground mining. Former brickworks occur near Worgret Heath Farm [SY 8935 8785 and 8948 8782] and on the south side of Trigon Hill [SY 892 891].

SAND AND GRAVEL

The principal sand and gravel resources occur in the Wareham Basin, and are the subject of a detailed report (Bristow et al., 2002a). They can be divided into two broad categories: bedrock sand deposits of Palaeo-

gene age and 'drift' gravel deposits of Quaternary age (Figure 47). Total production of sand and gravel in the basin is estimated to be about 2 million tonnes a year, of which about 75 per cent is sand and 25 per cent gravel. About 1.2 million tonnes of the total sand production is derived from bedrock deposits, almost entirely from the Poole Formation. Subsidiary resources occur in the overlying Branksome Sand, and in sand bodies in the London Clay (West Park Farm, Warmwell Farm Sand and Lytchett Matravers Sand members), although these are typically much finer grained. The remaining 0.8 million tonnes comes from river terrace deposits which, though extensive, are thin (2–3 m). Gravel also underlies the alluvium of river flood plains, but is unlikely to be worked because of operational and restoration difficulties.

LIME, MARL AND CEMENT

Chalk has been dug for lime across Dorset, and from all the main stratigraphical divisions within the group. Many of the former pits in the Grey Chalk Subgroup were worked for agricultural soil dressing, the crushed chalk reducing soil acidity and replacing leached calcium. The hardened Chalk of the Purbeck Hills has also been worked for road-metal. Around Church Knowle [SY 941 819], the Grey Chalk Subgroup and lower part of the White Chalk Subgroup were extensively worked for cement before the First World War (Arkell, 1947, p. 356), and argillaceous limestone in the Kimmeridge Clay near Kimmeridge; in the Lulworth Formation at Upwey and near Orchard (south-west of Corfe Castle) has been similarly exploited.

IRON ORE

The Abbotsbury Ironstone has an iron content of at least 30 per cent, and was investigated as a possible resource during the First World War (House, 1989). The iron occurs as berthierine (= 'chamosite'), but is often weathered to limonite, and siderite in sandstones and mudstones, but the high silica content of the ore (42 per cent) prevented its large-scale economic development (Pringle in Lamplugh et al., 1920; House, 1989; Wright and Cox, 2001).

BALL CLAY

Ball clays are fine-grained, highly plastic clays, which are essentially kaolinitic in character and are white when fired in an oxidising atmosphere. They are used predominantly in the manufacture of ceramic whitewares. The clays were originally hand cut into cubes, the sides of which rapidly rounded during handling, giving rise to the term 'ball clay'. High quality, white-firing ball clays have a limited distribution, both nationally and internationally, and Britain is a leading world producer and exporter. These deposits have been in continuous production for more than three centuries and there are records of white-firing ball clay from Dorset being used for tobacco pipe manufacture as early as the 1640s. Dorset typically accounts for 17 to 20 per cent of total UK output.

Figure 48
Distribution of ball-clay-bearing host clays in the Wareham Basin (from Bristow et al., 2002a).

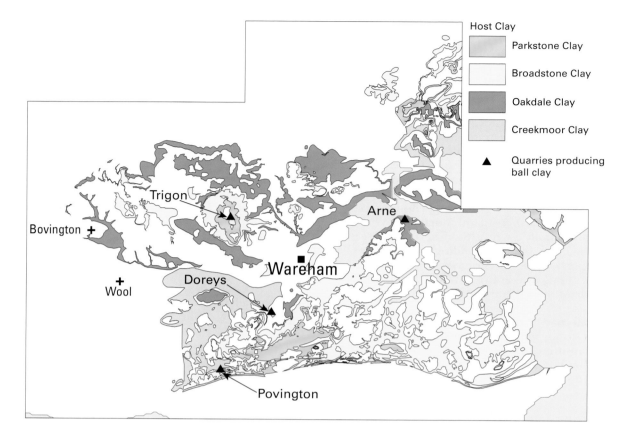

Host Clay

- Parkstone Clay
- Broadstone Clay
- Oakdale Clay
- Creekmoor Clay
- ▲ Quarries producing ball clay

Ball clays, which comprise a mixture of kaolinite (24 to 77 per cent), illite (12 to 35 per cent) and quartz (7 to 54 per cent), occur within clay units in the Poole Formation; these are interbedded with sand units in the central and eastern parts of the Wareham Basin (Figure 48). Minor components, in particular iron oxide and titanium oxide may modify the ceramic properties of the clay, and at levels above 3 per cent generally make the clay unusable for white-firing ceramic bodies. Dorset ball clays have

been described by Bristow et al. (2002a), Highley (1975, 1995) and Highley et al. (2002).

HYDROCARBONS

Petroleum production in the Wessex Basin is from Triassic (Sherwood Sandstone Group, Otter Sandstone Formation) and Jurassic (Bridport Sand and Cornbrash

Plate 41 A 'nodding donkey', used to pump oil to the surface from underground reservoir units at the Kimmeridge Oilfield [SY 9045 7928] (P673132).

formations) reservoirs. The oil is derived from organic-rich Lower Jurassic Lias Group mudstones (Ebukanson and Kinghorn, 1986a, b). Unlike the situation in the North Sea, the Kimmeridge Clay is too immature for oil generation (Ebukanson and Kinghorn, 1985, 1986a; Penn et al., 1987). The first commercial oilfield was discovered in 1959 in fractured Cornbrash limestones at Kimmeridge (Plate 41). It remains the only successful example of a Cenozoic (Tertiary) inversion anticline play within the Wessex Basin (Hawkes et al., 1998). Since 1973, however, it has been eclipsed by the Wytch Farm Oilfield in eastern Dorset. This oilfield was discovered after seismic surveying in 1970 and early 1971. Recent long-reach drilling from onshore sites and existing production locations has identified offshore extensions (McClure et al., 1995) that increase reserves to an estimated 500 million barrels, thereby putting the Wytch Farm field amongst the top ten fields in the UK.

Surface oil seepages in the Bencliff Grit Member of the Corallian Group (Oxfordian) at Osmington Mills [SY 738 805], and in the Wealden Formation (Lower Cretaceous) between Durdle Door [SY 806 803] and Worbarrow Bay [SY 860 799], do not appear to be related to commercial reserves at depth. However, an oil shale horizon in the Kimmeridge Clay, known as the 'Blackstone' or 'Kimmeridge Coal', has been considered to have economic potential; it occurs in the Burning Cliff [SY 7607 8160], named for the spontaneous combustion that occurred from 1826 to 1829 as a result of heat generated by pyrite oxidation (Gallois, 1979).

INFORMATION SOURCES

Further geological information held by the British Geological Survey relevant to the South Dorset and the World Heritage Coast of Dorset and East Devon is listed below. It includes published maps, memoirs and reports. Enquiries concerning geological data for the district should be addressed to the Manager, National Geological Records Centre, Keyworth. Geological advice for the area should be sought initially from the BGS Enquiries Service, Keyworth.

The Geological Data Index (GDI) is now available on the internet at: http://www.bgs.ac.uk. This includes the following themes:

- borehole records
- water wells
- site investigation reports
- drillcore
- samples
- geophysical logs
- well water levels
- aquifer properties
- geochemistry
- topography
- outline of BGS maps at 1:50 000 and 1:10 000 scale and 1:10 560 scale County Series aeromagnetic and gravity data recording stations

MAPS

Geological maps

1:1 500 000
Tectonic map of Britain, Ireland and adjacent areas, 1996

1:1 000 000
Pre-Permian geology of the United Kingdom, 1985

1:625 000
Solid geology map UK South Sheet, 2007; Quaternary geology, 1977

1:250 000
50N 04W Portland, Solid Geology, 1983

1:50 000
Sheet 327 Bridport, 2004
Sheet 328 Dorchester, 2001
Sheet 329 Bournemouth, 1991
Sheet 341/342 West Fleet and Weymouth, 2001
Sheet 342/343 Swanage, 2000
Sheet 326/340 Sidmouth, 2004
Sheet 339 Newton Abbot, 1976

1:10 000

Map No	Surveyor*	Date
ST00SE	RAEd	1987–1988
ST30SW	RWG, RJOH, ACP	1997–2000
ST30SE	FBAW, RWG, RJOH, ACP	1934–1935, 1997–2000
ST40SW	FBAW, SB	1932–1934
ST40SE	FBAW, CRB	1932–1935, 2000
ST50SW	FBAW, CRB	1932–1935, 1999–2000

Map No	Surveyor*	Date
ST50SE	FBAW, JAR, CRB	1932–1933, 1939, 1999–2000
ST60SW	FBAW, JAR, CRB	1933, 1936, 2000
ST80SW	CRB	1990
ST80SE	CMB	1990
ST90SW	CRB	1985
SY08NE	RAEd	1989, 1991, 1995
SY09NE	CRB, RAEd	1983, 1987–1988
SY09SE	RAEd	1988–1989
SY18NW	RAEd	1999–2000
SY18NE	AJN	1999
SY19NW	RAEd	1998
SY19NE	RAEl	1999
SY19SW	RAEd	1999–2000
SY19SE	AJN	1999
SY28NW	RWG	1996–2000
SY29NW	RWG, RAEl	1996–1997, 2000
SY29NE	RWG	1996–1997
SY29SW	RWG	1996–2000
SY29SE and part of SY28NE	RWG	1995–1996
SY39NW	RWG, RJOH	1996–2000
SY39NE	FBAW, RWG	1934–1936, 1994
SY39SW and part of SY38NW	RWG	1995
SY39SE	FBAW, RWG	1935–1936, 1994
SY48NE	WL	1931–1932
SY49NW	WL, FBAW, JAR	1932–1933, 1935–1936
SY49NE	WL, FBAW, JAR CRB	1932–1933, 1936, 2001
SY49SW	WL, FBAW, JAR	1932–1933, 1935–1936
SY49SE	FBAW, CRB	1932–1935, 2000
SY58NW	WL, FBAW, CRB	1931–1932, 1936, 1999–2000
SY58NE	JAR, FBAW, AJN, CRB	1935–1936, 1996, 1997
SY58SE	AJN	1996
SY59NW	FBAW, CRB	1932–1935, 2000
SY59NE	FBAW, CRB	1932–1935, 2000
SY59SW	WL, FBAW, JAR, CRB	1931, 1935, 2000
SY59SE	FBAW, JAR, CRB	1935–1936, 2000
SY66NE	AJN	1996
SY67NW	AS, CRB	1890, 1995
SY67NE and part of SY77NW	AS, CRB	1890, 1995
SY67SE and SY77SW	AJN	1996
SY68NW	JAR, FBAW, CRB	1936, 1997
SY68NE	RKW	1991–1992
SY68SW	AJN and CRB	1996
SY68SE	RKW	1996
SY69NW	JAR, FBAW, CRB	1933–1936, 2000
SY69NE	RKW	1991
SY69SW	JAR, FBAW, CRB	1936 and 2000
SY69SE	RKW	1991

Map No	Surveyor*	Date
SY78NW	CMB, CRB	1995
SY78NE	CMB, CRB	1995–1996
SY78SW	CMB	1995–1996
SY78SE	CMB, ECF	1995–1996
SY79NW	RKW	1991
SY79NE	RKW	1991
SY79SW	CRB, RKW	1991, 1995
SY79SE	CRB	1995
SY88NW	CMB	1996
SY88NE	CRB	1996
SY88SW and part of SY87NW	ECF	1995
SY88SE and part of SY87NE	CRB, RKW	1996
SY89NW	CRB	1990–1991
SY89NE	CRB	1990
SY89SW	CRB	1992, 1996
SY89SE	CRB	1991–1992, 1996
SY97NW	RKW	1996
SY97NE	AJN	1997
SY98NW	CRB	1986, 1996
SY98SW	RKW, CRB	1986, 1996
SY98SE	ECF, CRB	1986, 1997
SY99NW	CRB	1985
SY99NE	CRB	1985
SY99SW	CRB	1985–1986
SY99SE	ECF, CRB	1985, 1997
SZ08NW and part of SZ08NE	CRB, ECF	1984, 1986
SZ08SW and part of SZ08SE	CMB	1997
SZ09SW	CRB, ECF	1984
SZ09SE	CRB, ECF	1984
SZ19SW	ECF	1983
SZ19SE	CRB	1983

* CMB, C M Barton;   SB, S Buchan;   CRB, C R Bristow;
RAEd, R A Edwards;   RAEl, R A Ellison;   ECF, E C Freshney;
RWG, R W Gallois;   RJOH, R J O Hamblin;   WL, W Lloyd;
AJN, A J Newell;   ACP, A C Pople;   JAR, J A Robbie;   AS, A Strahan;
FBAW, F B A Welch;   RKW, R K Westhead

Digital geological map data

In addition to the printed publications noted above, many BGS maps are available in digital form. These data must be licensed for use. Details are available from the Intellectual Property Rights Manager at BGS Keyworth. The current availability of digital map datasets can be checked on the BGS web site at: http://www.bgs.ac.uk/products/digitalmaps/digmapgb.html

Geophysics

1:1 500 000
Colour shaded relief gravity anomaly map of Britian, Ireland and adjacent areas, 1997
Colour shaded relief magnetic anomaly map of Britain, Ireland and adjacent areas, 1998

1:250 000
50N 04W Portland, Bouguer gravity anomaly, 1978
50N 04W Portland, Aeromagnetic anomaly, 1978

Sea bed sediments map

1:250 000
50N 04W Portland, 1983

Groundwater vulnerability maps

1:100 000
50   East Devon and South Somerset, 1991
51   Dorset, 1990

Hydrogeological maps

1:100 000
Permo-Triassic and other aquifers of SW England, 1982
Chalk of Wessex, 1979

Geochemical maps

1:625 000
Methane, carbon dioxide and oil susceptibility, Great Britain (South Sheet), 1995
Radon potential based on solid geology, Great Britain (South Sheet), 1995
Distribution of areas with above national average background concentrations of potentially harmful elements (As, Cd, Cu, Pb and Zn), Great Britain (South Sheet), 1995

Minerals maps

1:1 000 000
Industrial minerals resources map of Britain, 1996

Minerals map and report

Dorset, Bournemouth and Poole: resources and constraints

BOOKS AND REPORTS

British Regional Geology: the Hampshire Basin
British Regional Geology: south-west England

Memoirs and Sheet Explanations

312/327 Bridport and Yeovil†
341, 342, 343 (and parts of 327, 328, 329) Weymouth, Swanage, Corfe and Lulworth
326/340 Sidmouth
†   out of print: facsimile copy is available at the cost of copying

Land Survey Technical reports

The following is a list of reports that provide geological notes and local details specific to 1:10 000 map sheets. Against each map sheet or sheets the report number, initials of the author and date of publication are shown.

Sheet number	Report No.	Author*	Date
ST80NE and ST80SE	WA/91/81	CMB	1992
ST80NW and ST80SW	WA/92/20	CRB	1992
ST90NW	WA/91/81	CMB	1992
ST90SW and ST90SE	WA/93/86	CRB	1993
ST91NW and ST91SW	WA/91/20	CRB	1991
SU00SW	WA/87/4	CRB	1987
SY58SE and SY58NE	WA/98/40	AJN	1998
SY66NE and SY67SE	WA/98/36	AJN	1998
SY68NE	WA/93/22	RKW	1993
SY68SE	WA/98/25	CMB and RKW	1998
SY68SW	WA/98/40	AJN	1998
SY69NE and SY69SE	WA/92/36	RKW	1992
SY77SW	WA/98/36	AJN	1998
SY78NE	WA/97/16	CMB	1997
SY78SE	WA/98/25	CMB and RKW	1998
SY78NW	WA/95/108	CMB and CRB	1995
SY78SW	WA/98/25	CMB and RKW	1998
SY79NE and SY79NW	WA/92/35	RKW	1992
SY79NE and SY79SW	WA/97/43	CRB	1997
SY87NE	WA/98/18	RKW	1998
SY88NE and SY88SE	WA/99/25	CRB	1999
SY88NW	WA/97/16	CMB	1997
SY89NW and SY89NE	WA/93/18	CRB	1993
SY97NE	WA/98/37	AJN	1998
SY97NW	WA/98/18	RKW	1998
SY98NW, SY98NE, SY98SW, SY98SE	WA/99/43	CRB	1999
SY99NW	WA/87/28	CRB	1987

SY99NW, SY99NE,	WA/86/4	CRB and ECF	1986
SY99SW, SY99SE	WA/87/28	CRB and ECF	1987
SY99SW	WA/87/28	CRB	1987
SZ07NW	WA/98/37	AJN	1998
SZ08NW and SZ08NE	WA/87/28	CRB and ECF	1987

* AJN A J Newell; CMB C M Barton; CRB C R Bristow; ECF E C Freshney; RKW R K Westhead

BGS Reports

In addition to BGS reports cited in the text and listed in the References, the following contain relevant information.

FORSTER, A. 1991. The engineering geology of the Exeter area. 1:50 000 geological map sheet 325. *British Geological Survey Technical Report*, WN/91/16.

NEWELL, A J. 1998. Fluvial sediments of the Tertiary Poole Formation (Dorset): depositional environments and sequence stratigraphic significance. *British Geological Survey Technical Report*, WA/98/05.

NEWELL, A J. 1999. Depositional environment of Eocene ball clays in the Hampshire Basin (Southern England). *British Geological Survey Technical Report*, WA/99/23.

WARRINGTON, G. 1999. Palynology report: Mercia Mudstone Group (Triassic), Axe outfall to Culverhole Point, south-east Devon (Sheet 326: Sidmouth). *British Geological Survey Technical Report* WH/99/73R.

WARRINGTON, G. 2000a. Palynology report: Mercia Mudstone Group (Triassic), River Axe outfall to Culverhole Point, south-east Devon (Sheet 326/340: Sidmouth and Lyme Regis). *British Geological Survey Technical Report* WH/00/25R.

WARRINGTON, G. 2000b. Palynology report: Blue Anchor Formation (Mercia Mudstone Group: Triassic), Culverhole foreshore, south-east Devon (Sheet 326/340: Sidmouth and Lyme Regis). *British Geological Survey Technical Report* WH/00/26R.

DOCUMENTARY COLLECTIONS

Boreholes
Borehole data for the district are catalogued in the BGS archives (National Geological Records Centre) at Keyworth on individual 1:10 000 scale sheets and are also held digitally. For further information contact: Chief Curator, National Geological Records Centre, BGS, Keyworth.

Geophysics
Gravity and aeromagnetic data are held digitally in the National Gravity Databank and the National Gravity Aeromagnetic Databank at BGS Keyworth.

Hydrogeology
BGS hydrogeology enquiry service; wells and springs and water borehole records are held at the British Geological Survey, Maclean Building, Crowmarsh Gifford, Wallingford, Oxfordshire OX10 8BB.

BGS Lexicon of named rock unit definitions
Definitions of the named rock units shown on the geological maps of the district are held in the Lexicon database. This is available on the BGS web site. Further information on the database can be obtained from the Lexicon manager, BGS, Keyworth.

MATERIALS COLLECTIONS

Palaeontological collection
Macrofossils and micropalaeontological samples collected from the district are held at BGS Keyworth. Enquiries concerning this material should be directed to the Chief Curator, BGS, Keyworth.

BGS Photographs
Copies of photographs used in this report are deposited for reference at BGS, Keyworth. BGS maintains a large collection of photographs that can be purchased. Some of the collection can be viewed on our web site. Please see GeoScenic at http://geoscenic.bgs.ac.uk

REFERENCES

British Geological Survey holds most of the references listed below, and copies may be obtained via the library service subject to copyright legislation (contact libuser@bgs.ac.uk for details). The library catalogue is available at: http://geolib.bgs.ac.uk

ABBINK, O A, CALLOMON, J H, RIDING, J B, WILLIAMS, P D B, and WOLFARD, A. 2001. Biostratigraphy of Jurassic–Cretaceous boundary strata in the Terschelling Basin, The Netherlands. *Proceedings of the Yorkshire Geological Society*, Vol. 53, 275–302.

AGER, D V. 1976. Discussion of Portlandian faunas. *Journal of the Geological Society of London*, Vol. 132, 335–336.

AINSWORTH, N R, BRAHAM, W, GREGORY, F J, JOHNSON, B, and KING, C. 1998. The lithostratigraphy and biostratigraphy of the latest Triassic to earliest Cretaceous of the English Channel and its adjacent areas. 103–164 *in* Development, evolution and petroleum geology of the Wessex Basin. UNDERHILL, J R (editor). *Geological Society of London Special Publication*, No. 133.

ALI, J R, KING, C, and HAILWOOD, E A. 1993. Magnetostratigraphic calibration of early Eocene depositional sequences in the Southern North Sea Basin. 99–125 *in* High resolution stratigraphy. HAILWOOD, E A, and KIDD R B (editors). *Geological Society of London Special Publication*, No. 70.

ALLEN, L G, and GIBBARD. 1993. Pleistocene evolution of the Solent river of southern England. *Quaternary Science Reviews*, Vol. 12, 503–528.

ALLEN, P A, and UNDERHILL, J R. 1989. Swaley cross-stratification produced by unidirectional flows, Bencliff Grit (Upper Jurassic), Dorset, UK. *Journal of the Geological Society of London*, Vol. 146, 241–252.

ALLEN, P A, and WIMBLEDON, W A. 1991. Correlation of NW European Purbeck–Wealden (nonmarine Lower Cretaceous) as seen from the English type-areas. *Cretaceous Research*, Vol. 12, 511–526.

ALLISON, R J. 1992. *The coastal landforms of west Dorset*. Geologists' Association Guide, No. 47. (London: The Geologists' Association.)

ALLISON, R J, and KIMBER, O G. 1998. Modelling failure mechanisms to explain rock slope change along the Isle of Purbeck Coast, UK. *Earth Surface Processes and Landforms*, Vol. 23, 731–750.

AMEEN, M S, and COSGROVE, J W. 1990. Kinematic analysis of the Ballard Fault, Swanage, Dorset. *Proceedings of the Geologists' Association*, Vol. 101, 119–129.

AMEEN, M S, and COSGROVE, J W. 1991. An upper strain detachment model for the Ballard Fault; reply. *Proceedings of the Geologists' Association*, Vol. 102, 315–320.

ANDERSON, F W. 1967. Ostracods from the Weald Clay of England. *Bulletin of the Geological Survey of Great Britain*, Vol. 27, 237–269.

ANDERSON, F W. 1985. Ostracod faunas in the Purbeck and Wealden of England. *Journal of Micropalaeontology*, Vol. 4, 1–68.

ANDERSON, F W, and BAZLEY, R A B. 1971. The Purbeck Beds of the Weald (England). *Bulletin of the Geological Survey of Great Britain*, No. 34.

ARBER, M A. 1940. The coastal landslips of south-east Devon. *Proceedings of the Geologists' Assocation*, Vol. 51, 257–271.

ARBER, M A. 1946. The valley system of Lyme Regis. *Proceedings of the Geologists' Association*, Vol. 57, 8–15.

ARBER, M A. 1973. Landslips near Lyme Regis. *Proceedings of the Geologists' Association*, Vol. 84, 121–133.

ARKELL, W J. 1933. *The Jurassic System in Great Britain*. (Oxford: Clarendon Press.)

ARKELL, W J. 1935–1948. A monograph on the ammonites of the English Corallian Beds. *Monograph of the Palaeontographical Society*, Vol. 88.

ARKELL, W J. 1936a. The Corallian Beds of Dorset. *Proceedings of the Dorset Natural History and Archaeological Society*, Vol. 57, 59–93.

ARKELL, W J. 1936b. The tectonics of the Purbeck and Ridgeway faults in Dorset. *Geological Magazine*, Vol. 73, 56–73.

ARKELL, W J. 1938. Three tectonic problems in the Lulworth district: studies in the middle limb of the Purbeck fold. *Quarterly Journal of the Geological Society of London*, Vol. 94, 1–54.

ARKELL, W J. 1947. The geology of the country around Weymouth, Swanage, Corfe and Lulworth. *Memoir of the Geological Survey of Great Britain*, Sheets 341, 342, 343 and parts of 327, 328 and 329 (England and Wales).

ARKELL, W J. 1956. *Jurassic geology of the World*. (Edinburgh: Oliver and Boyd Ltd.)

BADEN-POWELL, D F W. 1930. On the geological evolution of the Chesil Bank. *Geological Magazine*, Vol. 67, 499–513.

BAILEY, H W, GALE, A S, MORTIMORE, R N, SWIECICKI, A, and WOOD, C J. 1983. The Coniacian–Maastrichtian Stages of the United Kingdom, with particular reference to southern England. *Newsletters on Stratigraphy*, Vol. 12, 29–42.

BARKER, D, BROWN, C E, BUGG, S C, and COSTIN, J. 1975. Ostracods, land plants, and charales from the basal Purbeck Beds of Portesham Quarry, Dorset. *Palaeontology*, Vol. 18, 419–436.

BARTON, C M. 1992. Geology of the Blandford Forum district (Dorset). *British Geological Survey Technical Report*, WA/91/81.

BARTON, C M, and BRISTOW, C R. 1996. Geology of the Broadmayne district (Dorset). *British Geological Survey Technical Report*, WA/95/108.

BARTON, C M, IVIMEY-COOK, H C, LOTT, G K, and TAYLOR, R T. 1993. The Purse Caundle Borehole, Dorset: stratigraphy and sedimentology of the Inferior Oolite and Fuller's Earth in the Sherborne area of the Wessex Basin. *British Geological Survey Research Report*, SA/93/01.

BARTON, C M, EVANS, D J, BRISTOW, C R, FRESHNEY, E C, and KIRBY, G A. 1998. Reactivation of relay ramps and structural evolution of the Mere Fault and Wardour Monocline, northern Wessex Basin. *Geological Magazine*, Vol. 135, 383–395.

BATHURST, R G C. 1951. Wealden Beds and Lower Greensand. *Proceedings of the Dorset Natural History and Archaeological Society*, Vol. 72, 186–187.

BENTON, M J. 1990. The species of *Rhynchosaurus*, a rhynchosaur (Reptilia, Diapsida) from the Middle Triassic of England. *Philosophical Transactions of the Royal Society*, Vol. B328, 213–306.

BENTON, M J. 1997. The Triassic reptiles from Devon. *Proceedings of the Ussher Society*, Vol. 9, 141–152.

BENTON, M J, and GOWER, D J. 1997. Richard Owen's giant Triassic frogs: archosaurs from the Middle Triassic of England. *Journal of Vertebrate Paleontology*, Vol. 17, 74–88.

BENTON, M J, and SPENCER, P S. 1995. *Fossil reptiles of Great Britain. Geological Conservation Review Series*, No. 10. (London: Chapman and Hall.)

BENTON, M J, HART, M B, and CLAREY, T. 1993. A new rhynchosaur from the Middle Triassic of Devon. *Proceedings of the Ussher Society*, Vol. 8, 167–171.

BENTON, M J, WARRINGTON, G, NEWELL, A J, and SPENCER, P S. 1994. A review of the British Middle Triassic tetrapod assemblages. 131–160 in *In the shadow of the dinosaurs*. FRASER, N C, and SUES, H-D (editors). (Cambridge: Cambridge University Press.)

BENTON, M J, COOK, E, and TURNER, P. 2002. *Permian and Triassic Red Beds and the Penarth Group of Great Britain. Geological Conservation Review Series*, No. 24. (Peterborough: Joint Nature Conservation Committee.)

BLAKE, J F. 1875. On the Kimmeridge Clay of England. *Quarterly Journal of the Geological Society of London*, Vol. 31, 196–233.

BLAKE, J F. 1880. On the Portland rocks of England. *Quarterly Journal of the Geological Society of London*, Vol. 36, 189–236.

BLAKE, J F, and HUDLESTON, W H. 1877. The Corallian rocks of England. *Quarterly Journal of the Geological Society of London*, Vol. 33, 260–405.

BLOOS, G, and PAGE, K N. 2002. Global stratotype section and point for base of the Sinemurian Stage (Lower Jurassic). *Episodes*, Vol. 25, 22–28.

BOWMAN, M B J, McCLURE, N M, and WILKINSON, D W. 1993. Wytch Farm oilfield: deterministic reservoir description of the Triassic Sherwood Sandstone. 1513–1517 in *petroleum geology of northwest Europe: proceedings of the 4th conference*. PARKER, J R (editor). (London: The Geological Society.)

BRISTOW, C M. 1968. The derivation of the Tertiary sediments in the Petrockstow Basin, North Devon. *Proceedings of the Ussher Society*, Vol. 2, 29–35.

BRISTOW, C R. 1991. Geology of the Tollard Royal–Tarrant Hinton district. *British Geological Survey Technical Report*, WA/91/20.

BRISTOW, C R. 1999a. Geology of the Stokeford–East Lulworth area, Dorset. *British Geological Survey Technical Report*, WA/99/25.

BRISTOW, C R. 1999b. Geology of the Wareham, Arne, Creech and Corfe Castle area, Dorset. *British Geological Survey Technical Report*, WA/99/43.

BRISTOW, C R, and FRESHNEY, E C. 1986. Geology of the Poole–Bournemouth area. *British Geological Survey Technical Report*, WA/86/5.

BRISTOW, C R, and OWEN, H G. 1990. A temporary section in the Gault at Fontmell Magna, North Dorset. *Proceedings of the Dorset Natural History and Archaeological Society*, Vol. 112, 95–97.

BRISTOW, C R, FRESHNEY, E C, and PENN, I E. 1991. The geology of the country around Bournemouth. *Memoir of the British Geological Survey*, Sheet 329 (England and Wales).

BRISTOW, C R, BARTON, C M, FRESHNEY, E C, WOOD, C J, EVANS, D J, COX, B M, IVIMEY-COOK, H, and TAYLOR, R T. 1995. Geology of the country around Shaftesbury. *Memoir of the British Geological Survey*, Sheet 313 (England and Wales).

BRISTOW, C R, MORTIMORE, R N, and WOOD, C J. 1997. Lithostratigraphy for mapping the Chalk of southern England. *Proceedings of the Geologists' Association*, Vol. 108, 293–315.

BRISTOW, C R, BARTON, C M, HIGHLEY, D E, COWLEY, J F, FRESHNEY, E C, and WEBB, N R. 2002a. Mineral resources of east Dorset. *British Geological Survey Commissioned Report*, CR/01/138N.

BRISTOW, C R, WILKINSON, I P, WOOD, C J, and WOODS, M. 2002b. The base of the Portsdown Chalk Formation (Chalk Group, White Chalk Subgroup) in the BGS Big Almer Wood Borehole, Dorset, southern England. *Proceedings of the Geologists' Association*, Vol. 113, 37–45.

BRISTOW, H W. 1884. Section of the Purbeck strata of Darlston Bay, Dorset. 201–209 in DAMON, R F. *Geology of Weymouth, Portland and the coast of Dorsetshire from Swanage to Bridport-on-the-sea: with natural history and archaeological notes* (second edition). Weymouth.

BRISTOW, H W, and FISHER, O. 1857. Vertical Section Sheet 22. *Geological Survey of the United Kingdom.*

BRITISH GEOLOGICAL SURVEY. 1995. Exeter, England and Wales Sheet 325. Solid and Drift Geology. 1:50 000. (Southampton: Ordnance Survey for British Geological Survey.)

BROMLEY, R G, and GALE, A S. 1982. The lithostratigraphy of the English Chalk Rock. *Cretaceous Research*, Vol. 3, 273–306.

BROOKFIELD, M E. 1973. The palaeoenvironment of the Abbotsbury Ironstone (Upper Jurassic) of Dorset. *Palaeontology*, Vol. 16, 261–274.

BROOKFIELD, M E. 1978. The lithostratigraphy of the upper Oxfordian and the lower Kimmeridgian Beds of south Dorset, England. *Proceedings of the Geologists' Association*, Vol. 89, 1–32.

BROWN, P R. 1963. Algal limestones and associated sediments in the basal Purbeck of Dorset. *Geological Magazine*, Vol. 100, 565–573.

BRUNSDEN, D. 1974. The degradation of a coastal slope, Dorset, England. 79–98 in Progress in geomorphology. BROWN, E H, and WATERS, R S (editors). *Institute of British Geographers Special Publication*, No. 7.

BRUNSDEN, D. 1996. Landslides of the Dorset Coast — some unresolved questions. *Proceedings of the Ussher Society*, Vol. 9, 1–11.

BRUNSDEN, D, and JONES, K C. 1972. The morphology of degraded landslide slopes in south west Dorset. *Quarterly Journal of Engineering Geology*, Vol. 5, 205–222.

BRUNSDEN, D, and JONES, K C. 1976. The evolution of landslide slopes in Dorset. *Philosophical Transactions of the Royal Society of London*, Vol. A283, 605–631.

BRUNSDEN, D, and JONES, D K C. 1980. Relative time scales and formative events in coastal landslide systems. *Zeitschrift fur Geomorphologie*. Supplement 34, 1–19.

BRUNSDEN, D, COOMBE, K, GOUDIE A S, and PARKER A G. 1996. The structural geomorphology of the Island of Portland, southern England. *Proceedings of the Geologists' Association*, Vol. 107, 209–230.

BRYANT, I D, KANTOROWICZ, J D, and LOVE, C F. 1988. The origin and recognition of laterally continuous carbonate-cemented horizons in the Upper Lias Sands of southern England. *Marine and Petroleum Geology*, Vol. 5, 108–133.

BRYDONE, R M. 1914. The zone of *Offaster pilula* in the south English chalk. Part 1. *Geological Magazine*, Vol. 51, 359–369.

BUCKLAND, W. 1835. On the discovery of fossil bones of the *Iguanodon* in the iron sand of the Wealden Formation in the Isle of Wight and in the Isle of Purbeck. *Transactions of the Geological Society of London*, Vol. 3, 425.

BUCKLAND, W, and DE LA BECHE, H T. 1835. On the geology of the neighbourhood of Weymouth and the adjacent parts of the coast of Dorset. *Transactions of the Geological Society*, Vol. 4, 1–46.

BUCKMAN, S S. 1889. On the Cotteswold, Midford and Yeovil Sands, and the divisions between the Lias and Oolite. *Quarterly Journal of the Geological Society of London*, Vol. 45, 440–474.

BUCKMAN, S S. 1922. Jurassic chronology: II — preliminary studies. Certain Jurassic strata near Eypesmouth (Dorset): the Junction Bed of Watton Cliff and associated rocks. *Quarterly Journal of the Geological Society of London*, Vol. 78, 378–436.

BURLEY, S D. 1984. Patterns of diagenesis in the Sherwood Sandstone Group (Triassic), United Kingdom. *Clay Minerals*, Vol. 19, 403–440.

BURY, H. 1934. 'Creech Barrow', *Proceedings of the Bournemouth Natural Sciences Society*, Vol. 26, 68–72.

BUTLER, M. 1998. The geological history of the southern Wessex Basin — a review of new information from oil exploration. *Geological Society of London Special Publication*, Vol. 133, 67–86.

BUURMAN, P. 1980. Palaeosols in the Reading Beds (Paleocene) of Alum Bay, Isle of Wight, UK. *Sedimentology*, No. 27, 593–606.

CALLOMON, J H. 1964. *Notes on the Callovian and Oxfordian stages.* Coll. du Jurassique à Luxembourg 1962. Institut Grand du Section Science Natural Physique et Mathematiques, Luxembourg, 269–291.

CALLOMON, J H, and CHANDLER, R B. 1990. A review of the ammonite horizons of the Aalenian — Lower Bajocian Stages in the Middle Jurassic of southern England. 85–111 in Atti del meeting sulla stratigrafia del Baiociano. CRESTA, S, and PAVIA, G (editors). *Memorie Descrittive della Carta Geologica d'Italia*, Vol. 40.

CALLOMON, J H, and COPE, J C W. 1995. The Jurassic geology of Dorset. 51–103 in *Field geology of the British Jurassic.* TAYLOR, P D (editor). (London: The Geological Society.)

CALLOMON, J H, DIETL, G, and PAGE, K N. 1989. On the ammonite faunal horizons and standard zonations of the lower Callovian Stage in Europe. 359–376 in *[Proceedings] 2nd International Symposium on Jurassic Stratigraphy (Lisbon 1987).* ROCHA, R B, and SOARES, A F (editors). Vol. 1.

CARR, A P, and BLACKLEY, M W L. 1973. Investigations bearing on the age and development of Chesil Beach, Dorset and the associated area. *Transactions of the Institute of British Geographers*, Vol. 58, 99–111.

CARR, A P, and BLACKLEY, M W L. 1974. Ideas on the origin and development of Chesil Beach, Dorset. *Proceedings of the Dorset Natural History and Archaeological Society*, Vol. 95, 9–17.

CARTER, D J, and HART, M B. 1977. Aspects of mid Cretaceous stratigraphical micropalaeontology. *Bulletin of the British Museum (Natural History) Geology*, Vol. 29.

CARTER, H J. 1888. On some vertebrate remains in the Triassic strata of the south coast of Devonshire between Budleigh Salterton and Sidmouth. *Quarterly Journal of the Geological Society of London*, Vol. 44, 318–319.

CASEY, R. 1961. The stratigraphical palaeontology of the Lower Greensand. *Palaeontology*, Vol. 3, 487–622.

CASEY, R. 1963. The dawn of the Cretaceous period in Britain. *Bulletin of the South-Eastern Union Scientific Societies*, Vol. 17, 1–15.

CASEY, R. 1973. The ammonite succession at the Jurassic–Cretaceous boundary in eastern England. 193–266 in The Boreal Lower Cretaceous. CASEY, R, and RAWSON, P F (editors). *Geological Journal Special Issue*, No. 5.

CATT, J A. 1986. The nature, origin and geomorphological significance of clay-with-flints. 151–159 in *The Scientific study of flint and chert: Proceedings of the fourth international flint symposium held at Brighton Polytechnic 10–15 April 1983.* SIEVEKING, C DE G, and HART, M B (editors). (Cambridge: Cambridge University Press.)

CHADWICK, R A. 1985a. Upper Jurassic: late Oxfordian to early Portlandian. 49–51 in *Atlas of onshore sedimentary basins in England and Wales: post-Carboniferous tectonics and stratigraphy.* WHITTAKER, A (editor). (Glasgow: Blackie.)

CHADWICK, R A. 1985b. End Jurassic–early Cretaceous sedimentation and subsidence (late Portlandian to Barremian), and the late Cimmerian unconformity. 52–56 in *Atlas of onshore sedimentary basins in England and Wales: post-Carboniferous tectonics and stratigraphy.* WHITTAKER, A (editor). (Glasgow: Blackie.)

CHADWICK, R A. 1985c. Cretaceous sedimentation and subsidence (Aptian to Albian). 57–58 in *Atlas of onshore sedimentary basins in England and Wales: post-Carboniferous tectonics and stratigraphy.* WHITTAKER, A (editor). (Glasgow: Blackie.)

CHADWICK, R A. 1986. Extension tectonics in the Wessex Basin, southern England. *Journal of the Geological Society of London*, Vol. 143, 465–488.

CHADWICK, R A. 1993. Aspects of basin inversion in southern Britain. *Journal of the Geological Society of London*, Vol. 150, 311–322.

CHADWICK, R A, KENOULTY, N, and WHITTAKER, A. 1983. Crustal stucture beneath southern England from deep seismic reflection data. *Journal of the Geological Society of London*, Vol. 140, 893–911.

CHANDLER, J H, and BRUNSDEN, D. 1995. Steady state behaviour of the Black Ven Mudslide: the application of archival analytical photogrammetry to studies of landform change. *Earth Surface Processes and Landforms*, Vol. 20, 255–275

CHANDLER, M E J. 1962. The Lower Tertiary floras of southern England. II. *Flora of the Pipe-clay Series of Dorset (Lower Bagshot).* (London: British Museum (Natural History).)

CHANDLER, M E J. 1963. The Lower Tertiary floras of southern England. III. *Flora of the Bournemouth Beds*, the *Boscombe*, and the *Highcliff Sands.* (London: British Museum (Natural History).)

CLAYTON, C J. 1986. The chemical environment of flint formation in Upper Cretaceous chalks. 43–54 in *The scientific study of flint and chert: proceedings of the fourth international flint symposium held at Brighton Polytechnic 10–15 April, 1983.* SIEVEKING, G DE C, and HART, M B (editors). (Cambridge: Cambridge University Press.)

CLEEVELY, R J, MORRIS, N J, and BATE, G. 1983. An ecological consideration and comparison of the Punfield Marine Band (Lower Aptian). *Proceedings of the Dorset Natural History and Archaeological Society*, Vol. 105, 93–106.

CLEMENTS, R G. 1969. Annotated cumulative section of the Purbeck Beds between Peveril Point and the Zig-Zag Path, Durlston Bay. A35 in Excursion No. 1, Guide for Dorset and south Somerset. TORRENS, H S (editor). International Field Symposium on the British Jurassic. Unpublished document, University of Keele, April 1969.

CLEMENTS, R G. 1993. Type section of the Purbeck Limestone Group, Durlston Bay, Swanage. *Proceedings of the Dorset Natural History and Archaeological Society*, Vol. 114, 181–206.

CLEMMENSEN, L B, ØXNEVAD, I E I, and DE BOER, P L. 1994. Climatic controls on ancient desert sedimentation: some late Palaeozoic and Mesozoic examples from NW Europe and the Western Interior of the USA. *Special Publications, International Association of Sedimentologists*, Vol. 19, 439–457.

CLIFFORD, E, CORAM, R, JARZEMBOWSKI, E A, and ROSS, A J. 1993. A supplement to the insect fauna from the Purbeck Group of Dorset. *Proceedings of the Dorset Natural History and Archaeological Society*, Vol. 115, 143–146.

COCKS, L R M. 1989. Lower and Upper Devonian brachiopods from the Budleigh Salterton Pebble Bed, Devon. *Bulletin of the British Museum, Natural History* (Geology), Vol. 45, 21–37.

COCKS, L R M. 1993. Triassic pebbles, derived fossils and the Ordovician to Devonian palaeogeography of Europe. *Journal of the Geological Society of London*, Vol. 150, 219–226.

COE, A L. 1995. A comparison of the Oxfordian successions of Dorset, Oxfordshire and Yorkshire. 151–172 in *Field geology of the British Jurassic*. TAYLOR, P D (editor). (London: The Geological Society.)

COE, A L. 1996. Unconformities within the Portlandian Stage of the Wessex Basin and their sequence-stratigraphical significance. 109–143 in Sequence stratigraphy in British Geology. HESSELBO, S P, and PARKINSON, D N (editors). *Geological Society of London Special Publication*, No. 103.

COLTER, V S, and HAVARD D J. 1981. The Wytch Farm Oil Field, Dorset. 493–503 in *Petroleum geology of the continental shelf of north-west Europe*. ILLING, V C, and HOBSON, G D (editors). (London: Institute of Petroleum.)

CONWAY, B W. 1974a. East Cliff landslip Lyme Regis, Dorset. *Report of the Engineering Geology Unit of the Institute of Geological Sciences*, No. 74/10A.

CONWAY, B W. 1974b. The Black Ven landslip, Charmouth, Dorset. *Report of the Engineering Geology Unit of the Institute of Geological Sciences*, No. 74/3.

CONWAY, B W. 1976a. Coastal terrain evaluation and slope stability of the Charmouth/Lyme Regis area of Dorset. *Report of the Engineering Geology Unit of the Institute of Geological Sciences*, No. 76/10.

CONWAY, B W. 1976b. East Cliff landslip Lyme Regis, Dorset. *Report of the Engineering Geology Unit of the Institute of Geological Sciences*, No. 76/9.

CONWAY, B W. 1977a. East Cliff landslip Lyme Regis, Dorset. *Report of the Engineering Geology Unit of the Institute of Geological Sciences*, No. 77/13.

CONWAY, B W. 1977b. A regional study of coastal landslips in West Dorset. *Report of the Engineering Geology Unit of the Institute of Geological Sciences*, No. 77/10.

CONWAY, B W. 1979. East Cliff landslip Lyme Regis, Dorset. Summary 1974–1978. *Report of the Engineering Geology Unit of the Institute of Geological Sciences*, No. 79/10.

CONWAY, B W, and CULSHAW, M G. 1974. East Cliff landslip, Lyme Regis, Dorset. *Report of the Engineering Geology Unit of the Institute of Geological Sciences*, No. 74/10.

CONYBEARE, W D, BUCKLAND, W, and DAWSON, W. 1840. *Ten plates comprising a plan, sections and views representing the changes produced on the coast of East Devon between Axmouth and Lyme Regis by the subsidence of the land and the elevation of the bottom of the sea on 26th December, 1839 and 3rd February, 1840.* (London: John Murray.)

COPE, J C W. 1971. Abbotsbury Iron Ore at Litton Cheney. *Proceedings of the Dorset Natural History and Archaeological Society*, Vol. 92, 42.

COPE, J C W. 1980. Kimmeridgian correlation chart. 76–85 in *A correlation of Jurassic rocks in the British Isles. Part 2: Middle and Upper Jurassic*. COPE, J C W, DUFF, K L, PARSONS, C F, TORRENS, H S, WIMBLEDON, W A, and WRIGHT, J K. *Special Report of the Geological Society of London*, No. 15.

COPE, J C W. 1993. The Bolonian Stage: an old answer to an old problem. *Newsletters on Stratigraphy*, Vol. 28, 151–156.

COPE, J C W, HALLAM, A, and TORRENS, H S. 1969. Guide to Dorset and south Somerset. International Symposium on the British Jurassic, Excursion No. 1. Unpublished document, Geology Department, Keele University, April 1969.

COPE, J C W, GETTY, T A, HOWARTH, M K, MORTON, N, and TORRENS, H S. 1980. A correlation of Jurassic rocks in the British Isles. Part One: Introduction and Lower Jurassic. *Special Report of the Geological Society of London*, No. 14.

CORAM, R, and JARZEMBOWSKI, E A. 1997. Insect-bearing horizons in the type Purbeck and new Purbeck/Wealden flies (Diptera). *Proceedings of the Dorset Natural History and Archaeological Society*, Vol. 119, 135–140.

CORNFORD, C. 1984. Source rocks and hydrocarbon of the North Sea. 171–204 in *Introduction to the petroleum geology of the North Sea*. K W GLENNIE (editor). (Oxford: Blackwell Sciencific.)

COSTA, L I, and DOWNIE, C. 1976. The distribution of the dinoflagellate *Wetzeliella* in the Palaeogene of north-western Europe. *Palaeontology*, Vol. 19, 591–614.

COX, B M, and GALLOIS, R W. 1981. The stratigraphy of the Kimmeridge Clay of the Dorset type area and its correlation with some other Kimmeridgian sequences. *Report of the Institute of Geological Sciences*, 80/4.

COX, B M, and SUMBLER, M G. 2002. *British Middle Jurassic stratigraphy*. Geological Conservation Review Series, No. 26 (Peterborough: Joint Nature Conservation Committee.)

COX, B M, HUDSON, J D, and MARTILL, D M. 1993. Lithostratigraphic nomenclature of the Oxford Clay (Jurassic). *Proceedings of the Geologists' Association*, Vol. 102, 343–345.

COX, B M, SUMBLER, M G, and IVIMEY-COOK, H C. 1999. A formational framework for the Lower Jurassic of England and Wales (onshore area). *British Geological Survey Research Report*, RR/99/01.

COX, L R. 1925. The fauna of the Basal Shell Bed of the Portland Stone, Isle of Portland. *Proceedings of the Dorset Natural History and Antiquarian Field Club*, Vol. 46, 113–172.

COX, L R. 1947. Palaeontology and correlation. *In* The geology of the country around Weymouth, Swanage, Corfe and Lulworth. ARKELL, W J. *Memoir of the Geological Survey of Great Britain* Sheets 341, 342, 343 and parts of 327, 328 and 329, (England and Wales).

CULSHAW, M G. 1997. Landslide survey: West Fleet and Weymouth, East Dorset. *British Geological Survey Technical Report*, WN/97/28.

DALEY, B. 1999. Hampshire Basin: mainland localities. 159–212 in *British Tertiary Stratigraphy. Geological Conservation Review Series*, No. 15. DALEY, B, and BALSON, P (editors). (Peterborough: Joint Nature Conservation Committee.)

DALEY, B, and BALSON, P. 1999. *British Tertiary Stratigraphy. Geological Conservation Review Series*, No. 15. (Peterborough: Joint Nature Conservation Committee.)

DALEY, B, and STEWART, D J. 1979. Weekend field meeting: the Wealden Group in the Isle of Wight. *Proceedings of the Geologists' Association*, Vol. 90, 51–54.

DAMON, R. 1884. *Geology of Weymouth, Portland and the coast of Dorsetshire, from Swanage to Bridport-on-the-Sea: with natural history and archaeological notes. New and enlarged edition.* (London: E Stanford).

DARTON, D M, DINGWALL, R G, and McCANN, D M. 1981. Geological and geophysical investigations in Lyme Bay. *Report of the Institute of Geological Sciences*, No. 79/10.

DAVIES, D K. 1969. Shelf sedimentation: an example from the Jurassic of Britain. *Journal of Sedimentary Petrology*, Vol. 39, 1344–1370.

DAVIES, K H, and KEEN, D H. 1985. The age of Pleistocene marine deposits at Portland, Dorset. *Proceedings of the Geologists' Association*, Vol. 96, 217–225.

DAY, E C H. 1863. On the Middle and Upper Lias of the Dorsetshire coast. *Quarterly Journal of the Geological Society of London*, Vol. 19, 278–297.

DE LA BECHE, H T. 1829. Notice on the excavation of valleys. *Philosophy Magazine*, Vol. 2, 241–243. Reprinted in Geological Notes 1830.

DELAIR, J B. 1966. New records of dinosaurs and other fossil reptiles from Dorset. *Proceedings of the Dorset Natural History and Archaeological Society*, Vol. 87, 57–66.

DELAIR, J B, and WIMBLEDON, W A. 1993. Reptilia from the Portland Stone (Upper Jurassic) of England: a preliminary survey of the material and the literature. *Modern Geology*, Vol. 18, 331–348.

DENNESS, B. 1972. The reservoir principle of mass movement. *Report of the Institute of Geological Sciences*, No. 72/7.

DENNESS, B, CONWAY, B W, McCANN, D M, and GRAINGER, P. 1975. Investigation of a coastal landslip at Charmouth, Dorset. *Quarterly Journal of Engineering Geology*, Vol. 8, 119–140.

DESTOMBES, J P, and SHEPHARD-THORN, E R. 1971. Geological results of the Channel Tunnel Site investigation 1964–65. *Report of the Institute of Geological Sciences*, No. 71/11, 1–12.

DIKAU, R, BRUNSDEN, D, SCHROTT, L, and IBSEN, M (editors). 1996. *Landslide recognition*. (Chichester: John Wiley and Sons.)

DINELEY, D L, and METCALF, S J. 1999. *Fossil fishes of Great Britain. Geological Conservation Review Series*, No. 16. (Peterborough: Joint Nature Conservation Committee.)

DIVER, C. 1933. The physiography of South Haven peninsula, Studland Heath, Dorset. *Geographical Journal*, Vol. 81, 404–427.

DONOVAN, D T, and KELLAWAY, G A. 1984. *Geology of the Bristol district: the Lower Jurassic rocks.* Memoir of the Geological Survey of Great Britain, Special Sheet. (London: HMSO.)

DONOVAN, D T, BENNETT, R, BRISTOW, C R, CARPENTER, S C, GREEN, G W, HAWKES, C J, PRUDDEN, H C, and STANTON, W I. 1989. Geology of a gas pipeline from Ilchester (Somerset) to Pucklechurch (Avon). *Proceedings of the Somerset Archaeological and Natural History Society*, Vol. 132, 297–317.

D'ORBIGNY, A. 1842–1851. *Paléontologie française. Terrains jurassiques. I Céphalopodes.* (Paris: Victor Masson.)

DORHOFER, G, and NORRIS, G. 1977. Discrimination and correlation of highest Jurassic and lowest Cretaceous terrestrial palynofloras in north-west Europe. *Palynology*, Vol. 1, 79–93.

DOUGLAS, J A, and ARKELL, W J. 1928. The stratigraphical distribution of the Cornbrash. I. The south-western area. *Quarterly Journal of the Geological Society of London*, Vol. 84, 117–178.

DOUGLAS, J A, and ARKELL, W J. 1932. The stratigraphical distribution of the Cornbrash. II. The north-eastern area. *Quarterly Journal of the Geological Society of London*, Vol. 88, 112–170.

DRANFIELD, P, BEGG, S H, and CARTER, R R. 1987. Wytch Farm Oilfield: reservoir characterization of the Triassic Sherwood Sandstone for input to reservoir simulation studies. 149–160 in *Petroleum geology of north west Europe.* BROOKS, J, and GLENNIE, K (editors). (London: Graham and Trotman.)

DRUMMOND, P V O. 1970. The Mid Dorset Swell. Evidence of Albian–Cenomanian Movements in Wessex. *Proceedings of the Geologists' Association*, Vol. 81, 679–714.

DURRANCE, E M, and LAMING, D J C (editors). 1985. *The geology of Devon.* (Exeter: University of Exeter.)

EATON, G L. 1976. Dinoflagellate cysts from the Bracklesham Beds (Eocene) of the Isle of Wight, southern England. *Bulletin of the British Museum of Natural History* (Geology), Vol. 26, 225–332.

EBUKANSON, E J, and KINGHORN, R R F. 1985. Kerogen facies in the major Jurassic mudrock formations of southern England and their implication on the depositional environments of their precursors. *Journal of Petroleum Geology*, Vol. 8, 435–462.

EBUKANSON, E J, and KINGHORN, R R F. 1986a. Maturity of organic matter in the Jurassic of southern England and its relation to the burial history of the sediments. *Journal of Petroleum Geology*, Vol. 9, 259–280.

EBUKANSON, E J, and KINGHORN, R R F. 1986b. Oil and gas accumulations and their possible source rocks in southern England. *Journal of Petroleum Geology*, Vol. 9, 413–428.

EDWARDS, R A, and FRESHNEY, E C. 1987. Geology of the country around Southampton. *Memoir of the British Geological Survey*, Sheet 315 (England and Wales).

EDWARDS, R A, and GALLOIS, R W. 2004. Geology of the Sidmouth district — a brief explanation of the geological map. *Sheet Explanation of the British Geological Survey*, Sheets 326 and 340 (England and Wales).

EDWARDS, R A, and SCRIVENER, R C. 1999. Geology of the country around Exeter. *Memoir of the British Geological Survey.* Sheet 325 (England and Wales).

EDWARDS, R A, WARRINGTON, G, SCRIVENER, R C, JONES, N S, HASLAM, H W, and AULT, L. 1997. The Exeter Group, south Devon, England: a contribution to the early post-Variscan stratigraphy of north-west Europe. *Geological Magazine*, Vol. 134, 177–197.

EL-SHAHAT, A, and WEST, I M. 1983. Early and late lithification of aragonitic bivalve beds in the Purbeck Formation (Upper Jurassic–Lower Cretaceous) of southern England. *Sedimentary Geology*, Vol. 35, 15-41.

ENSOM, P C. 1977. A therapsid tooth from the Forest Marble (Middle Jurassic) of Dorset. *Proceedings of the Geologists' Association*, Vol. 88, 201–205.

ENSOM, P C. 1983. A temporary exposure in the Purbeck Limestone Formation (Upper Purbeck Beds) at Friar Waddon Pumping Station, Dorset. *Proceedings of the Dorset Natural History and Archaeological Society*, Vol. 105, 89–91.

ENSOM, P C. 1985a. An annotated section of the Purbeck Limestone Formation at Worbarrow Tout, Dorset. *Proceedings of the Dorset Natural History and Archaeological Society*, Vol. 106, 87–91.

ENSOM, P C. 1985b. Derived fossils in the Purbeck Limestone Formation, Worbarrow Tout, Dorset. *Proceedings of the Dorset Natural History and Archaeological Society*, Vol. 109, 166.

ENSOM, P C. 1987. A remarkable new vertebrate site in the Purbeck Limestone Formation on the Isle of Purbeck. *Proceedings of the Dorset Natural History and Archaeological Society*, Vol. 108, 205–206.

EVANS, D J, and HOPSON, P M. 2000. The seismic expression of synsedimentary channel features within the chalk of southern England. *Proceedings of the Geologists' Association*, Vol. 111, 219–230.

EVANS, D J, RHYS, J G, and HOLLOWAY, S. 1993. The Permian to Jurassic stratigraphy and structural evolution of the central Cheshire Basin. *Journal of the Geological Society of London*, Vol. 150, 857–870.

EVANS, D J, HOPSON, P M, KIRBY, G A, and BRISTOW, C R. 2003. The development and seismic expression of synsedimentary features within the Chalk of southern England. *Journal of the Geological Society of London*, Vol. 160, 797–813.

FEIST, M, LAKE, R D, and WOOD, C J. 1995. Charophyte biostratigraphy of the Purbeck and Wealden of southern England. *Palaeontology*, Vol. 38, 407–442.

FISHER, M J. 1985. Palynology of sedimentary cycles in the Mercia Mudstone and Penarth groups (Triassic) of south-west and central England. *Pollen et Spores*, Vol. 27, 95–112.

FISHER, O. 1856. On the Purbeck strata of Dorsetshire. *Transactions of the Cambridge Philosophical Society*, Vol. 9, 551–581.

FISHER, O. 1858. On some natural pits on the heaths of Dorsetshire. *Geologist*, Vol. 1, 527.

FISHER, O. 1859. On some natural pits on the heaths of Dorsetshire. *Quarterly Journal of the Geological Society of London*, Vol. 15, 187–188.

FITTON, W H. 1847. A stratigraphical account of the section from Atherfield to Rocken End on the south-west coast of the Isle of Wight. *Quarterly Journal of the Geological Society*, Vol. 3, 289–327.

FORBES, E. 1851. On the succession of strata and distribution of organic remains in the Dorsetshire Purbecks. *Report of the British Association for the Advancement of Science* (1850), Abstracts, 58 pp.

FORSTER, A. 1998. The engineering geology of the Sidmouth district. 1:50 000 Geological Sheet 326/340. *British Geological Survey Technical Report*, WN/98/1.

FRANCIS, J E. 1984. The seasonal environment of the Purbeck (Upper Jurassic) fossil forests. *Palaeogeography, Palaeoclimatology, Palaeoecology*, Vol. 48, 285–307.

FREEMAN, E F. 1976. A mammalian fossil from the Forest Marble (Middle Jurassic) of Dorset. *Proceedings of the Geologists' Association*, Vol. 87, 231–235.

FRESHNEY, E C, and EDWARDS, R A. 1983. Christchurch Borehole (SZ 2002 9301). 1–3 *in* IGS boreholes 1981. *Report of the Institute of Geological Sciences*, 82/11.

FÜRSICH, F T. 1976. The use of macroinvertebrate associations in interpreting Corallian (Upper Jurassic) environments. *Palaeogeography, Palaeoclimatology, Palaeoecology*, Vol. 20, 235–256.

FÜRSICH, F T. 1977. Corallian (Upper Jurassic) marine benthic associations from England and Normandy. *Palaeontology*, Vol. 20, 337–385.

FÜRSICH, F T, PALMER, T J, and GOODYEAR, K L. 1994. Growth and disintegration of bivalve-dominated patch reefs in the Upper Jurassic of southern England. *Palaeontology*, Vol. 37, 131–171.

GALE, A S. 1996. Turonian correlation and sequence stratigraphy of the Chalk in southern England. 177–195 *in* Sequence Stratigraphy in British Geology. HESSELBO, S P, and PARKINSON, D N (editors). *Geological Society of London Special Publication*, No. 103.

GALE, A S. 2000a. Early Cretaceous: rifting and sedimentation before the flood. 339–355 in *Geological history of Britain and Ireland*. WOODCOCK, N, and STRACHAN, R (editors). (Oxford: Blackwell Science.)

GALE, A S. 2000b. Late Cretaceous to Early Tertiary pelagic deposits: deposition on greenhouse Earth. 356–373 in *Geological history of Britain and Ireland*. WOODCOCK, N, and STRACHAN, R (editors). (Oxford: Blackwell Science.)

GALE, A S, WOOD, C J, and BROMLEY, R G. 1987. The lithostratigraphy and marker bed correlation of the White Chalk (Late Cenomanian–Campanian) in southern England. *Mesozoic Research*, Vol. 1, 107–118.

GALE, A W. 1992. *The building stones of Devon*. (Exeter: The Devonshire Association for the Advancement of Science.)

GALLOIS, R W. 1979. A pilot study of oil shale occurrences in the Kimmeridge Clay. *Report of the Institute of Geological Sciences*, No. 78/13.

GALLOIS, R W. 2000. The stratigraphy of the Kimmeridge Clay Formation (Upper Jurassic) in the RGGE Project boreholes at Swanworth Quarry and Metherhills, south Dorset. *Proceedings of the Geologists' Association*, Vol. 111, 265–280.

GALLOIS, R W. 2001. The lithostratigraphy of the Mercia Mudstone Group (Mid to Late Triassic) of the south Devon coast. *Geoscience in south-west England*, Vol. 10, 195–204.

GALLOIS, R W. 2003. The distribution of halite (rock-salt) in the Mercia Mudstone Group (Mid to Late Triassic) in south-west England. *Geoscience in south-west England*, Vol. 10, 383–389.

GALLOIS, R W. 2004. The type section of the junction of the Otter Sandstone Formation and the Mercia Mudstone Group (mid Triassic) at Pennington Point, Sidmouth. *Geoscience in south-west England*, Vol. 11, 51–58.

GASTER, C T A. 1924. The Chalk of the Worthing district, Sussex. *Proceedings of the Geologists' Association*, Vol. 35, 89–110.

GATRALL, M, JENKYNS, H C, and PARSONS, C F. 1972. Limonitic concretions from the European Jurassic, with particular reference to the 'snuff-boxes' of southern England. *Sedimentology*, Vol. 18, 79–103.

GEIGER, M E, and HOPPING, C A. 1968. Triassic stratigraphy of the Southern North Sea Basin. *Philosophical Transactions of the Royal Society of London*, Vol. B254, 1–36.

GOLDRING, R, and STEPHENSON, D G. 1972. The depositional environment of three starfish beds. *Neues Jahrbuch fur Geologie und Palaontologie Monatshefte*, Vol. H10, 611–624.

GOLDRING, R, ASTIN, T R, MARSHALL, J E A, GABBOTT, S, and JENKINS, C D. 1998. Towards an integrated study of the depositional environment of the Bencliff Grit (Upper Jurassic) of Dorset. 355–372 *in* Development, evolution and petroleum geology of the Wessex Basin. UNDERHILL, J R (editor). *Geological Society of London Special Publication*, No. 133.

GOUDIE, A, and BRUNSDEN, D. 1997. *Classic landforms of the east Dorset coast*. (Sheffield: Geographical Association in conjunction with the British Geomorphological Research Group.)

GRADSTEIN, F, and OGG, J. 1996. A Phanerozoic time scale. *Episodes*, Vol. 19, 3–5.

GRADSTEIN, F, OGG, J, and SMITH, A. (editors). 2004. *A Geological Time Scale 2004*. (Cambridge: Cambridge University Press.)

GRAINGER, P, and KALAUGHER, P G. 1987a. Cliff-top recession related to the development of coastal landsliding west of Budleigh Salterton, Devon. *Proceedings of the Ussher Society*, Vol. 6, 516–522.

GRAINGER, P, and KALAUGHER, P G. 1987b. Intermittent surging movements of a coastal landslide. *Earth Surface Processes and Landforms*, Vol. 12, 597–603.

GRAINGER, P, and KALAUGHER, P G. 1995. Renewed landslide activity at Pinhay, Lyme Regis. *Proceedings of the Ussher Society*, Vol. 8, 421–425.

GRAINGER, P, KALAUGHER, P G, and KIRK, S. 1996. The relation between coastal landslide activity at Pinhay, east Devon and rainfall and groundwater levels. *Proceedings of the Ussher Society,* Vol. 9, 12–16.

GRAINGER, P, TUBB, C D N, and NEILSON, A P M. 1985. Landslide activity at the Pinhay water source, Lyme Regis. *Proceedings of the Ussher Society,* Vol. 8, 421–425.

GROVES, A W. 1931. The unroofing of the Dartmoor Granite. *Quarterly Journal of the Geological Society,* Vol. 87, 70–72.

HALLAM, A. 1960a. The White Lias of the Devon coast. *Proceedings of the Geologists' Association,* Vol. 71, 47–60.

HALLAM, A. 1960b. A sedimentary and faunal study of the Blue Lias of Dorset and Glamorgan. *Philosophical Transactions of the Royal Society of London,* Vol. B234, 1–44.

HALLAM, A. 1967. An environmental study of the Upper Domerian and Lower Toarcian in Great Britain. *Philosophical Transactions of the Royal Society of London,* Vol. B252, 393–445.

HALLAM, A. 1969. A pyritized limestone hardground in the Lower Jurassic of Dorset (England). *Sedimentology,* Vol. 12, 231–240.

HALLAM, A. 1992. Jurassic. 325–354 in *Geology of England and Wales.* DUFF, P MC L D, and SMITH, A J (editors). (London: The Geological Society.)

HAMBLIN, R J O, and WOOD, C J. 1976. The Cretaceous (Albian–Cenomanian) stratigraphy of the Haldon Hills, south Devon, England. *Newsletters on Stratigraphy,* Vol. 4, 135–149.

HAMBLIN, R J O, CROSBY, A, BALSON, P S, JONES, S M, CHADWICK, R A, PENN, I E, and ARTHUR, M J. 1992. *United Kingdom offshore regional report: the geology of the English Channel.* (London: HMSO for the British Geological Survey.)

HAMILTON, D. 1961. Algal growth in the Rhaetic Cotham Marble of southern England. *Palaeontology,* Vol. 4, 324–333.

HARRISON, R K. 1975. Concretionary concentrations of the rarer elements in Permo-Triassic red beds of south-west England. *Bulletin of the British Geological Survey,* Vol. 52, 1–26.

HART, M B. 1994. The Mid-Dorset Swell: a re-assessment. *Proceedings of the Ussher Society,* Vol. 8, 308–312.

HARVEY, M J, and STEWART, S A. 1998. Influence of salt on the structural evolution of the Channel Basin. 241–266 *in* Development, evolution and petroleum geology of the Wessex Basin. UNDERHILL, J R (editor). *Geological Society of London Special Publication,* No. 133.

HAWKES, P W, FRASER, A J, and EINCHCOMB, C C G. 1998. The tectonostratigraphic development and exploration history of the Weald and Wessex basins, Southern England, UK. 39–65 *in* Development, evolution and petroleum geology of the Wessex Basin. UNDERHILL, J R (editor). *Geological Society of London Special Publication,* No. 133.

HEAP, W. 1951. The Carstone at Punfield Cove, Swanage, as shown in a section opened at the base of the Gault during the spring of 1950. *Proceedings of the Dorset Natural History and Archaeological Society,* Vol. 72, 133–134.

HENSON, M R. 1970. The Triassic rocks of south Devon. *Proceedings of the Ussher Society,* Vol. 2, 172–177.

HESSELBO, S P, and ALLEN, P A. 1991. Major erosion surfaces in the basal Wealden Beds, Lower Cretaceous, south Dorset. *Journal of the Geological Society of London,* Vol. 148, 105–113.

HESSELBO, S P, and JENKYNS, H C. 1995. A comparison of the Hettangian to Bajocian successions of Dorset and York-shire. 105–150 in *Field geology of the British Jurassic.* TAYLOR, P D (editor). (London: The Geological Society.)

HESSELBO, S P, and JENKYNS, H C. 1998. British Lower Jurassic sequence stratigraphy. 561–581 in Sequence stratigraphy of European basins. JAQUIN, T, DE GRACIANSKY, P, and HARDENBOL, J (editors). *Society of Economic Palaeontologists and Mineralogists, Special Publication,* No. 60.

HESSELBO, S P, ROBINSON, S A, and SURLYK, F. 2004. Sea-level change and facies development across potentialTriassic — Jurassic boundary horizons, south-west Britain. *Journal of the Geological Society of London,* Vol. 161, 365–379.

HIGHLEY, D E. 1975. *Ball Clay.* Mineral Dossier No. 11, Mineral Resources Consultative Committee. (London: HMSO.)

HIGHLEY, D E. 1995. The economic importance of ball clay. *British Geological Survey Technical Report,* WF/95/11.

HIGHLEY, D E, CAMERON, D G, SCRIVENER, R C, LOTT, G K, EVANS, D J, and WARRINGTON, G. 2001. Mineral resource information for development plans—Dorset, Bournemouth and Poole. *British Geological Survey Technical Report (Mineral Resources Series),* WF/01/01.

HIGHLEY, D E, BRISTOW, C R, COWLEY, J F, and WEBB, N R. 2002. Sustainable development issues for minerals extraction — the Wareham Basin of East Dorset. *British Geological Survey Commissioned Report,* CR/01/137N.

HILL, W, and JUKES-BROWN, A J. 1886. The Melbourne Rock and the zone of *Belemnitella Plena* from Cambridge to the Chiltern Hills. *Quarterly Journal of the Geological Society of London,* Vol. 42, 216–231.

HOGG, A J C, EVANS, I J, HARRISON, P F, MELING, T, SMITH, G S, THOMPSON, S D, and WATTS, G F T. 1999. Reservoir management of the Wytch Farm oilfield, Dorset, UK: providing options for growth into later life. 1157–1172 in *Petroleum geology of northwest Europe: proceedings of the 5th Conference.* FLEET, A J, and BOLDY, S A R (editors). (London: The Geological Society.)

HOLLOWAY, S. 1985. Lower Jurassic: the Lias. 37–40 in *Atlas of onshore sedimentary basins in England and Wales: post-Carbon-iferous tectonics and stratigraphy.* WHITTAKER, A (editor). (Glasgow and London: Blackie.)

HOLLOWAY, S, and CHADWICK, R A. 1986. The Sticklepath–Lustleigh fault zone: Tertiary sinistral reactivation of a Variscan dextral strike-slip fault. *Journal of the Geological Society of London,* Vol. 143, 4471–452.

HOLLOWAY, S, MILODOWSKI, A E, STRONG, G E, and WARRINGTON, G. 1989. The Sherwood Sandstone Group (Triassic) of the Wessex Basin, southern England. *Proceedings of the Geologists' Association,* Vol. 100, 383–394.

HOOKER, J J. 1977. The Creechbarrow Limestone — its biota and correlation. *Tertiary Research,* Vol. 1, 139–145.

HOOKER, J J. 1986. Mammals from the Bartonian (Mid/Late Eocene) of the Hampshire Basin, southern England. *Bulletin of the British Museum (Natural History) Geology,* Vol. 39, 191–478.

HOPSON, P M. 2005. Stratigraphical framework for the Upper Cretaceous Chalk of England and Scotland with statements on the Chalk of Northern Ireland and the UK Offshore Sector. *British Geological Survey Research Report,* RR/05/01.

HOPSON, P M, WILKINSON, I P, and WOODS, M A. 2008. A stratigraphical framework for the Lower Cretaceous of England. *British Geological Survey Research Report,* RR/08/03.

HORNE, D J. 1995. A revised ostracod biostratigraphy for the Purbeck–Wealden of England. *Cretaceous Research,* Vol. 16, 639–663.

HORNE, D J. 2002. Ostracod biostratigraphy and palaeo-ecology of the Purbeck Limestone Group in southern England. *Special Papers in Palaeontology,* Vol. 68, 53–70.

HOUNSLOW, M W, and McINTOSH, G. 2003. Magnetostratig-raphy of the Sherwood Sandstone Group (Lower and Middle Triassic), south Devon, UK: detailed correlation of the marine and non-marine Anisian. *Palaeo-geography, Palaeoclimatology, Palaeoecology,* Vol. 193, 325–348.

HOUSE, M R. 1958. *The Dorset coast from Poole to the Chesil Beach.* Geologists' Association Guides, No. 22. (Colchester: Benham and Co.)

HOUSE, M R. 1985. A new approach to an absolute timescale from the measurements of orbital cycles and sedimentary microrhythms. *Nature,* Vol. 316, 721–725.

HOUSE, M R. 1989. *Geology of the Dorset Coast.* Geologists' Asso-ciation Guide, No. 22, (London: The Geologists' Association.)

HOUSE, M R. 1993. *Geology of the Dorset Coast.* Second edition. Geologists' Association Guide, No. 22, (London: The Geolo-gists' Association.)

HOWARD, A S, WARRINGTON, G, AMBROSE, K, and REES, J G. 2008. A formational framework for the Mercia Mudstone Group of England and Wales. *British Geological Survey Research Report,* RR/08/04.

HOWARTH, M K. 1957. The Middle Lias of the Dorset coast. *Quarterly Journal of the Geological Society of London,* Vol. 113, 185–204.

HOWARTH, M K. 1992. The ammonite family Hildoceratidae in the Lower Jurassic of Britain. Part 1. *Monograph of the Palae-ontographical Society of London,* 1–106, pls 1–16. (No. 586, part of Vol. 145 for 1991.)

HUBBARD, R N L B, and BOULTER, M C. 1983. Reconstruction of Palaeogene climate from palynological evidence. *Nature,* Vol. 301, 147–150.

HUDLESTON, W H. 1902. Creechbarrow in Purbeck. *Geological Magazine,* Vol. 9, 241–256.

HUDSON, J D, and MARTILL, D M. 1991. Introduction. 11–34 in *Fossils of the Oxford Clay.* MARTILL, D M, and HUDSON, J D (editors). Palaeontological Association field guide to fossils, No. 4. (London: The Palaeontological Association.)

HUGHES, N F, and McDOUGALL, A B. 1987. Records of angio-spermid pollen entry into the English Early Cretaceous succes-sion. *Reviews in Palaeobotany and Palynology,* Vol. 50, 255–272.

HUGHES, T. 2003. Stone roofing in England. 32–127 *in* Stone roofing: conserving the materials and practice of traditional stone slate roofing in England. WOOD, C (editor). *English Heritage Research Transactions,* Vol. 9.

HUNT, C O. 1985. Miospores from the Portland Stone Forma-tion and the lower part of the Purbeck Formation (Upper Jurassic/Lower Cretaceous) from Dorset, England. *Pollen et Spores,* Vol. 27, 419–451.

HUTCHINSON, J N, and BHANDARI, R. 1977. Undrained loading: a fundamental mechanism in mudflows and other mass move-ments. *Geotechnique,* Vol. 21, 353–358.

HUXLEY, T H. 1869. On *Hyperodapedon. Quarterly Journal of the Geological Society of London,* Vol. 25, 138–152.

IVIMEY-COOK, H C. 1982. Biostratigraphy of the Lower Jurassic and Upper Triassic (Rhaetian) rocks of the Winterborne Kingston Borehole, Dorset. 97–106 in The Winterborne Kingston Borehole, Dorset, England. RHYS, G H, LOTT, G K, and CALVER, M A (editors). *Report of the Institute of Geological Sciences,* 81/3.

IVIMEY-COOK, H C, and DONOVAN, D T. 1983. Appendix 3: the fauna of the Lower Jurassic. 126–130 *in* Geology of the country around Weston-Super-Mare. WHITTAKER, A, and GREEN, G W. *Memoir of the British Geological Survey,* Sheet 279 (England and Wales).

JARVIS, I, and TOCHER, B A. 1987. Field Meeting: the Creta-ceous of south-east Devon, 14–16th March, 1986. *Proceedings of the Geologists' Association,* Vol. 98, 51–66.

JARVIS, I, and WOODROOF, P B. 1984. Stratigraphy of the Cenomanian and basal Turonian (Upper Cretaceous) between Branscombe and Seaton, south-east Devon, England. *Proceedings of the Geologists' Association,* Vol. 95, 193–215.

JARZEMBOWSKI, E A. 1993. A provisional checklist of fossil insects from the Purbeck Beds of Dorset. *Proceedings of the Dorset Natural History and Archaeological Society,* Vol. 115, 175–179.

JEANS, C V. 1978. The origin of the Triassic clay assemblages of Europe with special reference to the Keuper Marl and Rhaetic of parts of England. *Philosophical Transactions of the Royal Society of London,* Vol. A289, 549–639.

JEFFERIES, R P S. 1963. The stratigraphy of the *Actinocamax plenus* Subzone (Turonian) in the Anglo-Paris Basin. *Proceedings of the Geologists' Association,* Vol. 74, 1–33.

JENKYNS, H C, and SENIOR, J R. 1991. Geological evidence for intra-Jurassic faulting in the Wessex Basin and its margins. *Journal of the Geological Society of London,* Vol. 148, 245–260.

JOHNSTON-LAVIS, H J. 1876. On the Triassic strata which are exposed in the cliff-sections near Sidmouth, and a note on the occurrence of an ossiferous zone containing bones of a laby-rinthodon. *Quarterly Journal of the Geological Society of London,* Vol. 32, 274–277.

JONES, D K C, and LEE, E M. 1994. *Landsliding in Great Britain.* (London: HMSO.)

JONES, M E, ALLISON, R J, and GILLIGAN, J. 1983. On the rela-tionships between geology and coastal landforms in central southern England. *Proceedings of the Dorset Natural History and Archaeological Society,* Vol. 105, 107–118.

JONES, N S. 1992. Sedimentology of the Permo-Triassic of the Exeter area, south-west England. *British Geological Survey Tech-nical Report,* WH/92/122R.

JONES, N S. 1993. Sedimentology of selected Triassic and Cretaceous successions from the Sidmouth area, Devon. *British Geological Survey Technical Report,* WH/93/61R.

JUDD, J W. 1871. On the Punfield Formation. *Quarterly Journal of the Geological Society of London,* Vol. 27, 207–227.

JUKES-BROWNE, A J, and HILL, W. 1900. The Cretaceous rocks of Britain. Vol. 1. The Gault and Upper Greensand. *Memoir of the Geological Survey of Great Britain.*

JUKES-BROWNE, A J, and HILL, W. 1903. The Cretaceous rocks of Britain. Vol. 2. The Lower and Middle Chalk of England. *Memoir of the Geological Survey of Great Britain.*

JUKES-BROWNE, A J, and HILL, W. 1904. The Cretaceous rocks of Britain. Vol. 3 — The Upper Chalk of England. *Memoir of the Geological Survey of Great Britain.*

KALAUGHER, P G, GRAINGER, P, and HODGSON, R L P. 1987. Cliff stability evaluation using geomorphological maps based on oblique aerial photographs. 155–161 *in* Planning and engineering geology. CULSHAW, M G, BELL, F G, CRIPPS, J C, and O'HARA, M (editors). *Geological Society Engineering Geology Special Publication,* No. 4.

KALAUGHER, P G, GRAINGER, P, and HODGSON, R L P. 1995. Tidal influence on the intermittent surging movements of a coastal landslide. *Proceedings of the Ussher Society,* Vol. 8, 416–420.

KALAUGHER, P G, HODGSON, R L P, and GRAINGER, P. 2000. Pre-failure strains as precursor of sliding in a coastal mudslide. *Quarterly Journal of Engineering Geology and Hydrogeology,* Vol. 33, 325–334.

KATTENHORN, S A, and POLLARD, D D. 2001. Integrating 3D seismic data, field analogs, and mechanical models in the analysis of segmented normal faults in the Wytch Farm oil field, southern England, United Kingdom. *Bulletin of the American Association of Petroleum Geology*, Vol. 85, 1183–1210.

KEEN, D H. 1995. Raised beaches and sea-levels in the English Channel in the Middle and Late Pleistocene: problems of interpretation and implications for the isolation of the British Isles. 63–74 *in* Island Britain: a Quaternary perspective, PREECE, R C (editor). *Geological Society of London Special Publication*, No. 96.

KEEPING, H. 1910. On the discovery of Bembridge Limestone fossils on Creechbarrow Hill, Isle of Purbeck. *Geological Magazine*, Vol. 7, 436–439.

KELLAWAY, G A, and WILSON, V. 1941. An outline of the geology of Yeovil, Sherborne and Sparkford Vale. *Proceedings of the Geologists' Association*, Vol. 52, 131–174.

KELLY, S R A. 1988. *Laevitrigonia cineris* sp. nov., a bivalve from near the Jurassic–Cretaceous boundary in the Durlston Formation (Purbeck Limestone Group) of Dorset. *Proceedings of the Dorset Natural History and Archaeological Society*, Vol. 109, 113–116.

KENNEDY, W J. 1970. A correlation of the uppermost Albian and the Cenomanian of south-west England. *Proceedings of the Geologists' Association*, Vol. 81, 613–677.

KING, C. 1988. The Hampshire Basin. 32–35 *in* Lithostratig-raphy. KOCKEL, F. (compiler) 1. *In* The Northwest European Tertiary Basin. Results of the International Geological Correlation Programme, Project, No. 124. VINKIN, R. (compiler). *Geologisches Jahrbuch*, Reihe A, Vol. 100.

KIRKALDY, J F. 1947. The provenance of pebbles in the Lower Cretaceous rocks. *Proceedings of the Geologists' Association*, Vol. 58, 223–241.

KNOX, R W O'B. 1982. The petrology of the Penarth Group (Rhaetian) of the Winterborne Kingston borehole, Dorset. 127–134 *in* The Winterborne Kingston borehole, Dorset, England. RHYS, G H, LOTT, G K, and CALVER, M A (editors). *Report of the Institute of Geological Sciences*, 81/3.

KNOX, R W O'B, and HARLAND, R. 1979. Stratigraphical rela-tionships of the early Palaeogene ash series of NW Europe. *Journal of the Geological Society of London*, Vol. 136, 463–470.

KNOX, R W O'B, MORTON, A C, and LOTT, G K. 1982. Petrology of the Bridport Sands in the Winterborne Kingston borehole, Dorset. 107–121 *in* The Winterborne Kingston borehole, Dorset, England. RHYS, G H, LOTT, G K, and CALVER, M A (editors). *Report of the Institute of Geological Sciences*, 81/3.

KOH, A. 1992. Black Ven. 67–79 in *The coastal landforms of west Dorset*. Geologists' Association Guide, No. 47. ALLISON, R J (editor). (London: The Geologists' Association.)

LAKE, S D, and KARNER, G D. 1987. The structure and evolu-tion of the Wessex Basin, southern England: an example of inversion tectonics. *Tectonophysics*, Vol. 137, 347–378.

LAMPLUGH, G W, WEDD, C B, and PRINGLE, J. 1920. Iron ores: bedded ores of the Lias Oolites and later formations in England. *Special Reports on the Mineral Resources of Great Britain*, No. 12. *Memoir of the Geological Survey*.

LANG, W D. 1914. The geology of the Charmouth cliffs, beach and foreshore. *Proceedings of the Geologists' Association*, Vol. 25, 293–360.

LANG, W D. 1924. The Blue Lias of the Devon and Dorset coasts. *Proceedings of the Geologists' Association*, Vol. 35, 169–185.

LANG, W D. 1927. Landslips in Dorset. *Natural History Magazine*, Vol. 9, 201–209.

LANG, W D. 1932. The Lower Lias of Charmouth and the Vale of Marshwood. *Proceedings of the Geologists' Association*, Vol. 43, 97–126.

LANG, W D. 1936. The Green Ammonite Beds of the Dorset Lias. *Quarterly Journal of the Geological Society of London*, Vol. 92, 423–455.

LANG, W D. 1939. Mary Anning (1799–1847), and the pioneer geologists of Lyme. *Proceedings of the Dorset Natural History and Archaeological Society*, Vol. 60, 142–164.

LANG, W D, and SPATH, L F. 1926. The Black Marl of Black Ven and Stonebarrow, in the Lias of the Dorset coast. With notes on the Lamellibranchia by L R Cox; on the Brachiopoda by H M Muir-Wood; on certain Echioceratidae by A E Trueman and D M Williams. *Quarterly Journal of the Geological Society of London*, Vol. 82, 144–187.

LANG, W D, SPATH, L F, and RICHARDSON, W A. 1923. Shales-with-'Beef', a sequence in the Lower Lias of the Dorset coast. *Quarterly Journal of the Geological Society of London*, Vol. 79, 47–99.

LANG, W D, SPATH, L F, COX, L R, and MUIR-WOOD, H M. 1928. The Belemnite Marls of Charmouth, a series in the Lias of the Dorset coast. *Quarterly Journal of the Geological Society of London*, Vol. 84, 179–257.

LEONARD, A J, MOORE, A G, and SELWOOD, E B. 1982. Ventifacts from a deflation surface marking the top of the Budleigh Salt-erton Pebble Beds, east Devon. *Proceedings of the Ussher Society*, Vol. 5, 333–339.

LOTT, G K. 1982. The sedimentology of the Lower Chalk (Middle–Upper Cenomanian) of the Winterborne Kingston borehole, Dorset. 28–34 *in* The Winterborne Kingston Borehole, Dorset, England. RHYS, G H, LOTT, G K, and CALVER, M A (editors). *Report of the Institute of Geological Sciences*, No. 81/3.

LOTT, G K, and STRONG, G E. 1982. The petrology and petrog-raphy of the Sherwood Sandstone Group (? Middle Triassic) of the Winterborne Kingston borehole, Dorset. 135–142 *in* The Winterborne Kingston Borehole, Dorset, England. RHYS, G H, LOTT, G K, and CALVER, M A (editors). *Report of the Institute of Geological Sciences*, No. 81/3.

LOTT, G K, SOBEY, R A, WARRINGTON, G, and WHITTAKER, A. 1982. The Mercia Mudstone Group (Triassic) in the western Wessex Basin. *Proceedings of the Ussher Society*, Vol. 5, 340–346.

LYELL, C. 1855. *Manual of elementary geology*. Fifth edition. (London: John Murray.)

MADER, D. 1985a. *Beiträge zur Genese des germanischen Buntsand-steins*. (Hannover: Sedimo-Verlag.)

MADER, D. 1985b. Braidplain, floodplain and playa lake, alluvial-fan, aeolian and palaeosol facies composing a diversi-fied lithogenetical sequence in the Permian and Triassic of south Devon (England). 15–64 *in* Aspects of fluvial sedimen-tation in the Lower Triassic Buntsandstein of Europe. MADER, D (editor). *Lecture Notes in Earth Sciences*, Vol. 4.

MADER, D. 1990. *Palaeoecology of the flora in Buntsandstein and Keuper in the Triassic of Middle Europe*. (Stuttgart: Gustav Fischer Verlag.)

MADDY, D. 1997. Uplift-driven valley incision and river terrace formation in southern England. *Journal of Quaternary Science*, Vol. 12, 539–545.

MATHERS, S J. 1982. The sand and gravel resources of the country between Dorchester and Wareham, Dorset: descriptions of parts of 1:25 000 sheets SY68, 69, 78, 79, 88, 89 and 99. *Mineral Assess-ment Report of the Institute of Geological Sciences*, No. 103.

MAYALL, M J. 1983. An earthquake origin for synsedimentary deformation in a late Triassic (Rhaetian) lagoonal sequence, southwest Britain. *Geological Magazine*, Vol. 120, 613–622.

McCLURE, N M, WILKINSON, D W, FROST, D P, and GEEHAN, G W. 1995. Planning extended reach wells in Wytch Farm Field, UK. *Petroleum Geoscience*, Vol. 1, 115–127.

McKIE, T, AGGETT, J, and HOGG, A J C. 1998. Reservoir architecture of the upper Sherwood Sandstone, Wytch Farm field, southern England. 399–406 *in* Development, evolution and petroleum geology of the Wessex Basin. UNDERHILL, J R (editor). *Geological Society of London Special Publication*, No. 133.

METCALFE, A T. 1884. On further discoveries of vertebrate remains in the Triassic strata of the south coast of Devonshire, between Budleigh Salterton and Sidmouth. *Quarterly Journal of the Geological Society of London*, Vol. 40, 257–262.

MILIORIZOS, M, and RUFFELL, A. 1998. Kinematics of the Watchet–Cothelstone–Hatch Fault System: implications for the fault history of the Wessex Basin and adjacent areas. 311–330 *in* Development, evolution and petroleum geology of the Wessex Basin. UNDERHILL, J R (editor). *Geological Society of London Special Publication*, No. 133.

MILNER, A R, GARDINER, B G, FRASER, N C, and TAYLOR, M A. 1990. Vertebrates from the Middle Triassic Otter Sandstone Formation of Devon. *Palaeontology*, Vol. 33, 873–892.

MOGHADAM, H V, and PAUL, C R C. 2000. Trace fossils of the Jurassic, Blue Lias, Lyme Regis, southern England. *Ichnos*, Vol. 8, 1–24.

MORGANS-BELL, H S, COE, A L, HESSELBO, S P, JENKYNS, H C, WEEDON, G P, MARSHALL, J E A, TYSON, R V, and WILLIAMS, C J. 2001. Integrated stratigraphy of the Kimmeridge Clay Formation (Upper Jurassic) based on exposures and boreholes in south Dorset, UK. *Geological Magazine*, Vol. 138, 511–539.

MORTER, A A. 1982. The macrofauna of the Lower Cretaceous rocks of the Winterbourne Kingston borehole, Dorset. 35–38 *in* The Winterbourne Kingston Borehole, Dorset, England. RHYS, G H, LOTT, G K, and CALVER, M A (editors). *Report of the Institute of Geological Sciences*, No. 81/3.

MORTER, A A. 1984. Purbeck–Wealden Mollusca and their relationship to ostracod biostratigraphy, stratigraphical correlation and palaeoecology in the Weald and adjacent areas. *Proceedings of the Geologists' Association*, Vol. 95, 217–234.

MORTIMORE, R N. 1983. The stratigraphy and sedimentation of the Turonian–Campanian in the southern Province of England. *Zitteliana*, Vol. 10, 515–529.

MORTIMORE, R N. 1986a. Stratigraphy of the Upper Cretaceous White Chalk of Sussex. *Proceedings of the Geologists' Association*, Vol. 97, 97–139.

MORTIMORE, R N. 1986b. Controls on Upper Cretaceous sedimentation in the South Downs, with particular reference to flint distribution. 21–42 in *The scientific study of flint and chert*. SIEVEKING, G DE C, and HART, M B (editors). (London: Cambridge University Press.)

MORTIMORE, R N, and POMEROL, B. 1987. Correlation of the Upper Cretaceous White Chalk (Turonian to Campanian) in the Anglo-Paris Basin. *Proceedings of the Geologists' Association*, Vol. 98, 97–143.

MORTIMORE, R N, and POMEROL, B. 1991. Upper Cretaceous tectonic disruptions in a placid Chalk sequence in the Anglo-Paris Basin. *Journal of the Geological Society of London*, Vol. 148, 391–404.

MORTIMORE, R N, WOOD, C J, POMEROL, B, and ERNST, G. 1998. Dating the phases of the Subhercynian tectonic epoch: Late Creta-ceous tectonics and eustatics in the Cretaceous basins of northern Germany compared with the Anglo-Paris Basin. *Zentralblatt, Geologie Paläontologie*, Teil I, H. 11/12, 1349–1401.

MORTIMORE, R N, WOOD, C J, and GALLOIS, R W. 2001. *British Upper Cretaceous Stratigraphy. Geological Conservation Review Series*, No. 23. (Peterborough: Joint Nature Conservation Committee.)

MORTON, A C. 1982. Heavy minerals of Hampshire Basin Palaeogene strata. *Geological Magazine*, Vol. 119, 463–476.

MUIR-WOOD, H M. 1936. A monograph on the Brachiopoda of the British Great Oolite Series. Part I. The Brachiopoda of the Fuller's Earth. *Monograph of the Palaeontographical Society*.

MURRAY, J W. 1992. Palaeogene and Neogene. 141–148 *in* Atlas of Palaeogeography and Lithofacies. COPE, J C W, INGHAM, J K, and RAWSON, P F (editors). *Geological Society of London Memoir*, No. 13.

NEWELL, A J. 1998. Corallian lithostratigraphy of the Abbots-bury district (Dorset): a revised interpretation based on new borehole evidence. *Technical Report of the British Geological Survey*, WA/98/04.

NEWELL, A J. 2000. Fault activity and sedimentation in a marine rift basin (Upper Jurassic, Wessex Basin, UK). *Journal of the Geological Society of London*, Vol. 157, 83–92.

NEWELL, A J. 2001. Bounding surfaces in a mixed aeolian-fluvial system (Rotliegend, Wessex Basin, SW UK). *Marine and Petroleum Geology*, Vol. 18, 339–347.

NOMINATION. 2000. *Nomination of the Dorset and east Devon coast for inclusion in the World Heritage List*. (Dorset: Dorset County Council.)

NORRIS, G. 1969. Miospores from the Purbeck Beds and marine Upper Jurassic from southern England. *Palaeontology*, Vol. 12, 574–620.

NORRIS, G. 1970. Palynology of the Jurassic–Cretaceous boundary in southern England. *Geoscience and Man*, Vol. 1, 57–65.

ORBELL, G. 1973. Palynology of the British Rhaeto-Liassic. *Bulletin of the British Geological Survey*, Vol. 44, 1–44.

ORD, W T. 1914. The geology of the Bournemouth to Boscombe Cliff section. *Proceedings of the Bournemouth Natural Science Society*, Vol. 5, 118–135.

OWEN, H G. 1971. Middle Albian stratigraphy in the Anglo-Paris Basin. *Bulletin of the British Museum (Natural History) Geology*, Supplement 8.

OWEN, H G. 1975. The stratigraphy of the Gault and Upper Greensand of the Weald. *Proceedings of the Geologists' Association*, Vol. 86, 475–498.

OWEN, H G. 1984. The Albian Stage: European province chronology and ammonite zonation. *Cretaceous Research*, Vol. 5, 329–344.

OWEN, H G. 1996. Boreal and Tethyan late Aptian to late Albian ammonite zonation and palaeobiogeography. *Mitteilungen aus dem Geologisches—Palaontologisches Institut der Universitat Hamburg*, Vol. 77, 461–481.

OWEN, H G. 1999. Correlation of Albian European and Tethyan ammonite zonations and the boundaries of the Albian Stage and substages: some comments. *Scripta Geologica Special Issue*, No. 3, 129–149.

OWEN, H G, and MUTTERLOSE, J. 2006. Late Albian ammonites from offshore Suriname: implications for biostratigraphy and palaeobiogeography. *Cretaceous Research*, Vol. 27, 717–727.

OWENS, B. 1972. A derived lower Tournaisian miospore assemblage from the Permo-Triassic deposits of south Devon, England. *Compte Rendu du 7me Congrés International du Stratigra-phie et Geologie du Carbonifère (Krefeld, 1971)*, Vol. 1, 325–343.

PAGE, K N. 1989. A stratigraphical revision for the English Lower Callovian. *Proceedings of the Geologists' Association*, Vol. 100, 363–382.

PAGE, K N. 1992. The sequence of ammonite correlated horizons in the British Sinemurian (Lower Jurassic). *Newsletters on Stratigraphy*, Vol. 27, 129–156.

PAGE, K N. 1995. East Quantoxhead, Somerset, England; a potential global stratotype section and point (GSSP) for the base of the Sinemurian stage (Lower Jurassic). *Proceedings of the Ussher Society*, Vol. 8, 210–214.

PAGE, K N. 2002. A review of the ammonite faunas and standard zonation of the Hettangian and Lower Sinemurian succession (Lower Jurassic) of the east Devon coast (south-west England). *Geoscience in south-west England*, Vol. 10, 293–303.

PAGE, K N, and BLOOS, G. 1998. The base of the Jurassic System in West Somerset, south-west England — new observations on the succession of ammonite faunas of the lowest Hettangian stage. *Geoscience in south-west England*, Vol. 9, 231–235.

PALMER, C P. 1966. The fauna of Day's Shell Bed in the Middle Lias of the Dorset coast. *Proceedings of the Dorset Natural History and Archaeological Society*, Vol. 87, 69–80.

PALMER, T J, and WILSON, M A. 1990. Growth of ferruginous oncoliths in the Bajocian (Middle Jurassic) of Europe. *Terra Nova*, Vol. 2, 142–147.

PARSONS, C F. 1980. Aalenian and Bajocian Correlation Chart. 3–21 *in* A correlation of Jurassic rocks in the British Isles. Part Two: Middle and Upper Jurassic. COPE, J C W, DUFF, K L, PARSONS, C F, TORRENS, H S, WIMBLEDON, W A, and WRIGHT, J K. *Special Report of the Geological Society of London*, No. 15.

PATON, R L. 1974. Capitosauroid labyrinthodonts from the Trias of England. *Palaeontology*, Vol. 17, 253–289.

PENN, I E. 1982. Middle Jurassic stratigraphy and correlation of the Winterborne Kingston borehole, Dorset. 53–76 *in* Winterborne Kingston borehole, Dorset, England. RHYS, G H, LOTT, G K, and CALVER, M A (editors). *Report of the Institute of Geological Sciences*, No. 81/3.

PENN, I E, MERRIMAN, R J, and WYATT, R J. 1979. The Bathonian strata of the Bath–Frome area. 1. A proposed type section for the Fuller's Earth (Bathonian), based on the Horsecombe Vale No.15 Borehole, near Bath, with details of contiguous strata. *Report of the Institute of Geological Sciences*, No. 78/22.

PENN, I E, CHADWICK, R A, HOLLOWAY, S, ROBERTS, G, PHARAOH, T C, ALLSOP, J M, HULBERT, A G, and BURNS, I M. 1987. Principal features of the hydrocarbon prospectivity of the Wessex–Channel Basin, UK. 109–118 *in Petroleum geology of north-west Europe*, Vol. 1. BROOKS, J, and GLENNIE, K (editors). (London: Graham and Trotman.)

PERRY, C T. 1994. Freshwater tufa stromatolites in the basal Purbeck Formation (Upper Jurassic), Isle of Portland, Dorset. *Geological Journal*, Vol. 29, 119–135.

PHELPS, M C. 1985. A refined ammonite biostratigraphy for the Middle and Upper Carixian (*ibex* and *davoei* zones, Lower Jurassic) in north-west Europe and stratigraphical details of the Carixian–Domerian boundary. *Geobios*, Vol. 18, 321–362.

PITTS, J. 1974. The Bindon Landslip of 1839. *Proceedings of the Dorset Natural History and Archaeological Society*, Vol. 95, 18–29.

PITTS, J. 1981a. Landslides of the Axmouth–Lyme Regis Undercliffs Nature Reserve, Devon. Unpublished PhD thesis, University of London.

PITTS, J. 1981b. A historical survey of the landslips of the Axmouth–Lyme Regis Undercliffs, Devon. *Proceedings of the Dorset Natural History and Archaeological Society*, Vol. 103, 106.

PITTS, J. 1983. The temporal and spatial development of landslides in the Axmouth–Lyme Regis Undercliffs National Nature Reserve, Devon. *Earth Surface Processes and Landforms*, Vol. 8, 589–603.

PITTS, J, and BRUNSDEN, D. 1987. A reconsideration of the Bindon Landslide of 1839. *Proceedings of the Geologists' Association*, Vol. 98, 1–18.

PLINT, A G. 1982. Eocene sedimentation and tectonics in the Hampshire Basin. *Journal of the Geological Society of London*, Vol. 139, 249–254.

PLINT, A G. 1983. Facies, environments and sedimentary cycles in the Middle Eocene, Bracklesham Formation of the Hampshire Basin: evidence for global sea-level changes? *Sedimentology*. Vol. 30, 625–653.

POWELL, A J. 1992. Dinoflagellate cysts of the Tertiary System. 155–251 in *A stratigraphic index of dinoflagellate cysts*. POWELL, A J (editor). British Micropalaeontological Society Publications Series. (London: Chapman and Hall.)

POWELL, H P. 1987. A megalosaurid dinosaur jawbone from the Kimmeridge Clay of the sea bed of West Bay, Dorset. *Proceedings of the Dorset Natural History and Archaeological Society*, Vol. 109, 105–108.

PUGH, M E. 1968. Algae from the Lower Purbeck Limestones of Dorset. *Proceedings of the Geologists' Association*, Vol. 79, 513–523.

PUGH, M E. 1969. Algae from the Lower Purbeck Limestones of Dorset. *Proceedings of the Geologists' Association*, Vol. 79, 51–523.

PURVIS, K, and WRIGHT, V P. 1991. Calcretes related to phreatophytic vegetation from the Middle Triassic Otter Sandstone of south-west England. *Sedimentology*, Vol. 38, 539–551.

RADLEY, J D. 2002. Distribution and palaeoenvironmental significance of molluscs in the Late Jurassic–Early Cretaceous Purbeck Formation of Dorset, southern England: A review. *Special Papers in Palaeontology*, No. 68, 41–51.

RAWSON, P F, and RILEY, L A. 1982. Latest Jurassic–Early Cretaceous events and the 'late Cimmerian Unconformity' in the North Sea. *American Association of Petroleum Geologists Bulletin*, Vol. 12, 2628–2648.

RAWSON, P F, CURRY, D, DILLEY, F C, HANCOCK, J M, KENNEDY, W J, NEALE, J W, WOOD, C J, and WORSSAM, B C. 1978. A correlation of the Cretaceous rocks in the British Isles. *Special Report of the Geological Society of London*, No. 9.

RAWSON, P F, ALLEN, P, and GALE, A S. 2001. The Chalk Group — a revised lithostratigraphy. *Geoscientist*, Vol. 11, 21.

REID C. 1899. The geology of the country around Dorchester. *Memoir of the Geological Survey of Great Britain*, Sheet 328 (England and Wales).

RHYS, G H, LOTT, G K, and CALVER, M A (editors). 1982. The Winterborne Kingston borehole, Dorset, England. *Report of the Institute of Geological Sciences*, No. 81/3.

RICHARDSON, L. 1906. On the Rhaetic and contiguous deposits of Devon and Dorset. *Proceedings of the Geologists' Association*, Vol. 19, 401–409.

RICHARDSON, L. 1928–1930. The Inferior Oolite and contiguous deposits of the Burton Bradstock–Broadwindsor district, Dorset. *Proceedings of the Cotteswold Naturalists' Field Club*, Vol. 23, 35–68 (1928), 149–185 (1929); Vol. 24, 253–264 (1930).

ROBERTS, G. 1840. *An account of and guide to the Mighty Landslip of Dowlands and Bindon in the parish of Axmouth near Lyme Regis, December 25, 1839* (fifth edition). (Lyme Regis: Daniel Dunster.)

ROWE, A W. 1901. The zones of the white Chalk of the English coast. II — Dorset. *Proceedings of the Geologists' Association*, Vol. 17, 1–76.

ROWE, A W. 1903. The zones of the White Chalk of the English coast. III — Devon. *Proceedings of the Geologists' Association*, Vol. 18, 1–51.

RUFFELL, A H, and BATTEN, D J. 1994. Uppermost Wealden facies and Lower Greensand Group (Lower Cretaceous) in Dorset, southern England: correlation and palaeoenvironment. *Proceedings of the Geologists' Association*, Vol. 105, 53–69.

RUFFELL, A H, and OWEN, H G. 1995. The Sandgate Formation of the M20 Motorway near Ashford, Kent, and its correlation. *Proceedings of the Geologists' Association*, Vol. 106, 1–9.

RUFFELL, A, and SHELTON, R. 1999. The control of sedimentary facies by climate during phases of crustal extension: examples from the Triassic of onshore and offshore England and Northern Ireland. *Journal of the Geological Society of London*, Vol. 156, 779–789.

SEELEY, H G. 1876. On the posterior portion of a lower jaw of *Labyrinthodon* (*L. Lavisi*) from the Trias of Sidmouth. *Quarterly Journal of the Geological Society of London*, Vol. 32, 278–284.

SELLWOOD, B W. 1970. The relation of trace fossils to small-scale sedimentary cycles in the British Lias. 489–504 in *Trace fossils*, CRIMES, T P, and HARPER, J C (editors). *Special Issue of the Geological Journal*, No. 3.

SELLWOOD, B W, and JENKYNS, H C. 1975. Basins and swells and the evolution of a epeiric sea (Pliensbachian–Bajocian of Great Britian). *Journal of the Geological Society of London*, Vol. 131, 373–388.

SELLWOOD, B W, and WILSON, R C L. 1990. *Field Guide No. 7: Jurassic sedimentary environments of the Wessex Basin.* (Cambridge: British Sedimentological Research Group.)

SELLWOOD, B W, DURKIN, M K, and KENNEDY, W J. 1970. Field meeting on the Jurassic and Cretaceous rocks of Wessex. *Proceedings of the Geologists' Association*, Vol. 81, 715–732.

SELWOOD, E B, EDWARDS, R A, SIMPSON, S, CHESHER, J A, HAMBLIN, R J O, HENSON, M R, RIDDOLLS, B W, and WATERS, R A. 1984. Geology of the country around Newton Abbot. *Memoir of the British Geological Survey*, Sheet 339 (England and Wales).

SENIOR, J R, PARSONS, C F, and TORRENS, H S. 1970. New sections in the Inferior Oolite of South Dorset. *Proceedings of the Dorset Natural History and Archaeological Society*, Vol. 91, 114–119.

SIMMS, M J. 1989. British Lower Jurassic Crinoids. *Monograph of the Palaeontographical Society*, London: 1–103, pls. 1–15 (Publ. No. 581, part of Vol. 142 for 1988).

SIMMS, M J. 2003. Uniquely extensive seismile from the latest Triassic of the United Kingdom: evidence for bolide impact? *Geology*, Vol. 19, 401–409.

SIMMS, M J. 2004. Pinhay Bay to Fault Corner and East Cliff, Dorset. 60–81 in *British Lower Jurassic Stratigraphy*, SIMMS, M J, CHIDLAW, N, MORTON, N, and PAGE, K N (editors). *Geological Conservation Review Series*, No. 30 (Peterborough: Joint Nature Conservation Committee.)

SIMMS, M J, CHIDLAW, N, MORTON, N, and PAGE, K N. 2004. *British Lower Jurassic Stratigraphy. Geological Conservation Review Series*, No. 30 (Peterborough: Joint Nature Conservation Committee.)

SIMPSON, M I. 1983. Decapod Crustacea and associated fauna of the Punfield Marine Band (Lower Cretaceous; Lower Aptian), Punfield, Dorset. *Proceedings of the Dorset Natural History and Archaeological Society*, Vol. 104, 143–146.

SIMPSON, M I. 1985. The stratigraphy of the Atherfield Clay Formation (Lower Aptian, Lower Cretaceous) at the type and other localities in southern England. *Proceedings of the Geologists' Association*, Vol. 96, 23–45.

SMITH, C, and HATTON, I R. 1998. Inversion tectonics in the Lyme Bay–west Dorset area of the Wessex Basin, UK. 267–281 in Development, evolution and petroleum geology of the Wessex Basin, UNDERHILL, J R (editor). *Geological Society of London Special Publication*, Vol. 133.

SMITH, S A. 1990. The sedimentology and accretionary styles of an ancient gravel-bed stream: the Budleigh Salterton Pebble Beds (Lower Triassic), south-west England. *Sedimentary Geology*, Vol. 67, 199–219.

SMITH, S A, and EDWARDS, R A. 1991. Regional sedimentological variations in Lower Triassic fluvial conglomerates (Budleigh Salterton Pebble Beds), south-west England: some implications for palaeogeography and basin evolution. *Geological Journal*, Vol. 26, 65–83.

SMITH, W E. 1957. The Cenomanian Limestone of the Beer District, South Devon. *Proceedings of the Geologists' Association*, Vol. 68, 115–135.

SMITH, W E. 1961a. The Cenomanian deposits of south-east Devonshire: the Cenomanian limestones and contiguous deposits west of Beer. *Proceedings of the Geologists' Association*, Vol. 72, 91–133.

SMITH, W E. 1961b. The detrital mineralogy of the Cretaceous rocks of south-west England with particular reference to the Cenomanian. *Proceedings of the Geologists' Association*, Vol. 72, 303–331.

SMITH, W E. 1965. The Cenomanian deposits of south-east Devonshire: The Cenomanian Limestone east of Seaton. *Proceedings of the Geologists' Association*, Vol. 76, 121–136.

SPATH, L F. 1926. On the zones of the Cenomanian and uppermost Albian. *Proceedings of the Geologists' Association*, Vol. 37, 420–432.

SPATH, L F. 1933. A monograph of the Ammonoidea of the Gault. *Monograph of the Palaeontological Society*, Volume 2, pt. 10, 411–442.

SPATH, L F. 1934. A monograph of the Ammonoidea of the Gault. *Monograph of the Palaeontological Society*, Volume 2, pt. 11, 443–496.

SPATH, L F. 1943. A monograph of the Ammonoidea of the Gault. *Monograph of the Palaeontological Society*, Volume 2, pt. 16, 721–787.

SPENCER, P S, and ISAAC, K P. 1983. Triassic vertebrates from the Otter Sandstone Formation of Devon, England. *Proceedings of the Geologists' Association*, Vol. 94, 267–269.

SPENCER, P S, and STORRS, G W. 2002. A re-evaluation of small tetrapods from the Middle Triassic Otter Sandstone Formation of Devon, England. *Palaeontology*, Vol. 44, 447–467.

SPERLING, C H B, GOUDIE, A S, STODDART, D R, and POOLE, G G. 1977. Dolines of the Dorset Chalklands and other areas in southern Britain. *Transactions of the Institute of British Geographers*, Vol. 2, 205–223.

STANIER, P. 1995. *Quarries of England and Wales: An historic photographic record.* (Truro: Twelveheads Press.)

STEVENSON, C R, and WARRINGTON, G. 1971. Jurassic and Cretaceous rocks of Wessex: highest Keuper deposits. Written discussion to report of field meeting. *Proceedings of the Geologists' Association*, Vol. 82, 297–300.

STEVENSON, W. 1812. *General view of the agriculture of the County of Dorset.* (London: Board of Agriculture.)

STONELEY, R. 1982. The structural development of the Wessex Basin. *Journal of the Geological Society of London*, Vol. 139, 543–552.

STRAHAN, A. 1895. Overthrusts of Tertiary date in Dorset. *Quarterly Journal of the Geological Society of London*, Vol. 51, 549–562.

STRAHAN, A. 1898. The geology of the Isle of Purbeck and Weymouth. *District memoir of the Geological Survey of Great Britain.*

STRONG, G E, and MILODOWSKI, A E. 1987. Aspects of the diagenesis of the Sherwood Sandstones of the Wessex Basin and their influence on reservoir characteristics. 325–337 *in* Diagenesis of sedimentary sequences, MARSHALL, J D (editor). *Geological Society of London Special Publication*, No. 36.

SUN, S Q. 1989. A new interpretation of the Corallian (Upper Jurassic) cycles of the Dorset coast, southern England. *Geological Journal*, Vol. 24, 139–158.

SWIFT, A. 1995. Conodonts from the Late Permian and Late Triassic of Britain. *Monograph of the Palaeontographical Society of London*, No. 598. (London: Palaeontographical Society.)

SWIFT, A, and MARTILL, D M. 1999. Fossils of the Rhaetian Penarth Group. *Field Guides to Fossils*, No. 9 (London: The Palaeontological Association.)

SYKES, R M, and CALLOMON, J H. 1979. The *Amoeboceras* zonation of the Boreal Upper Oxfordian. *Palaeontology*, Vol. 22, 839–903.

SYLVESTER-BRADLEY, P C. 1949. The ostracod genus *Cypridea* and the Zones of the Upper and Middle Purbeckian. *Proceedings of the Geologists' Association*, Vol. 60, 125–153.

TALBOT, M R. 1973. Major sedimentary cycles in the Corallian Beds (Oxfordian) of southern England. *Journal of Sedimentary Petrology*, Vol. 41, 261–273.

TAYLOR, M A, and BENTON, M J. 1985. Reptiles from the Upper Kimmeridge Clay (Kimmeridgian, Upper Jurassic) of the vicinity of Egmont Bight, Dorset. *Proceedings of the Dorset Natural History and Archaeological Society*, Vol. 107, 121–125.

THOMAS, J. 1990. The lesser known building materials of west Dorset. *Proceedings of the Geologists' Association*, Vol. 101, 289–301.

THOMAS, J. 1993. The Building stones of Dorset. Part 1. The Western parishes — Upper Greensand Chert and Lower Lias. *Proceedings of the Dorset Natural History and Archaeological Society*, Vol. 114, 161–168.

THOMAS, J. 1994. Building stones of Dorset. Part 2. Chideock to Broadwindsor–Middle and Upper Lias. *Proceedings of the Dorset Natural History and Archaeological Society*, Vol. 115, 133–138.

THOMAS, J. 1995. Building stones of Dorset. Part 3. Inferior Oolite, Forest Marble, Cornbrash and Corallian Limestones. *Proceedings of the Dorset Natural History and Archaeological Society*, Vol. 116, 61–70.

THOMAS, J. 1998. Stone Quarrying. *Discover Dorset.* (Stanbridge: Dovecote Press.)

TICKELL, C. 1996. *Mary Anning of Lyme Regis.* (Lyme Regis: Philpot Museum.)

TORRENS, H S (editor). 1969. Excursion No.1. Guide for Dorset and south Somerset International Field Symposium on the British Jurassic (University of Keele, April, 1969).

TORRENS, H S. 1980a. Jurassic stratigraphy in practice. 2–4 *in* A correlation of Jurassic rocks in the British Isles. Part One: Introduction and Lower Jurassic. COPE, J C W, GETTY, T A, HOWARTH, M K, MORTON, N, and TORRENS, H S. *Special Report of the Geological Society of London*, No. 14.

TORRENS, H S. 1980b. Bathonian Correlation Chart. 21–45 *in* A correlation of Jurassic rocks in the British Isles. Part 2: Middle and Upper Jurassic. COPE, J C W, DUFF, K L, PARSONS, C F, TORRENS, H S, WIMBLEDON, W A, and WRIGHT, J K. *Special Report of the Geological Society of London*, No. 15.

TORRENS, H S. 1998. Life, times and legacy of Mary Anning (1799–1847) Fossilist. *Transactions of the Leicester Literary and Philosophical Society*, Vol. 92, 4–5.

TORRENS, H S, and GETTY, T A. 1980. The base of the Jurassic System. 17–22 *in* A correlation of Jurassic rocks in the British Isles. Part One: Introduction and Lower Jurassic. COPE, J C W, GETTY, T A, HOWARTH, M K, MORTON, N, and TORRENS, H S. *Special Report of the Geological Society of London*, No. 14.

TOWNSON, W G. 1975. Lithostratigraphy and deposition of the type Portlandian. *Journal of the Geological Society of London*, Vol. 131, 619–638.

UNDERHILL, J R. 2002. Evidence for structural controls on the deposition of the Late Jurassic – Early Cretaceous Purbeck Limestone Group, Dorset, southern England. *Special Papers in Palaeontology*, Vol. 68, 21–40.

UNDERHILL, J R, and PATERSON, S. 1998. Genesis of tectonic inversion structures: seismic evidence for the development of key structures along the Purbeck–Isle of Wight Disturbance. *Journal of the Geological Society of London*, Vol. 155, 975–992.

VELLACOT, C H. 1908. *Victoria County History, Dorset* — Vol. 2. (London: Archibald Constable and Co. Ltd.)

WARRINGTON, G. 1971. Palynology of the New Red Sandstone sequence of the south Devon coast. *Proceedings of the Ussher Society*, Vol. 2, 307–314.

WARRINGTON, G. 1974. Les évaporites du Trias britannique. *Bulletin de la Société géologique de France*, Série 7, Vol. 16, 708–723.

WARRINGTON, G. 1982. Palynology of cores from the basal Lias and the Permian(?)–Triassic sequence of the Winterborne Kingston borehole, Dorset. 122–126 *in* The Winterborne Kingston borehole, Dorset, England. RHYS, G H, LOTT, G K, and CALVER, M A (editors). *Report of the Institute of Geological Sciences*, No. 81/3.

WARRINGTON, G. 1997. The Lyme Regis Borehole, Dorset — palynology of the Mercia Mudstone, Penarth and Lias groups (Upper Triassic–Lower Jurassic). *Ussher Society.* Annual conference 1997, 153–157.

WARRINGTON, G. 2005. The Charmouth 16A Borehole, Dorset — palynology of the Mercia Mudstone, Penarth and basal Lias groups (Upper Triassic–Lower Jurassic). *Geoscience in South-West England*, Vol. 11, 109–116.

WARRINGTON, G, and IVIMEY-COOK, H C. 1992. Triassic. 97–106 *in* Atlas of palaeogeography and lithofacies, COPE, J C W, INGHAM, J K, and RAWSON, P F (editors). *Geological Society of London Memoir*, No. 13.

WARRINGTON, G, and SCRIVENER, R C. 1980. The Lyme Regis (1901) Borehole succession and its relationship to the Triassic sequence of the east Devon coast. *Proceedings of the Ussher Society*, Vol. 5, 24–32.

WARRINGTON, G, and SCRIVENER, R C. 1988. Late Permian fossils from Devon: regional geological implications. *Proceedings of the Ussher Society*, Vol. 7, 95–96.

WARRINGTON, G, and SCRIVENER, R C. 1990. The Permian of Devon, England. *Review of Palaeobotany and Palynology*, Vol. 66, 263–272.

WARRINGTON, G, AUDLEY-CHARLES, M G, ELLIOTT, R E, EVANS, W B, IVIMEY-COOK, H C, KENT, P E, ROBINSON, P L, SHOTTON, F W, and TAYLOR, F M. 1980. A correlation of Triassic rocks in the

British Isles. *Special Report of the Geological Society of London,* No. 13.

WEEDON, G P. 1986. Hemiplagic shelf sedimentation and climatic cycles: basal Jurassic (Blue Lias) of South Britain. *Earth and Planetary Science Letters,* Vol. 76, 321–335.

WEEDON, G P, and JENKYNS, H C. 1990. Regular and irregular climatic cycles and the Belemnite Marls (Pliensbachian, Lower Jurassic, Wessex Basin). *Journal of the Geological Society of London,* Vol. 147, 915–918.

WEST, I M. 1964. Evaporite diagenesis in the Lower Purbeck Beds of Dorset. *Proceedings of the Yorkshire Geological Society,* Vol. 34, 315–330.

WEST, I M. 1975. Evaporites and associated sediments of the basal Purbeck Formation (Upper Jurassic) of Dorset. *Proceedings of the Geologists' Association,* Vol. 86, 205–225.

WEST, I M. 1979. Sedimentary environments and diagenesis of Purbeck strata (Upper Jurassic–Lower Cretaceous) of Dorset, UK. Unpublished PhD thesis, University of Southampton.

WEST, I M, SHEARMAN, D J, and PUGH, M E. 1969. Whitsun field meeting in the Weymouth area, 1966. *Proceedings of the Geologists' Association,* Vol. 80, 331–340.

WESTHEAD, R K, and MATHER, A E. 1996. An updated litho-stratigraphy for the Purbeck Limestone Group in the Dorset type-area. *Proceedings of the Geologists' Association,* Vol. 107, 117–128.

WHALLEY, P E S. 1985. The systematics and palaeogeography of the Lower Jurassic insects of Dorset, England. *Bulletin of the British Museum (Natural History) Geology,* Vol. 39, 107–18.

WHITAKER, W. 1869. On the succession of beds in the 'New Red' on the south coast of Devon, and on the locality of a new specimen of *Hyperodapedon*. *Quarterly Journal of the Geological Society of London,* Vol. 25, 152–158.

WHITE, H J O. 1917. Geology of the country around Bournemouth. *Memoir of the Geological Survey of Great Britain.* Sheet 329 (England and Wales).

WHITE, H J O. 1923. Geology of the country south and west of Shaftesbury. *Memoir of the Geological Survey of Great Britain.* Sheet 313 (England and Wales).

WHITTAKER, A (editor). 1985. *Atlas of onshore sedimentary basins in England and Wales: post-Carboniferous tectonics and stratigraphy.* (Glasgow: Blackie.)

WHITTAKER, A, and CHADWICK, R A. 1984. The large scale structure of the Earth's crust beneath southern Britain. *Geological Magazine,* Vol. 121, 621–624.

WHITTAKER, A, HOLLIDAY, D W, and PENN, I E. 1985. Geophysical logs in British stratigraphy. *Geological Society of London Special Report,* No. 18.

WIGNALL, P B. 1994. Black Shales. *Oxford Monographs on geology and geophysics,* No. 30 (Oxford: Clarendon).

WIGNALL, P B. 2001. Sedimentology of the Triassic–Jurassic boundary beds in Pinhay Bay (Devon, south-west England). *Proceedings of the Geologists' Association,* Vol. 112, 349–360.

WILLIAMS, C L. 1986. The cherts of the Upper Greensand (Cretaceous) of south-east Devon. 63–70 in *The scientific study of flint and chert: proceedings of the fourth international flint symposium held at Brighton Polytechnic 10-15 April, 1983.* SIEVEKING, G DE C, and HART, M B (editors). (Cambridge: Cambridge University Press.)

WILSON, V, WELCH, F B A, ROBBIE, J A, and GREEN, G W. 1958. Geology of the country around Bridport and Yeovil. *Memoir of the British Geological Survey,* Sheets 327 and 312 (England and Wales).

WIMBLEDON, W A. 1980. Portlandian correlation chart. 85–93 in A correlation of Jurassic rocks in the British Isles. Part 2: Middle and Upper Jurassic. COPE, J C W, DUFF, K L, PARSONS, C F, TORRENS, H S, WIMBLEDON, W A, and WRIGHT, J K. *Special Report of the Geological Society of London,* No. 15.

WIMBLEDON, W A. 1987. Rhythmic sedimentation in the Late Jurassic–Early Cretaceous. *Proceedings of the Dorset Natural History and Archaeological Society,* Vol. 108, 127–133.

WIMBLEDON, W A, and COPE, J C W. 1978. The ammonite faunas of the English Portland Beds and the zones of the Portlandian Stage. *Journal of the Geological Society of London,* Vol. 135, 183–190.

WOODS, M A, WOOD, C J, and LOTT, G K. 2009. The Albian–Cenomanian boundary at Eggardon Hill, Dorset (England): an anomaly resolved? *Proceedings of the Geologists' Association,* Vol. 120, 108–120.

WOODWARD, H B. 1893. The Jurassic rocks of Britain. Vol 3. The Lias of England and Wales (Yorkshire excepted). *Memoir of the Geological Survey of Great Britain.*

WOODWARD, H B. 1894. The Jurassic rocks of Britain. Vol. 4. The Lower Oolitic rocks of England. *Memoir of the Geological Survey of Great Britain.*

WOODWARD, H B. 1895. The Jurassic rocks of Britain. Vol. 5. The Middle and Upper Oolitic Rocks of England (Yorkshire excepted). *Memoir of the Geological Survey of Great Britain.*

WORSSAM, B C, and IVIMEY-COOK, H C. 1984. Comments on the paper 'The Portland–Purbeck junction (Portlandian–Berriasian) in the Weald, and correlation of latest Jurassic–early Cretaceous rocks in southern England' by W A WIMBLEDON, and C O HUNT. *Geological Magazine,* Vol. 120, 267–280.

WRIGHT, C W. 1947. Albian Stage: Gault and Upper Greensand. 178–194 in The geology of the country around Weymouth, Swanage, Corfe and Lulworth. ARKELL, W J. *Memoir of the Geological Survey of Great Britain,* Sheets 341, 342, 343 and parts of 327, 328 and 329 (England and Wales).

WRIGHT, C W, and KENNEDY, W J. 1981. The Ammonoidea of the Plenus Marls and the Middle Chalk. *Monograph of the Palaeontographical Society of London.* Publ. No. 560, part of Vol. 134 for 1980.

WRIGHT, C W, and KENNEDY, W J. 1984. The Ammonoidea of the Lower Chalk. Part I. *Monograph of the Palaeontographical Society of London.* Publ. No. 567, part of Vol. 137 for 1983.

WRIGHT, J K. 1980. Oxfordian correlation chart. 61–76 in A correlation of Jurassic rocks in the British Isles. Part 2: Middle and Upper Jurassic. COPE, J C W, DUFF, K L, PARSONS, C F, TORRENS, H S, WIMBLEDON, W A, and WRIGHT, J K. *Special Report of the Geological Society of London,* No. 15.

WRIGHT, J K. 1986. A new look at the stratigraphy, sedimentology and ammonite fauna of the Corallian Group (Oxfordian) of south Dorset. *Proceedings of the Geologists' Association,* Vol. 97, 1–21.

WRIGHT, J K, and COX, B M. 2001. *British Upper Jurassic Stratigraphy (Oxfordian to Kimmeridgian).* Geological Conservation Review Series No. 21. (Peterborough: Joint Nature Conservation Committee.)

WRIGHT, V P, MARRIOTT, S B, and VANSTONE, S D. 1991. A 'reg' paleosol from the Lower Triassic of south Devon: stratigraphic and palaeoclimatic implications. *Geological Magazine,* Vol. 128, 517–523.

ZIEGLER, B. 1962. Die Ammonitengattung in Oberjura (Taxionomie, Stratigraphie, Biologie). *Palaeontographica,* A119, 1–172.

APPENDIX 1

List of boreholes referred to in the text

Name	Grid reference	BGS Index Number
Abbotsbury 1	SY 5847 8533	SY58NE3
Abbotsbury 2	SY 5851 8505	SY58NE4
Arne G1	SY 9575 8704	SY98NE5
Bere Regis	SY 8644 9563	SY89NE1
Big Almer Wood	ST 9154 0016	ST90SW80
Bransgore	SZ 1958 9505	SZ19NE26
Bushey Farm A1	SY 9693 8306	SY98SE4
Chaldon Down G1	SY 8066 8196	SY88SW2
Chaldon Down G2	SY 8323 8130	SY88SW1
Chaldon Herring G2	ST 7832 8358	SY78SE5
Chaldon Herring G3	SY 7837 8402	SY78SE1
Coombe Keynes	SY 8240 8412	SY88SW48
Chickerell	SY 6573 8222	SY68SE26
Christchurch	SZ 2002 9301	SZ29SW12
Combe Throop	ST 7260 2350	ST72SW1
Cranborne	SU 0341 0907	SU00NW1
Creech	SY 9005 8249	SY98SW14
Encombe	SY 9412 7832	SY97NW2
Hewish	SY 6429 8439	SY68SW4
Hurn	SU 0999 0071	SU00SE215
Kimmeridge 5	SY 9042 7935	SY97NW9
Langton Herring	SY 6063 8171	SY68SW2
Lulworth Banks	SY 7851 7710	SY77NE1
Lyme Regis	SY 336 930	SY39SW14
Lytchett	SY 9339 9286	SY99SW81
Mappowder	ST 7288 0580	ST70NW1

Name	Grid reference	BGS Index Number
Martinstown	SY 6418 8664	SY68NW3
Marshwood	SY 3885 9880	SY39NE1
Metherhills 1	SY 9112 7911	SY97NW14
Monks Wall S10	SY 091 847	SY08SE45
Musbury	SY 2670 9510	SY29NE21
Nettlecombe	SY 5052 9544	SY59NW1
Osmington	SY 7170 8360	SY78SW1
Purse Caundle	ST 7012 1826	ST71NW7
Seabarn Farm	SY 6263 8054	SY68SW3
Seaborough	ST 4348 0620	ST40NW1
Shapwick	ST 9428 0134	ST90SW1
Southard Quarry	SZ 0234 7775	SZ07NW9
Spetisbury	ST 8881 0269	ST80SE1
Stoborough	SY 9126 8661	SY98NW5
Swanworth Quarry 1	SY 9676 7823	SY97NE8
Upton 2	SY 7395 8339	SY78SW27
Waddock Cross	SY 8035 9125	SY89SW16
Wareham 2	SY 9093 8834	SY98NW3
Wareham 3	SY 9059 8721	SY98NW4
West Lulworth	SY 8225 8076	SY88SW3
Winterborne Kingston	SY 8470 9799	SY89NW1
Woodlands	SU 0659 0627	SU00NE5
Wytch Farm X14	SY 9804 8526	SY98NE15
Wytch Farm F15	SZ 0104 8574	SZ08NW10
Wytch Farm 25	SZ 0094 8705	SZ08NW92
98/11–2 (offshore borehole)	Latitude: 50°37'49.7N	Longitude: 001°50'28.6W

APPENDIX 2

Author citations for fossil species

Triassic

Chlamys valoniensis (Defrance, 1825)
Protocardia rhaetica (Merian, 1853)
Rhaetavicula contorta (Portlock, 1843)
Rhynchosaurus spenceri Benton, 1990

Jurassic

Acanthothyris powerstockensis (Buckman & Walker, 1889)
Amaltheus margaritatus de Montfort, 1808
Amaltheus bifurcus (Howarth, 1958)
Amaltheus gibbosus (Schlotheim, 1820)
Amaltheus margaritatus de Montfort, 1808
Amaltheus stokesi (J Sowerby, 1818)
Amaltheus striatus Howarth, 1955
Amaltheus subnodosus (Young & Bird, 1828)
Amaltheus wertheri (Lange, 1932)
Amauroceras ferrugineum (Simpson, 1855)
Amoeboceras transitorium Spath, 1935
Aptyxiella portlandica (J de C Sowerby, 1836)
Arnioceras semicostatum (Young & Bird, 1828)
Aspidoceras perarmatum (J Sowerby, 1822)
Astarte obliqua Deshayes, 1830
Astarte supracorallina d'Orbigny, 1850
Aulacostephanus autissiodorensis (Cotteau, 1853)
Avonothyris bradfordensis (Walker in Davidson, 1878)
Bositra buchii (Roemer, 1836)
Caenisites turneri (J de C Sowerby, 1824)
Caloceras johnstoni (J de C Sowerby, 1824)
Cardioceras scarburgense (Young & Bird, 1828)
Catinula alimena (d'Orbigny, 1850)
Cererithyris intermedia (J Sowerby, 1812)
Chlamys fibrosus (J Sowerby, 1816)
Clydoniceras discus (J Sowerby, 1813)
Corbula prora Sauvage, 1871
Crendonites gorei (Salfeld, 1913)
Dactylioceras athleticum (Simpson, 1884)
Dactylioceras directum (S S Buckman, 1926)
Deltoideum delta (Wm. Smith, 1817)
Digonella digona (J Sowerby, 1815)
Dimorphodon macronyx (Buckland, 1828)
Diplocraterion habichi (Lisson, 1904)
Diplocraterion parallelum Torell, 1870
Galbanites okusensis (Salfeld, 1913)
Gibbirhynchia muirwoodae Ager, 1954
Gibbirhynchia thorncombiensis (S S Buckman, 1922)
Glaucolithites caementarius (S S Buckman, 1926)
Glomerula gordialis (Schlotheim, 1820)
Goliathiceras capax (Young & Bird, 1822)
Goniorhynchia boueti (Davidson, 1852)
Gryphaea arcuata Lamarck, 1801
Gryphaea (Bilobissa) dilobotes Duff, 1978
Gryphaea cymbium Lamarck, 1801
Gryphaea dilatata J Sowerby, 1816

Gryphaea lituola Lamarck, 1819
Gyrochorte comosa Heer, 1865
Isognomon cordati (Uhlig, 1882)
Kepplerites (Gowericeras) gowerianus (J de C Sowerby, 1827)
Kerberites audax (Buckman, 1927)
Kerberites kerberus Buckman, 1924
Kosmoceras (Lobokosmoceras) phaeinum (S S Buckman, 1924)
Liparoceras obtusinodum Trueman, 1919
Lytoceras fimbriatum (J Sowerby, 1817)
Macrocephalites dolius (Buckman, 1922)
Meleagrinella braamburiensis (Phillips, 1829)
Microderoceras birchi J Sowerby, 1820
Modiolus bipartitus J Sowerby, 1818
Myophorella clavellata (Parkinson, 1811)
Nanogyra nana (J Sowerby, 1822)
Neocrassina extensa (Phillips, 1835)
Neocrassina modiolaris (Lamarck) in Deshayes, 1830
Neocrassina hilpertonensis (Lycett, 1863)
Obovothyris obovata (J Sowerby, 1812)
Ornithella [Microthyridina] lagenalis (Schlotheim, 1820)
Ornithella [Microthyridina] siddingtonensis (Walker, 1878)
Oxytoma inequivalve (J Sowerby, 1819)
Palaeocoma milleri (Phillips, 1829)
Palaeonucula menkii (Röemer, 1836)
Paracraspedites opressus Casey, 1973
Parkinsonia parkinsoni (J Sowerby, 1821)
Pavlovia rotunda (J Sowerby, 1821)
Pectinatites wheatleyensis Neaverson, 1925
Pentacrinites fossilis Blumenbach, 1804
Perisphinctes (Arisphinctes) helenae de Riaz, 1898
Perisphinctes (Pseudarisphinctes) shortlakensis Arkell, 1935
Plagiostoma giganteum J Sowerby, 1814
Pleuroceras solare (Phillips, 1829)
Pleuromya uniformis (J Sowerby, 1813)
Praeexogyra hebridica (Forbes, 1851)
Praeexogyra hebridica var. *elongata* (Dutertre, 1931)
Prionorhynchia serrata (J de C Sowerby, 1825)
Progalbanites albani Arkell, 1935
Protogrammoceras occidentale Dommergues, 1982
Protogrammoceras paltum (S S Buckman, 1922)
Pseudopecten aequivalvis (J Sowerby, 1816)
Psiloceras planorbis (J de C Sowerby, 1824)
Quenstedtoceras lamberti (J Sowerby, 1819)
Rhynchonelloidella curvivarians S S Buckman, 1918
Rhynchonelloidella smithi (Davidson, 1878)
Rhynchonelloidella wattonensis (Muir-Wood, 1936)
Ringsteadia anglica Salfeld, 1917
Rudirhynchia egretta (Eudes-Deslongchamps, 1858)
Scelidosaurus harrisoni Owen, 1861
Sigaloceras calloviense (J Sowerby, 1815)
Thamnasteria arachnoides (Parkinson, 1808)
Titanites anguiformis Wimbledon & Cope, 1978
Titanites bononiensis (de Loriol, 1873)
Titanites giganteus (J Sowerby, 1816)

Titanites pseudogigas (Blake, 1880)
Titanites titan S S Buckman, 1921
Tmetoceras scissum (Benecke, 1868)
Torquirhynchia inconstans (J Sowerby, 1821)
Tragophylloceras loscombi (J Sowerby, 1817)
Trigonia pullus J de C Sowerby, 1826

Cretaceous

Actinoceramus concentricus (Parkinson, 1819)
Amphidonte obliquatum (Pulteney, 1813)
Anahoplites picteti Spath, 1926
Anahoplites planus (Mantell, 1822)
Aptolinter aptiensis (Pictet & Campiche, 1866)
Belemnitella mucronata (Schlotheim, 1813)
Callihoplites horridus Spath, 1927
Callihoplites vraconensis (Pictet & Campiche, 1860)
Calycoceras (Newboldiceras) hippocastanum
 (J de C Sowerby, 1826)
Cheloniceras (Cheloniceras) gottschei (Kilian, 1910)
Cladoceramus undulatoplicatus (Röemer, 1855)
Conulus albogalerus Leske, 1778
Costagyra digitata (J Sowerby, 1817)
Crateraster quinqueloba (Goldfuss, 1826)
Cretirhynchia woodwardi (Davidson, 1855)
Deshayesites forbesi Casey, 1961
Echinocorys brydonei Gale MS
Echinocorys cincta Brydone, 1912
Echinocorys depressula Griffith & Brydone, 1911
Echinocorys elevata Brydone, 1912
Echinocorys subconicula Griffith & Brydone, 1911
Echinocorys tectiformis Brydone, 1912
Echinocorys truncata Griffith & Brydone, 1911
Eomicraster leskei magna Drummond, 1983
Freiastarte subcostata (d'Orbigny, 1850)
Hemicidaris purbeckensis Forbes, 1850
Hoplites dentatus (J Sowerby, 1812)
Hysteroceras varicosum (J de C Sowerby, 1824)
Inoceramus cuvieri (J Sowerby, 1814)
Inoceramus lamarcki Parkinson, 1819
Magas chitoniformis (Schlotheim, 1813)
Marsupites testudinarius (Schlotheim, 1820)
Micraster coranguinum (Leske, 1778)
Micraster leskei (Desmoulins, 1837)
Mortoniceras (Deiradoceras) albense Spath, 1933
Mortoniceras (Deiradoceras) cunningtoni Spath, 1933
Mortoniceras (Mortoniceras) inflatum (J Sowerby, 1818)
Mytiloides hattini Elder, 1991
Mytiloides hercynicus (Petrascheck, 1903)
Mytiloides kossmati (Heinz, 1930)
Mytiloides mytiloides (Mantell, 1822)
Mytiloides subhercynicus (Seitz, 1934)
Neithea gibbosa (Pulteney, 1813)
Nuculana scapha (d'Orbigny, 1844)

Nuthetes destructor Owen, 1854
Offaster pilula (Lamarck, 1816)
Panopea gurgitis (Brongniart, 1822)
Paraglauconia strombiformis (Schlotheim, 1820)
Parahoplites maximus Sinzow, 1907
Parahoplites nutfieldiensis (J Sowerby, 1815)
Plectomya anglica Woods, 1909
Pleurohoplites renauxianus (d'Orbigny, 1840)
Praeactinocamax plenus (Blainville, 1825)
Praeexogyra [Liostrea] distorta (J de C Sowerby, 1836)
'Protocardia' major (J de C Sowerby, 1826)
Protocardia purbeckensis (de Loriol, 1865)
Pseudoptera subdepressa (d'Orbigny, 1850)
Pycnodonte vesiculare (Lamarck, 1806)
Roveacrinus communis Douglas, 1908
Sciponoceras baculoides (Mantell, 1822)
Serpula coacervata Blumenbach, 1803
Sternotaxis plana (Mantell, 1822)
Terebratulina lata Etheridge, 1881
Turrilites acutus Passy, 1832
Volviceramus involutus (J de C Sowerby, 1828)

Palaeogene

Adnatosphaeridium multispinosum Williams & Downie,
 1966
Apectodinium homomorphum (Deflandre & Cookson
 1955) Lentin & Williams, 1977
Apectodinium quinquelatum (Williams & Downie, 1966)
 Costa & Downie, 1979
Brazilea parva (Cookson & Dettmann, 1959)
 Backhouse 1988
Callialasporites dampieri (Balme, 1957) Sukh Dev 1961
Caryapollenites simplex (Potonie, 1931) Raatz 1937
Cleistosphaeridium diversispinosum Davey et al., 1966
Corsinipollenites oculusnoctis (Thiergart, 1940)
 Nakoman, 1965
Dracodinium simile (Eisenack, 1954) Costa & Downie, 1979
Eatonicysta ursulae (Morgenroth, 1966) Stover & Evitt, 1978
Homotryblium tenuispinosum Davey & Williams, 1966
Hystrichokolpoma cinctum Klump, 1953
Lejeunecysta hyalina (Gerlach, 1961) Artzner &
 Dörhöfer, 1978
Milfordia hungarica (Kedves, 1965) Krutzsch & Van
 Hoorne, 1970
Muratodinium fimbriatum (Cookson & Eisenack, 1967)
 Drugg, 1970
Plicapollis pseudoexcelsus (Krutzsch, 1958) Krutzsch, 1961
Pompeckjoideapollenites subhercynicus (Krutzsch, 1954)
 Krutzsch in Góczán et al. 1967
Spinizonocolpites baculatus Muller, 1968
Taxodiaceaepollenites hiatus Potonié, 1932 ex Potonié, 1958
Thalassiphora delicata Williams & Downie, 1966
Wetzeliella articulata Eisenack, 1938

INDEX